THE
CONCORDIA
HYMNAL

THE

Concordia

HYMNAL

*A Hymnal for Church,
School and Home*

Published by

Augsburg Publishing House

MINNEAPOLIS   MINNESOTA

THE CONCORDIA HYMNAL
REVISED AND ENLARGED

Twenty-second Printing
To date: 194,000

Manufactured in the United States of America
Printed by Augsburg Publishing House, Minneapolis 15, Minnesota
. . . 9820 . . .

Speaking one to another in psalms and hymns and spiritual songs, singing and making melody with your heart to the Lord.

Eph. 5:19.

TABLE OF CONTENTS

General Classification of the Hymns

General Classification of the Hymns

INTRODUCTION

THE revised and enlarged *Concordia* is a collection of hymns and spiritual songs selected for church, school, home, and private use. Hence, materials of different types from as many styles and sources as possible have been included. For example, besides the bulk of general hymns, there are numbers which, although useful for congregational singing, are, perhaps, more suitable for sacred solos and easy choir songs. In all cases the object has been to include only material of a distinctive and upbuilding character, consistent with good taste and spiritual demands.

The chorale with its centuries of unparalleled expressiveness and churchliness remains as the backbone of the collection. To aid organists and worshippers to a right understanding and interpretation of the chorales, they are, in nearly all cases, presented in modern notation and time signatures. The best of the indispensable English and American hymns are included. German and Scandinavian sources have been richly utilized. Other ancient and modern numbers appear, together with many new translations of old favorites which have not been rendered in English before. New combinations have been effected to insure more unity in spirit between text and music. In several cases new and better tunes have been joined to old beautiful hymns which hitherto have been fettered by inferior music. A great number of the beloved standard hymns which have had faulty meter and accents, and other curable misfits, have been carefully revised with as little alteration as possible of the original. Then, much effort has been expended to find and adapt tunes and texts that might prove effective in the branches of Christian work where the so-called Gospel hymns have been found useful; songs simple and singable, yet of wholesome appeal and musically sound. The attempt should be to find appropriate hymns of elevating qualities to displace the crude, characterless, and often degrading material so abundantly in use. Again folk music furnishes the ideal and the supply. The compilers feel that one of the unique features of this hymnal is the large group of fine folk-tunes which appear here for the first time in hymn form, and with sacred texts. We feel in duty bound to be spokesmen, translators, and incorporators of the religious treasures and folk-music idioms to which we are related. We believe that, to a great extent, American hymnology shall be enriched in proportion as each racial group discovers and adapts its own peculiar gifts, and in that way makes its distinctive contribution.

It is hoped that in the important field of sacred song our people, and especially the leaders, shall exercise the same care and faithfulness that they covet in keeping the Word of God pure and prominent; that they shall strive to develop sufficient discrimination to recognize and prize their choicest treasures, learn and use them for spiritual nourishment, and teach them to their children. Our heritage in this respect is so immeasurable that to leave it for *greener pastures across the stream* would be tragic.

The Orders of Service, Scripture readings and prayers for family devotions are other features which, it is hoped, will help to make the new *Concordia* serviceable and a source of joy and blessing to many.

The Editors are greatly indebted to publishers, authors and composers for material used in this book.

Of special value are the hymns borrowed by kind permission, from the Augustana Book Concern, Rock Island, Ill.; The Lutheran Book Concern, Columbus, Ohio; and the Danish Lutheran Publishing House, Blair, Neb.

From *The Hymnal* (A. B. C.) are taken the following: Nos. 43 (text and music), 122 (text), 173 (text and music), 200 (text), 295 (text), 316 (text and music), 368 (text and music), 429 (text).

From *Songs of the Church Year* by Anna Hoppe (A. B. C.), Nos. 48, 116, 137, 179.

From *American Lutheran Hymnal* (L. B. C.), texts Nos. 165, 218, 246, 274, 280, 292, 345; 312 (text and music).

From *Hymnal for Church and Home* (D. L. P. H.), Nos. 69 (text and music), 153 (text), 224 (text).

Highly appreciated are the contributions of new original hymns and translations by the authors and translators whose names appear on the pages of the book, as is also the privilege of using other good material from sources old and new and any assistance otherwise rendered.

Grateful recognition is especially due Dr. T. F. Gullixson, President of Luther Theological Seminary, St. Paul, Minn., for his assistance in compiling the Orders of Service, the Scripture Selections and the Prayers included in the book.

Editors:

ANDREAS BERSAGEL   T. O. BURNTVEDT

V. E. BOE   OSCAR R. OVERBY

S. O. SIGMOND

THE HYMNS

I. Worship in General

1 All Glory Be to Thee, Most High

ALL GLORY BE TO THEE 87, 87, 887

Nicolaus Decius, 1539
Tr Catherine Winkworth, 1863, alt

Val. Schumann's Geistliche Lieder, 1539
Nicolaus Decius, 1539

1. All glo-ry be to Thee, Most High, To Thee all ad-o-ra-tion!
2. We praise, we wor-ship Thee, we trust, And give Thee thanks for-ev-er,
3. O Je-sus Christ, our God and Lord, Son of the Heav'n-ly Fa-ther,
4. O Ho-ly Ghost, Thou pre-cious gift, Thou Com-fort-er un-fail-ing,

In grace and truth Thou draw-est nigh To of-fer us sal-
O Fa-ther, for Thy rule is just And wise and chang-es
O Thou who hast our peace re-stored, Thy stray-ing sheep dost
From Sa-tan's snares our souls up-lift, And let Thy pow'r a-

va-tion Thou show-est Thy good will to men, And
nev-er. Thy hand al-might-y o'er us reigns, Thou
gath-er, Thou Lamb of God, to Thee on High Out
vail-ing, A-void our woes and calm our dread; For

peace shall reign on earth a-gain; We praise Thy name for-ev-er.
do-est what Thy will or-dains; 'Tis well for us Thou rul-est.
of the depths we sin-ners cry: Have mer-cy on us Je-sus!
us the Sav-iour's blood was shed, We trust in Thee to save us!

3

2 Praise, My Soul, the King of Heaven

EASTER MORROW 8 7 6L

Henry F. Lyte, 1834   Ludvig M. Lindeman, 1812-1887

1. Praise my soul, the King of heav-en, To His feet thy
2. Praise Him for His grace and fav-or To our 'fa - thers
3. Fa - ther-like, He tends and spares us; Well our fee - ble
4. An - gels in the height, a - dore Him; Ye be-hold Him

trib - ute bring; Ran - somed, healed, re - stored, for - giv - en,
in dis - tress; Praise Him, still the same as ev - er,
frame He knows; In His hands He gent - ly bears us,
face to face; Saints tri - um - phant, bow be - fore Him;

Ev - er - more His prais - es sing! Hal - le - lu - jah!
Slow to chide, and swift to bless; Hal - le - lu - jah!
Res - cues us from all our foes; Hal - le - lu - jah!
Gath - ered in from ev - 'ry race. Hal - le - lu - jah!

Hal - le - lu - jah! Praise the ev - er - last - ing King.
Hal - le - lu - jah! Glo - rious in His faith - ful - ness.
Hal - le - lu - jah! Wide - ly as His mer - cy goes.
Hal - le - lu - jah! Praise with us the God of grace.

4

3 Praise to the Lord, the Almighty

PRAISE TO THE LORD 14 14, 4 7 8

Joachim Neander, 1680
Tr Catherine Winkworth, 1863

German, 1668
Arr. F. Melius Christiansen, 1907

1. Praise to the Lord, the Al-might-y, the King of cre-a-tion! O my soul praise Him, for He is thy health and sal-va-tion! All ye who hear, Now to His tem-ple draw near, Join me in glad a-do-ra-tion.

2. Praise to the Lord, who o'er all things so won-drous-ly reign-eth, Shel-ters thee un-der His wings, yea, so gent-ly sus-tain-eth; Hast thou not seen How thy de-sires e'er have been Grant-ed in what He or-dain-eth?

3. Praise to the Lord, who doth pros-per thy work and de-fend thee; Sure-ly His good-ness and mer-cy here dai-ly at-tend thee; Pon-der a-new What the Al-might-y can do If with His love He be-friend thee!

4. Praise to the Lord, who with mar-vel-ous wis-dom hath made thee; Decked thee with health, and with faith-ful-ness guid-ed and stayed thee; How oft in grief Hath He not brought thee re-lief, Spread-ing His wings to o'er-shade thee!

5. Praise to the Lord! O let all that is in me a-dore Him! All that hath life and hath breath, come with prais-es be-fore Him! Let the A-men Sound from His peo-ple a-gain; Glad-ly for aye we a-dore Him.

5

4 O Savior, Precious Savior

CRUX CHRISTI 7 6 8L

Frances R Havergal, 1870

Arthur Henry Mann, 1897

1. O Sav - ior, pre - cious Sav - ior, Whom yet un - seen we love,
2. O Bring - er of sal - va - tion, Who won - drous - ly hast wrought,
3. In Thee all full - ness dwell - eth, All grace and pow'r di - vine;
4. O grant the con - sum - ma - tion Of this our song a - bove,

O Name of might and fa - vor, All oth - er names a - bove!
Thy - self the rev - e - la - tion Of love be - yond our thought·
The glo - ry that ex - cell - eth, O Son of God, is Thine;
In end - less a - do - ra - tion, And ev - er - last - ing love;

We wor - ship Thee, we bless Thee, To Thee, O Christ, we sing;
We wor - ship Thee, we bless Thee, To Thee, O Christ, we sing;
We wor - ship Thee, we bless Thee, To Thee, O Christ, we sing;
Then shall we praise and bless Thee Where per - fect prais - es ring,

We praise Thee, and con - fess Thee Our ho - ly Lord and King.
We praise Thee, and con - fess Thee Our gra - cious Lord and King.
We praise Thee, and con - fess Thee Our glo - rious Lord and King.
And ev - er - more con - fess Thee Our Sav - ior and our King.

5 Give Praise to God Our King

SUNRISE 6 5, 6 5, 6 5, 6 6 5

Arthur T Russell, 1854

Zinck's Koralbog, 1801
Arr. F. Melius Christiansen, 1907

1 Give praise to God our King, O earth and heav - en!
2 O Ho - ly Ghost, our guide To heav'n - ly glo - ry,
3 Lift we our hearts on high In a - do - ra - tion,

Of grace and mer - cy sing, So free - ly giv - en O Sav - ior,
In all our hearts a - bide, Lord, we im - plore Thee; In us, blest
Our Lord is ev - er nigh With con - so - la - tion. Let ev - 'ry

who hast died, Our ex - pi - a - tion, Thy name be glo - ri - fied,
Spir - it, reign, Thine aid be - stow - ing, Our souls with peace sus - tain,
grief be still; Light He will send us; In life, in death, He will,

Thy name be glo - ri - fied By all cre - a - tion.
Our souls with peace sus - tain, Peace still o'er - flow - ing
In life, in death, He will Al - ways de - fend us.

6 Beautiful Savior, King of Creation

CRUSADERS' HYMN Irregular

Münster Gesangbuch, 1677
Tr Joseph A Seiss, 1873

Silesian Folk-Tune
Hoffmann von Fallersleben's Volkslieder, 1842

1. Beau - ti - ful Sav - ior! King of cre - a - tion!
2. Fair are the mead - ows, Fair - er the wood - lands,
3. Fair is the sun - shine, Fair - er the moon - light
4. Beau - ti - ful Sav - ior! Lord of the na - tions!

Son of God and Son of Man! Tru - ly I'd love Thee,
Robed in flow'rs of bloom - ing spring; Je - sus is fair - er;
And the spark - ling stars on high; Je - sus shines bright - er,
Son of God and Son of Man! Glo - ry and hon - or,

Tru - ly I'd serve Thee, Light of my soul, my joy, my crown!
Je - sus is pur - er; He makes our sorrow - ing spir - it sing.
Je - sus shines pur - er; Than all the an - gels in the sky.
Praise, a - dor - a - tion, Now and for ev - er - more be Thine!

7 All Hail the Power of Jesus' Name

CORONATION C M

Edward Perronet, 1779

Oliver Holden, 1793

1. All hail the pow'r of Je - sus' name! Let an - gels pros - trate fall;
2. Ye seed of Is - rael's chos - en race, Ye ran - somed from the fall,
3. Hail Him, ye heirs of Da - vid's line, Whom Da - vid Lord did call,
4. Let ev - 'ry kin - dred, ev - 'ry tribe, On this ter - res - tial ball,
5. O that with yon - der sa - cred throng We at His feet may fall;

8

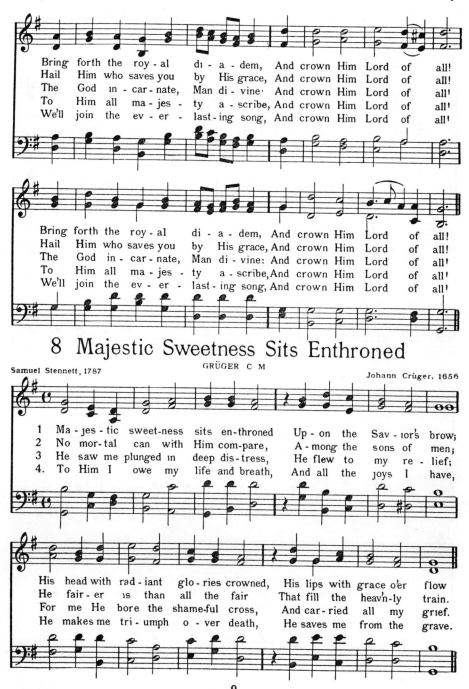

Bring forth the roy-al di-a-dem, And crown Him Lord of all!
Hail Him who saves you by His grace, And crown Him Lord of all!
The God in-car-nate, Man di-vine· And crown Him Lord of all!
To Him all ma-jes-ty a-scribe, And crown Him Lord of all!
We'll join the ev-er-last-ing song, And crown Him Lord of all!

Bring forth the roy-al di-a-dem, And crown Him Lord of all!
Hail Him who saves you by His grace, And crown Him Lord of all!
The God in-car-nate, Man di-vine: And crown Him Lord of all!
To Him all ma-jes-ty a-scribe, And crown Him Lord of all!
We'll join the ev-er-last-ing song, And crown Him Lord of all!

8 Majestic Sweetness Sits Enthroned

GRÜGER C M

Samuel Stennett, 1787

Johann Crüger, 1656

1 Ma-jes-tic sweet-ness sits en-throned Up-on the Sav-ior's brow;
2 No mor-tal can with Him com-pare, A-mong the sons of men;
3 He saw me plunged in deep dis-tress, He flew to my re-lief;
4. To Him I owe my life and breath, And all the joys I have,

His head with rad-iant glo-ries crowned, His lips with grace o'er flow
He fair-er is than all the fair That fill the heav'n-ly train.
For me He bore the shame-ful cross, And car-ried all my grief.
He makes me tri-umph o-ver death, He saves me from the grave.

9

9 My Soul, Now Bless Thy Maker

MY SOUL, NOW BLESS 7 8, 7 8, 7 6, 7 6, 7 6, 7 6

Johannes Graumann, 1540
Tr Catherine Winkworth, 1863

Ludvig M Lindeman, 1812 - 1887

1 My soul, now bless thy Mak-er! Let all with-in me bless His name,
2 He shows to man His trea-sure Of judg-ment, truth, and right-eous-ness,
3. For, as a ten-der fa-ther Hath pit-y on his chil-dren here,
4. God's grace a-lone en-dur-eth, And chil-dren's chil-dren yet shall prove

Who mak-eth thee par-tak-er Of mer-cies more than thou dar'st claim.
His love be-yond all meas-ure, His yearn-ing pit-y o'er dis-tress;
He in His arms doth gath-er All who are His in child-like fear:
How He with strength as-sur-eth The hearts of all that seek His love

For-get Him not, whose meek-ness For-giv-eth all thy sin;
Nor treats us as we mer-it, But lays His an-ger by;
He knows how frail our pow-ers, Who but from dust are made:
In heav'n is fixed His dwell-ing, His rule is o-ver all;

Who heal-eth all thy weak-ness, Re-news thy life with-in;
The hum-ble, con-trite spir-it, Finds His com-pas-sion nigh;
We flour-ish as the flow-ers, And ev-en so we fade;
An-gels, in might ex-cell-ing, Bright hosts, be-fore Him fall.

10 O for a Thousand Tongues to Sing

CHESTERFIELD C. M.

Charles Wesley, 1738   Thomas Haweis, 1733-1820

11 Sweet Hour of Prayer

SWEET HOUR OF PRAYER L.M. 8L.

William W Walford

William B Bradbury, 1859

1. Sweet hour of pray'r, sweet hour of pray'r! That calls me from a world of care,
2. Sweet hour of pray'r, sweet hour of pray'r, The joy I feel, the bliss I share
3. Sweet hour of pray'r, sweet hour of pray'r, Thy wings shall my pe - ti - tion bear

And bids me at my Fa - ther's throne Make all my wants and wish - es known:
Of those whose anx-ious spir - its burn With strong de-sires for thy re - turn!
To Him, whose truth and faith-ful - ness, En - gage the wait-ing soul to bless;

In sea-sons of dis - tress and grief, My soul has oft - en found re - lief;
With such I hast - en to the place, Where God, my Sav - ior, shows His face,
And since He bids me seek His face, Be - lieve His word, and trust His grace,

And oft es-caped the temp-ter's snare, By thy re-turn, sweet hour of pray'r!
And glad - ly take my sta - tion there, And wait for thee, sweet hour of pray'r.
I'll cast on Him my ev - 'ry care, And wait for thee, sweet hour of pray'r.

12

12 Thee, God, We Praise, Thy Holy Name We Bless

FINLANDIA 10 10, 10 8, 10 8

Te Deum, Latin of 4th Century, adapted

Jean Sibelius, b 1865
Arr. Gunnar J Malmin, 1932

1 Thee, God, we praise, Thy ho-ly name we bless,
2 O Thou most ho-ly, ho-ly, ho-ly Lord,

Thee, Lord of all, We hum-bly do con-fess. The whole cre-
Thou, God of hosts, by all, by all a-dored Earth and the

a-tion ev-er wor-ships Thee, The Fa-ther of e-
heav'ns are ev-er full of Thee, Thy light, Thy pow'r, Thy

ter-ni-ty. The whole cre-a-tion ev-er wor-ships
maj-es-ty The earth and heav'ns are ev-er full of

Thee, The Fa-ther of e-ter-ni-ty
Thee, Thy light, Thy pow'r, Thy maj-es-ty

13

13 Pass Me Not, O Gentle Savior

PASS ME NOT 8 5 4L and Chorus

Fanny J Crosby, 1868   William Howard Doane, 1831-1915

1 Pass me not, O gen - tle Sav - ior, Hear my hum - ble cry;
2 Let me at Thy throne of mer - cy Find a sweet re - lief;
3 Trust-ing on - ly in Thy mer - it, Would I seek Thy face;
4 Thou, the Spring of all my com - fort, More than life to me,

While on oth - ers Thou art smil - ing, Do not pass me by
Kneel-ing there in deep con - tri - tion, Help my un - be - lief
Heal my wound-ed, bro - ken spir - it, Save me by Thy grace.
Whom have I on earth be - side Thee? Whom in heav'n but Thee?

CHORUS

Sav - ior, Sav - ior, hear my hum - ble cry, While on

oth ers Thou art call - ing, Do not pass me by

14 Lord of Our Life, and God of Our Salvation

FATHER MOST HOLY 11 11, 11 5

Matthæus A. von Löwenstern, 1644
Tr Philip Pusey, 1840

Johann Crüger, 1640

1 Lord of our life, and God of our sal - va - tion, Star of our night, and hope of ev - 'ry na - tion, Hear and re - ceive Thy Church's sup - pli - ca - tion, Lord God Al - might - y Thou canst pre - serve us.

2. See round Thine Ark the hun-gry bil - lows curl - ing, See how Thy foes their ban -ners are un - furl - ing; Lord, while their darts en - ven-omed they are hurl - ing, Thou canst pre - serve us.

3. Lord, Thou canst help when earth - ly ar - mor fail - eth; Lord, Thou canst save when dead - ly sin as - sail - eth, Lord, o'er Thy Church nor death nor hell pre - vail - eth: Grant us Thy peace, Lord

4. Peace in our hearts, our e - vil thoughts as-suag-ing, Peace in Thy Church where broth-ers are en - gag - ing, Peace, when the bus - y world its war is wag-ing, Send us, O Sav - ior.

5 Grant us Thy help till foes are back-ward driv - en; Grant them Thy truth, that they may be for - giv - en; Grant peace on earth, and, af - ter we have striv - en, Peace in Thy heav - en

15

15 O Can You Sing the New Song of Salvation

O CAN YOU SING THE NEW SONG 11 9, 11 9, 9 9, 11 9

J. Traasdal
Tr. V. E Boe, 1921

Norwegian Folk-Tune
Arr. Oscar R Overby, 1932

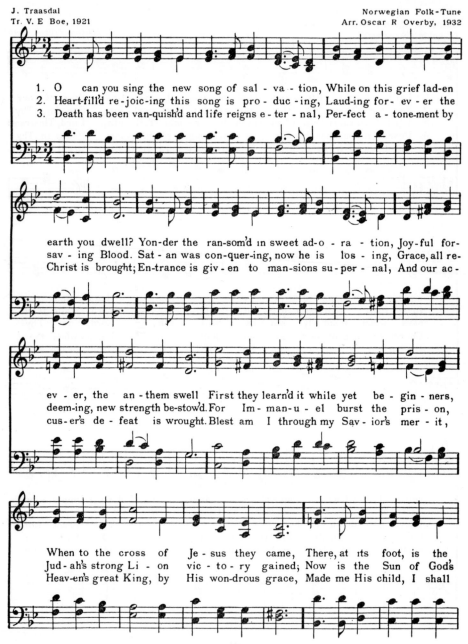

1. O   can you sing the new song of sal - va - tion, While on this grief lad-en
2. Heart-fill'd re-joic-ing this song is pro - duc - ing, Laud-ing for- ev - er the
3. Death has been van-quish'd and life reigns e - ter - nal, Per-fect a - tone-ment by

earth you dwell? Yon-der the ran-som'd in sweet ad-o - ra - tion, Joy-ful for-
sav - ing Blood. Sat - an was con-quer-ing, now he is los - ing, Grace, all re-
Christ is brought; En-trance is giv-en to man-sions su-per - nal, And our ac-

ev - er, the an - them swell First they learn'd it while yet be - gin - ners,
deem-ing, new strength be-stow'd. For Im - man-u - el burst the pris - on,
cus-er's de - feat is wrought. Blest am I through my Sav - ior's mer - it,

When to the cross of Je - sus they came, There, at its foot, is the
Jud - ah's strong Li - on vic - to - ry gained; Now is the Sun of God's
Heav-en's great King, by His won-drous grace, Made me His child, I shall

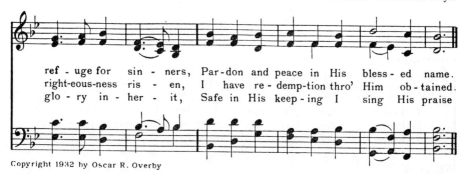

ref - uge for sin - ners, Par-don and peace in His bless - ed name.
right-eous-ness ris - en, I have re - demp-tion thro' Him ob - tained.
glo - ry in - her - it, Safe in His keep - ing I sing His praise

16 Thee God We Praise, Thy Name We Bless

OLD HUNDREDTH L. M.

Te Deum, Latin of 4th Century

Louis Bourgeois, 1551

1. Thee God we praise, Thy name we bless, Thee Lord of all we do con-fess;
2. To Thee a - loud all an-gels cry, The heav'ns and all the pow'rs on high,
3. O ho - ly, ho - ly, ho - ly Lord, Thou God of hosts by all a-dored,
4. Th'a - pos-tles join the glo-rious throng The pro-phets swell th'im-mor-tal song,

The whole cre - a - tion wor-ships Thee, The Fa-ther of e - ter - ni - ty.
The cher - ubs and the ser-aphs join, And thus they hymn Thy praise di-vine:
The heav'ns and earth are full of Thee, Thy light, Thy pow'r, Thy maj - es - ty.
The white-robed hosts of mar-tyrs bright All serve and praise Thee day and night.

5   The holy Church in ev'ry place
    Throughout the world exalts Thy praise,
    And ever doth acknowledge Thee,
    O Lord of boundless majesty.

6   O God eternal, mighty King,
    We unto Thee our praises bring;
    And to Thy true and only Son,
    And Holy Spirit, Three in One.

17

17 Praise Ye the Father

INTEGER VITÆ 11 11, 11 5

Elizabeth Charles, 1828-1896

Friedrich F. Flemming, 1778-1813

1. Praise ye the Fa - ther for His lov - ing kind - ness:
2. Praise ye the Sav - ior, great is His com - pas - sion;
3. Praise ye the Spir - it, Com-fort - er of Is - rael,

Ten - der - ly cares He for His er - ring chil - dren; Praise Him, ye
Gra - cious - ly cares He for His chos-en peo - ple; Young men and
Sent of the Fa - ther and the Son to bless us, Praise ye, the

an - gels, praise Him in the heav - ens, Praise ye Je - ho - vah.
maid - ens, ye old men and chil - dren, Praise ye the Sav - ior.
Fa - ther, Son, and Ho - ly Spir - it, Praise ye the Tri - une God.

18 Prayer Is the Soul's Sincere Desire

AZMON C. M

James Montgomery, 1818

Carl G. Gläser, 1828
Arr. Lowell Mason, 1839

1. Pray'r is the soul's sin - cere de - sire, Un - ut - tered or ex - pressed;
2. Pray'r is the sim - plest form of speech That in - fant lips can try;
3. Pray'r is the Chris-tian's vi - tal breath, The Chris-tian's na - tive air;
4. O Thou, by Whom we come to God, The Life, the Truth, the Way!

18

The mo-tion of a hid-den fire That trem-bles in the breast.
Pray'r, the sub-lim-est strains that reach The Ma-jes-ty on high.
His watch-word at the gates of death: He en-ters heav'n with pray'r.
The path of pray'r Thy-self hast trod; Lord, teach us how to pray.

19 My God! How Wonderful Thou Art

DUNDEE C. M

Frederick William Faber, 1849

Scottish Psalter, 1615

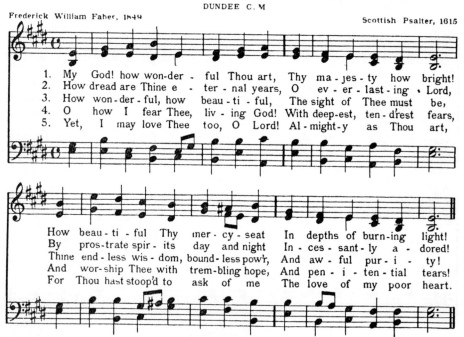

1. My God! how won-der-ful Thou art, Thy ma-jes-ty how bright!
2. How dread are Thine e-ter-nal years, O ev-er-last-ing Lord,
3. How won-der-ful, how beau-ti-ful, The sight of Thee must be,
4. O how I fear Thee, liv-ing God! With deep-est, ten-d'rest fears,
5. Yet, I may love Thee too, O Lord! Al-might-y as Thou art,

How beau-ti-ful Thy mer-cy-seat In depths of burn-ing light!
By pros-trate spir-its day and night In-ces-sant-ly a-dored!
Thine end-less wis-dom, bound-less pow'r, And aw-ful pur-i-ty!
And wor-ship Thee with trem-bling hope, And pen-i-ten-tial tears!
For Thou hast stoop'd to ask of me The love of my poor heart.

6 No earthly father loves like Thee,
   No mother e'er so mild,
   Bears and forbears, as Thou hast done
   With me, Thy sinful child.

7. My God, how wonderful Thou art,
   Thou everlasting Friend!
   On Thee I stay my trusting heart,
   Till faith in vision end.

20 We Praise Thee, O God

KREMSER 12 11 4L.

Julia Bulkley Cady, 1882   Old Netherlands Melody

1. We praise Thee, O God, our Re - deem - er, Cre - a - tor,
2. We wor - ship Thee, God of our fa - thers, we bless Thee;
3. With voic - es u - nit - ed our prais - es we of - fer,

In grate - ful de - vo - tion our trib - ute we bring.
Thro' trou - ble and temp - est our Guide hast Thou been.
To Thee, great Je - ho - vah, glad an - thems we raise.

We lay it be - fore Thee, we kneel and a - dore Thee,
When per - ils o'er - take us, es - cape Thou wilt make us,
Thy strong arm will guide us, our God is be - side us,

We bless Thy ho - ly name, glad prais - es we sing.
And with Thy help, O Lord, our bat - tles we win.
To Thee, our great Re - deem - er, for - ev - er be praised.

21 Mighty God, While Angels Bless Thee

AUSTRIA 8 7 8L

Robert Robinson, 1758

Franz Joseph Haydn, 1797

1. Might-y God, while an-gels bless Thee, May a mor-tal lisp Thy name?
2. For the grand-eur of Thy na-ture, Grand be-yond a ser-aph's tho't;
3. But Thy rich, Thy free re-demp-tion, Bright, tho' veil'd in dark-ness long;
4. From the high-est throne of glo-ry To the cross of deep-est woe,

Lord of men as well as an-gels, Thou art ev-'ry crea-ture's theme.
For the won-ders of cre-a-tion, Works with skill and kind-ness wrought;
Thought is poor, and poor ex-pres-sion, Who can sing that won-drous song?
Thou didst stoop to ran-som cap-tives; Flow my praise, for ev-er flow.

Lord of ev-'ry land and na-tion, An-cient of e-ter-nal days,
For Thy pro-vi-dence that gov-erns Thru Thine em-pires wide do-main,
Bright-ness of the Fa-ther's glo-ry, Shall Thy praise un-ut-tered lie?
Re-a-scend, im-mor-tal Sav-ior, Leave Thy foot-stool, take Thy throne;

Sound-ed thru the wide cre-a-tion Be Thy just and end-less praise.
Wings an an-gel, guides a spar-row, Bless-ed be Thy gen-tle reign.
Break, my tongue, such guil-ty sil-ence, Sing the Lord who came to die.
Thence re-turn, and reign for-ev-er; Be the king-dom all Thine own.

22 Blessing, and Honor, and Glory, and Power

AMERICAN HYMN 10 10 4L .

Horatius Bonar, 1808-1889

Matthias Keller, 1813-1890

1. Bless-ing, and hon-or, and glo-ry, and pow'r, Wis-dom, and
2. Dwell-eth the light of the glo-ry with Him, Light of a
3. Ev-er as-cend-eth the song and the joy, Ev-er de-
4. Life of all life, and true Light of all light, Star of the

rich-es, and strength ev-er-more, Give ye to Him who our
glo-ry that can-not grow dim, Light in its si-lence and
scend-eth the love from on high, Bless-ing, and hon-or, and
dawn-ing, un-chang-ing-ly bright, Sing we the song of the

bat-tle hath won, Whose are the king-dom, the crown, and the
beau-ty and calm, Light in its glad-ness and bright-ness and
glo-ry, and praise, This is the theme of the hymns that we
Lamb that was slain, Dy-ing in weak-ness, but ris-ing to

throne, Whose are the king-dom, the crown, and the throne.
balm, Light in its glad-ness and bright-ness and balm.
raise, This is the theme of the hymns that we raise.
reign, Dy-ing in weak-ness, but ris-ing to reign.

23 Heaven and Earth, and Sea and Air

NATURE'S PRAISES 7 7, 7 7 4

Joachim Neander, 1680
Tr. James D. Burns, 1823 - 1864

Danish Folk - Tune

1. Heav'n and earth, and sea and air, Still their Mak - er's
2. See, the sun his pow'r a - wakes, As through clouds his
3. See how God this roll - ing globe, Swathes with beau - ty
4. Through the air Thy prais - es meet, Birds are sing - ing

praise de - clare; Thou, my soul, as loud - ly sing,
glo - ry breaks; See the moon and stars of light,
as a robe; For - ests, fields, and liv - ing things,
clear and sweet; Fire, and storm, and wind, Thy will

To thy God thy prais - es bring, Thy prais - es bring.
Prais - ing God in still - est night, In still - est night.
Each its Mas - ter's glo - ry sings, His glo - ry sings.
As Thy min - is - ters ful - fill, Thy will ful - fill.

5.
Ocean waves Thy glory tell,
At Thy touch they sing and swell;
From the well-spring to the sea,
Rivers murmer, Lord, of Thee,
O Lord, of Thee.

6.
O my God, what wonders lie
Hid in Thine infinity!
Stamp upon my inmost heart
What I am, and what Thou art,
And what Thou art.

24 Give to Our God Immortal Praise

DUKE STREET L.M

Isaac Watts, 1719

John Hatton, 1790

1. Give to our God im - mor - tal praise! Mer-cy and truth are all His ways;
2. Give to the Lord of lords re - nown, The King of kings with glo-ry crown;
3. He built the earth, He spread the sky, And fixed the star - ry lights on high:
4. He sent His Son with pow'r to save From guilt and dark-ness, and the grave:

Won-ders of grace to God be - long: Repeat His mer - cies in your song.
His mer-cies ev - er shall en - dure, When lords and kings are known no more.
Won-ders of grace to God be - long; Repeat His mer - cies in your song.
Won-ders of grace to God be - long; Repeat His mer - cies in your song.

25 There Is an Eye That Never Sleeps

EVAN C M

James C Wallace, 1793-1841

William H Havergal, 1846

1. There is an eye that nev - er sleeps Be - neath the wing of night;
2. There is an arm that nev - er tires, When hu-man strength gives way;
3. But there's a pow'r which man can wield When mor-tal aid is vain,
4. That pow'r is pray'r, which soars on high, Thru Je - sus, to the throne;

There is an ear that nev - er shuts When sink the beams of light.
There is a love that nev - er fails, When earth-ly loves de - cay.
That eye, that arm, that love to reach, That list-'ning ear to gain.
And moves the hand which moves the world, To bring sal - va - tion down!

26 My Heart Is Longing to Praise My Savior

PRINCESS EUGENIE 10 10 4L.

Princess Eugenie of Sweden
Tr. P. A Sveeggen, 1931

Norwegian Folk-Tune

1. My heart is long-ing to praise my Sav-ior, And glo-ri-fy His name in song and pray'r; For He has shown me His won-d'rous fav-or And of-fered me all heav'n with Him to share.

2. I walked in blind-ness; my soul was dy-ing; The prince of dark-ness held me in his pow'r. In pain I turned, to my Fa-ther cry-ing; He broke my chains and saved me in that hour.

3. O bless-ed Je-sus, what Thou hast giv-en, Thru dy-ing on the cross in bit-ter pain, Has filled my heart with the peace of heav-en; My win-ter's gone and spring is mine a-gain.

4. O Chris-tian friends, let our song as-cend-ing, Give hon-or, praise to Him who set us free! Our trib-ul-a-tions may seem un-end-ing; But soon with Him we shall for-ev-er be.

5. Soon we are home and shall stand be-fore Him; What mat-ter then, tho' we have suf-fered here. Then He shall crown us, while we a-dorn Him; So death and all our pains will dis-ap-pear.

6. To Thee, O Savior, our adoration
    Shall rise forever for Thy precious blood
   Which blotted out all the accusation
    Of sin and guilt which once against us stood.

7. What blessed joy overflows my spirit,
    Because Thy wondrous grace was granted me.
   Thy work complete, that I may inherit
    At last eternal life in heaven with Thee!

27 Ye Lands, to the Lord Make a Jubilant Noise

YE LANDS, TO THE LORD 11 5, 11 9

Vilhelm Koren, 1674
Tr Harriet R Spaeth, 1898

Erik Hoff, b 1832

1. Ye lands, to the Lord make a ju - bi - lant noise;
2. Not we, but the Lord is our Mak - er, our God;
3. O en - ter His gates with thanks - giv - ing and praise;
4. For good is the Lord, and His mer - cy is sure;

Glo - ry be to God! O serve Him with joy, in His pres - ence now re -
Glo - ry be to God! His peo - ple we are, and the sheep led by His
Glo - ry be to God! To bless Him and thank Him, our voic - es we will
Glo - ry be to God! To all gen - er - a - tions His truth shall still en -

joice; Sing praise un - to God out of Zi - on!____
rod; Sing praise un - to God out of Zi - on!____
raise; Sing praise un - to God out of Zi - on!____
dure; Sing praise un - to God out of Zi - on!____

28 Lord Teach Us How to Pray Aright

EVAN C.M.

James Montgomery, 1818, alt.

William H. Havergal, 1846

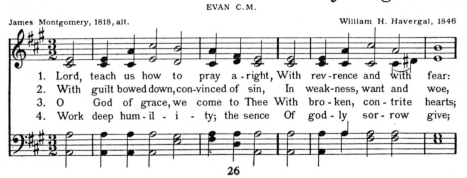

1. Lord, teach us how to pray a - right, With rev - rence and with fear:
2. With guilt bowed down, con - vinced of sin, In weak - ness, want and woe,
3. O God of grace, we come to Thee With bro - ken, con - trite hearts;
4. Work deep hum - il - i - ty; the sence Of god - ly sor - row give;

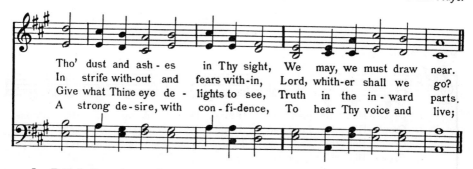

Tho' dust and ash-es in Thy sight, We may, we must draw near.
In strife with-out and fears with-in, Lord, whith-er shall we go?
Give what Thine eye de-lights to see, Truth in the in-ward parts.
A strong de-sire, with con-fi-dence, To hear Thy voice and live;

5. Faith in the only sacrifice
   That can for sin atone,
   To cast our hopes, to fix our eyes,
   On Christ, on Christ alone.

6. Give these, and then Thy will be done;
   Thus strengthened with all might,
   We, through Thy Spirit and Thy Son,
   Shall pray, and pray aright.

29 My God, Is Any Hour So Sweet

HOUR OF PRAYER 8 8, 8 4

Charlotte Elliot, 1835

H. Matthias Hansen

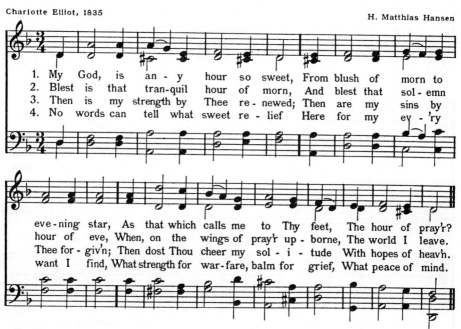

1. My God, is an-y hour so sweet, From blush of morn to
2. Blest is that tran-quil hour of morn, And blest that sol-emn
3. Then is my strength by Thee re-newed; Then are my sins by
4. No words can tell what sweet re-lief Here for my ev-'ry

eve-ning star, As that which calls me to Thy feet, The hour of pray'r?
hour of eve, When, on the wings of pray'r up-borne, The world I leave.
Thee for-giv'n; Then dost Thou cheer my sol-i-tude With hopes of heav'n.
want I find, What strength for war-fare, balm for grief, What peace of mind.

5. Hushed is each doubt, gone every fear,
   My spirit seems in heaven to stay,
   And e'en the penitential tear
   Is wiped away.

6. Lord, till I reach that blissful shore,
   No privilege so dear shall be
   As thus my inmost soul to pour
   In pray'r to Thee.

30 Crown Him with Many Crowns

DIADEMATA 6 6,8 6 8L.

Matthew Bridges, 1857 George Job Elvey, 1816-1893

1. Crown Him with man - y crowns, The Lamb up - on His throne;
2. Crown Him the Lord of Love; Be - hold His hands and side,
3. Crown Him the Lord of Peace; Whose pow'r a scep - tre sways
4. Crown Him the Lord of years, The Po - ten - tate of time,

Hark! how the heav'n-ly an - them drowns All mu - sic but its own.
Rich wounds yet vis - i - ble a - bove In beau - ty glo - ri - fied.
From pole to pole, that wars may cease, And all be pray'r and praise.
Cre - a - tor of the roll - ing spheres, In - ef - fa - bly sub - lime.

A - wake, my soul, and sing Of Him who died for thee,
No an - gel in the sky Can ful - ly bear that sight,
His reign shall know no end, And 'round His pierc - ed feet
All hail, Re - deem - er, hail! For Thou hast died for me;

And hail Him as thy match-less King Thro' all e - ter - ni - ty.
But down-ward bends His burn - ing eye At mys - ter - ies so bright.
Fair flow'rs of Par - a - dise ex - tend There fra - grance ev - er sweet.
Thy praise shall nev - er, nev - er fail Thru-out e - ter - ni - ty.

31 Come, Thou Fount of Every Blessing

NETTLETON 8 7 8L.

Robert Robinson, 1758

Asahel Nettleton, 1825

1. Come, Thou Fount of ev - 'ry bless - ing, Tune my heart to sing Thy grace;
2. Here I raise my Eb - en - e - zer, Hith - er by Thy help I'm come;
3. O to grace how great a debt - or, Dai - ly I'm con - strained to be;

Streams of mer - cy, nev - er ceas - ing, Call for songs of loud - est praise.
And I hope, by Thy good pleas - ure, Safe - ly to ar - rive at home.
Let that grace now like a fet - ter, Bind my wan - d'ring heart to Thee.

While the hope of end - less glo - ry Fills my heart with joy and love,
Je - sus sought me when a stran - ger, Wand - 'ring from the fold of God;
Prone to wan - der, Lord, I feel it, Prone to leave the God I love;

Teach me ev - er to a - dore Thee, May I still Thy good-ness prove.
He, to res - cue me from dan - ger, In - ter - posed His pre - cious blood.
Here's my heart, O take and seal it, Seal it from Thy courts a - bove.

32 Ye Servants of God, Your Master Proclaim

LYONS 10 10, 11 11

Charles Wesley, 1744

Johann Michael Haydn, 1770

1. Ye ser - vents of God, your Mas - ter pro - claim,
2. God rul - eth on high, al - might - y to save;
3. Sal - va - tion to God, who sits on the throne,
4. Then let us a - dore and give Him His right,

And pub - lish a - broad His won - der - ful name;
And still He is nigh His pres - ence we have;
Let all cry a - loud and hon - or the Son;
All glo - ry, and pow'r, and wis - dom and might;

The name all vic - to - rious of Je - sus ex - tol;
The great con - gre - ga - tion His tri - umph shall sing,
The prais - es of Je - sus the an - gels pro - claim,
All hon - or and bless - ing, with an - gels a - bove,

His king - dom is glo - rious, He rules o - ver all.
As - crib - ing sal - va - tion to Je - sus our King.
Fall down on their fa - ces and wor - ship the Lamb.
And thanks nev - er ceas - ing, and in - fi - nite love.

33 What a Friend We Have in Jesus

ERIE 8 7 8L.

Joseph Scriven, ca. 1855

Charles C. Converse, 1868

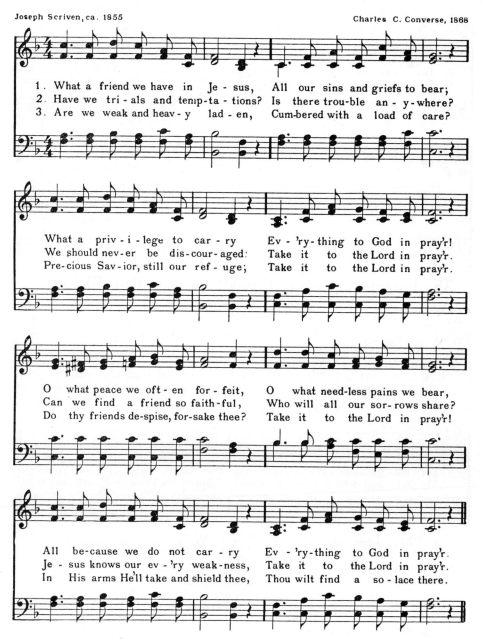

1. What a friend we have in Je - sus, All our sins and griefs to bear;
2. Have we tri - als and temp-ta - tions? Is there trou-ble an - y-where?
3. Are we weak and heav - y lad - en, Cum-bered with a load of care?

What a priv - i - lege to car - ry Ev - 'ry-thing to God in pray'r!
We should nev - er be dis-cour-aged: Take it to the Lord in pray'r.
Pre-cious Sav - ior, still our ref - uge; Take it to the Lord in pray'r.

O what peace we oft - en for - feit, O what need-less pains we bear,
Can we find a friend so faith-ful, Who will all our sor-rows share?
Do thy friends de-spise, for-sake thee? Take it to the Lord in pray'r!

All be-cause we do not car - ry Ev - 'ry-thing to God in pray'r.
Je - sus knows our ev - 'ry weak-ness, Take it to the Lord in pray'r.
In His arms He'll take and shield thee, Thou wilt find a so - lace there.

31

34 All Glory, Laud and Honor

Theodulph of Orleans, d. 821 ALL GLORY, LAUD 7 6 4L.
Tr. John Mason Neale, 1854, alt. 1859 Ludvig M. Lindeman, 1812-1887

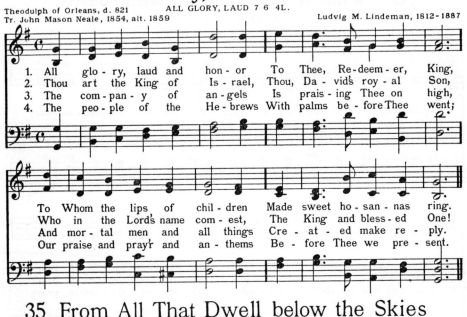

1. All glo - ry, laud and hon - or To Thee, Re - deem - er, King,
2. Thou art the King of Is - rael, Thou, Da - vid's roy - al Son,
3. The com - pan - y of an - gels Is prais - ing Thee on high,
4. The peo - ple of the He - brews With palms be - fore Thee went;

To Whom the lips of chil - dren Made sweet ho - san - nas ring.
Who in the Lord's name com - est, The King and bless - ed One!
And mor - tal men and all things Cre - at - ed make re - ply.
Our praise and pray'r and an - thems Be - fore Thee we pre - sent.

35 From All That Dwell below the Skies

OLD HUNDREDTH L.M.

Isaac Watts, 1719 Louis Bourgeois, 1551

1. From all that dwell be - low the skies, Let the Cre - a - tor's praise a - rise:
2. E - ter - nal are Thy mer - cies, Lord! E - ter - nal truth at - tends Thy word:

Let the Re - deem - er's name be sung, Thro' ev - 'ry land by ev - 'ry tongue.
Thy praise shall sound from shore to shore, Till suns shall rise and set no more.

36 Praise God, from Whom (Doxology)

Thomas Ken, 1637-1710 OLD HUNDREDTH L.M.

Praise God, from whom all blessings flow;
Praise Him, all creatures here below;
Praise Him above, ye heavenly host:
Praise Father, Son, and Holy Ghost.

See also:

37 Father, Again in Jesus' Name We Meet

BENEDICTION 10 10 4L.

Lucy E G. Whitmore, 1824

Edward J. Hopkins, 1867

1. Fa - ther, a - gain in Je - sus' name we meet, And bow in pen - i -
2. O we would bless Thee for Thy cease-less care, And all Thy work from
3. A - las, un - worth - y of Thy bound-less love, Too oft with care-less
4. O by that Name in Whom all ful - ness dwells, O by that love which

tence be-neath Thy feet; A - gain to Thee our fee - ble voic - es raise
day to - day de - clare; Is not our life with hour - ly mer - cies crowned?
feet from Thee we rove; But now, en - cour - aged by Thy voice, we come,
ev - 'ry love ex - cels, O by that blood so free - ly shed for sin,

To sue for mer - cy, and to sing Thy praise.
Does not Thine arm en - cir - cle us a - round?
Re - turn - ing sin - ners to a Fa - ther's home.
O - pen, blest mer - cy's gate, and take us in.

38 Love Divine, All Love Excelling

BEECHER 8 7 8L

Charles Wesley, 1747   John Zundel, 1870

1 Love di-vine, all love ex-cel-ling, Joy of heav'n to earth come down!
2. Breathe, O breathe Thy lov-ing Spir-it In-to ev-'ry trou-bled breast!
3 Come, Al-might-y to de-liv-er, Let us all Thy life re-ceive;
4 Fin-ish, then, Thy new cre-a-tion, Pure and spot-less let us be;

Fix in us Thy hum-ble dwell-ing, All Thy faith-ful mer-cies crown
Let us all in Thee in-her-it, Let us find Thy prom-ised rest.
Gra-cious-ly re-turn, and nev-er, Nev-er more Thy tem-ples leave!
Let us see Thy great sal-va-tion, Per-fect-ly re-stored in Thee,

Je-sus, Thou art all com-pas-sion, Pure, un-bound-ed love Thou art;
Take a-way the love of sin-ning, Al-pha and O-me-ga be;
Thee we would be al-ways bless-ing, Serve Thee as Thy hosts a-bove,
Changed from glo-ry in-to glo-ry, Till in heav'n we take our place,

Vis-it us with Thy sal-va-tion, En-ter ev-'ry trem-bling heart.
End of faith, as its be-gin-ning, Set our hearts at lib-er-ty.
Pray and praise Thee with-out ceas-ing, Glo-ry in Thy per-fect love
Till we cast our crowns be-fore Thee, Lost in won-der, love, and praise

39 Dearest Jesus, Draw Thou Near Me

SCHOP 8 7, 8 7, 7 7, 8 8

Thomas Kingo, 1699
Tr. C.K. Solberg, 1908, alt.

Johann Schop, 1642

1. Dear-est Je-sus, draw Thou near me, Let Thy Spir-it dwell with mine;
2. Un-der-neath Thy wings a-bid-ing, In Thy Church, O Sav-ior dear,
3. Thou, earth's great-est joy and glad-ness, And sal-va-tion, full and free,

O-pen now my ear to hear Thee, Take my heart and seal it Thine;
Let me dwell, in Thee con-fid-ing, Hold me in Thy faith and fear;
Let Thy pre-sence cheer my sad-ness, And pre-pare my soul for Thee!

Keep me, lead me on my way, Thee to fol-low and o-bey,
Take a-way from me each thought That with wick-ed-ness is fraught,
In the hour when I de-part, Touch my spir-it, lips and heart,

E'er to do Thy will and fear Thee, And re-joice to know and hear Thee.
Tempt-ing me to dis-o-bey Thee, Root it out, O Lord, I pray Thee.
With Thy word as-sure, up-hold me Till the heav'n-ly gates en-fold me.

40 Lord Jesus Christ, Be Present Now

LORD JESUS CHRIST, BE PRESENT NOW L.M.

Wilhelm II, Duke of Saxe-Weimar, 1648
Tr Catherine Winkworth, 1863, alt.

Cantionale Sacrum Gotha, 1651
Arr. F. Melius Christiansen, 1907

1. Lord Je - sus Christ, be pre - sent now, Our
2. Un - seal our lips to sing Thy praise, Our
3. Un - til we join the hosts that cry, "Thou
4. All glo - ry to the Fa - ther, Son, And

hearts in true de - vo - tion bow, Thy Spir - it send with
souls to Thee in wor - ship raise, Our faith in - crease, our
ho - ly art, O Lord most high!" And 'mid the light of
Ho - ly Spir - it, Three in One! To Thee, O bless - ed

light di - vine, And let Thy truth with - in us shine.
minds en - light, That we may know Thy name a - right.
that blest place Shall gaze up - on Thee face to face.
Trin - i - ty, Be praise through-out e - ter - ni - ty!

41 Lord Jesus, Though but Two or Three

LORD JESUS CHRIST, BE PRESENT NOW L.M.

1. Lord Jesus, though but two or three
In Thy dear name assembled be,
Thou wilt among them show Thy face,
And bless them with Thy saving grace.

2. In Thy dear name again we meet,
And worship humbly at Thy feet,
Thou wilt Thy gracious word fulfill,
And cheer us with Thy presence still.

3. O Thou from whom all blessings flow,
Thy peace and comfort now bestow;
Abide with us till life is o'er,
And make us Thine for evermore.

42 The Chimes of the Sabbath Re-echo Abroad

SABBATH CHIMES 11 9, 11 9, 5 5 9

Oscar R. Overby, 1931

Norwegian Folk-Tune
Arr. Oscar R. Overby, 1931

1 The chimes of the sab-bath re - ech - o a - broad, An-nounc-ing a
2. The tones of the tem-ple are lad - en with peace, In meas-ures of
3. When sab-bath with glad in - ton - a - tion of chimes As-cends where the
4. To God be the glo - ry whose mes-sage of love, Be-stowed on my

fes - tive oc - ca - sion. Ar - ray thee, my soul, for the tem-ple of
heav-en - ly splen - dor. Be-deck thee, my soul, let thy slum-ber sur -
shad-ows dis - sev - er, Be lift - ed, my soul, to ce - les - tial
low - ly sur - round - ing, Fore-shad-ows a wor-ship in tem-ples a -

God; Draw near to the fount of sal - va - tion. Be cleansed and made
cease, And hast-en thy wor-ship to ren - der. The call is di -
climes, Re-leased from thy earth-ly en - deav - or. In - vit - ed by
bove, With an-thems an - gel - ic a - bound - ing. My spir- it, with

whole; Be strengthened, my soul, By Him who re-stores His cre - a - tion.
vine; Re - demp-tion is thine, Thro' Je - sus, thy ho - ly de - fend - er.
grace, Com - mit all thy ways To Him who pre-serves thee for - ev - er.
joy Thy prais-es em - ploy, As - cend with the chimes now re - sound - ing.

43 With God and His Mercy

WITH GOD AND HIS MERCY 11 11 11, 6 6 11

Carl Olof Rosenius, 1816-1868
Tr. E. W. Olson

Oskar Ahnfelt, 1813-1882

1. With God and His mer-cy, His Spir-it, and word, And lov-ing com-mun-ion at al-tar and board, We meet with as-sur-ance the dawn of each day: The Shep-herd is with us, The Shep-herd is with us, To lead and pro-tect us, and teach us the way

2. In per-il-ous times, a-mid temp-est and night, A band press-es on through the gloom to-ward light; Though hum-ble, and meek, and dis-owned by the world, They fol-low the Sav-ior, They fol-low the Sav-ior, And march on to glo-ry, with ban-ners un-furled

3. While grov-el-ing world-lings with dross are con-tent, And ev-er on sin and trans-gres-sion are bent, I fol-low, vic-to-ri-ous hosts, at your word, And march on to glo-ry, And march on to glo-ry, We march on to glo-ry, our cap-tain the Lord.

4. The sign of the cross we tri-um-phant-ly bear, Though none of my kin-dred that em-blem may wear; I joy-ful-ly fol-low the cham-pions of right, Who march on to glo-ry, Who march on to glo-ry, Who march on to glo-ry, with weap-ons of might.

5. O Shep-herd, a-bide with us, care for us still, And feed us and lead us and teach us Thy will; And when in Thy heav-en-ly folds we shall be, Our thanks and our prais-es, Our thanks and our prais-es, Our thanks and our prais-es we'll ren-der to Thee

44 O Day of Rest and Gladness

AURELIA 7 6 8L.

Christopher Wordsworth, 1862

Samuel S. Wesley, 1864

1. O day of rest and glad-ness, O day of joy and light,
2. On thee at the cre - a - tion, The light first had its birth;
3. Thou art a port pro - tect - ed From storms that round us rise;
4. To - day on wear - y na - tions The heav'n - ly man - na falls;
5. New grac - es ev - er gain - ing From this our day of rest,

O balm of care and sad - ness, Most beau - ti - ful, most bright,
On thee, for our sal - va - tion, Christ rose from depths of earth;
A gar - den in - ter - sect - ed With streams of Par - a - dise;
To ho - ly con - vo - ca - tions The sil - ver trum - pet calls,
We reach the rest re - main - ing To spir - its of the blest.

On thee, the high and low - ly, Through ag - es joined in tune,
On thee, our Lord, vic - to - rious, The Spir - it sent from heav'n,
Thou art a cool - ing foun - tain, In life's dry, drear - y sand;
Where gos - pel light is glow - ing With pure and ra - diant beams,
To Ho - ly Ghost be prais - es; To Fa - ther, and to Son; .

Sing Ho - ly, Ho - ly, Ho - ly! To the great God Tri - une.
And thus on Thee, most glo - rious, A tri - ple light was giv'n,
From thee, like Pis - gah's moun - tain, We view our prom - ised land.
And liv - ing wa - ter flow - ing With soul - re - fresh - ing streams.
The Church her voice up - rais - es To Thee, blest Three in One.

45 Open Now Thy Gates of Beauty

AMEN, JESUS 8 7, 8 7, 7 7

Benjamin Schmolck, 1732
Tr. Catherine Winkworth, 1863

Andreas Peter Berggren, 1849

1. O - pen now thy gates of beau - ty, Zi - on, let me en - ter there,
2. Lord, my God, I come be - fore Thee, Do not hide Thy face from me;
3. Here Thy praise is glad - ly chant - ed, Here Thy seed is du - ly sown:
4. Thou my faith in-crease and quick-en, Let me keep Thy gift di - vine;
5. Speak, O God, and I will hear Thee; Let Thy will be done in - deed;

Where my soul, in joy-ful du - ty, Waits for Him who an-swers pray'r;
Where we find Thee, and a - dore Thee There a heav'n on earth must be;
Let my soul, where it is plant - ed, Bring forth pre-cious sheaves a - lone,
How - so - e'er temp-ta-tions thick-en, May Thy word for - ev - er shine
May I un - dis-turbed draw near Thee While Thou dost Thy peo - ple feed;

O how bless - ed is this place, Fill'd with sol - ace, light, and grace
To my heart, O en - ter Thou, Let it be Thy tem - ple now.
So that all I hear may be Fruit-ful un - to life in me.
As my guid - ing star through life, As my com-fort in the strife.
Here the liv - ing wa - ters flow, Here is balm for all our woe.

46 Blessed Jesus, at Thy Word

BLESSED JESUS, AT THY WORD 7 8, 7 8, 8 8

Tobias Clausnitzer, 1663
Tr. Catherine Winkworth, 1858

Johann Rudolph Ahle, 1664

1. Bless-ed Je - sus, at Thy word We are gath-ered all to hear Thee;
2. All our know-ledge, sense, and sight Lie in deep-est dark-ness shroud-ed,
3. Glo-rious Lord, Thy-self im-part! Light of light, from God pro-ceed - ing,

Let our hearts and souls be stirred Now to seek and love and fear Thee;
Till Thy spir - it breaks our night With the beams of truth un-cloud-ed.
O - pen Thou our ears and heart, Help us by Thy Spir - it's plead-ing;

By Thy teach-ings sweet and ho - ly, Drawn from earth to love Thee sole - ly.
Thou a - lone to God canst win us, Thou must work all good with-in us.
Hear the cry Thy peo - ple rais-es, Hear, and bless our pray'rs and prais - es.

47 Lord, We Come before Thee Now

LAST HOPE 7 7 4L.

William Hammond, 1745

Louis Gottschalk, 1867
Arr Edwin P. Parker, 1836

1. Lord, we come be - fore Thee now, At Thy feet we hum-bly bow;
2. Lord, on Thee our souls de - pend; In com - pas - sion, now de-scend,
3. In Thine own ap-point-ed way, Now we seek Thee, here we stay;
4. Send some mes-sage from Thy word, That may joy and peace af-ford;

O do not our suit dis - dain, Shall we seek Thee, Lord, in vain?
Fill our hearts with Thy rich grace, Tune our lips to sing Thy praise.
Lord, we know not how to go, Till a bless-ing Thou be - stow.
Let Thy Spir - it now im - part Full sal - va - tion to each heart.

5. Comfort those who weep and mourn,
   Let the time of joy return;
   Those that are cast down lift up,
   Strong in faith, in love, in hope.

6. Grant that those who seek may find
   Thee a God sincere and kind;
   Heal the sick, the captive free,
   Let us all rejoice in Thee.

41

48 Eternal God, Our Father

O BREAD OF LIFE 7 7 6, 7 7 8

Anna Hoppe, 1928

Heinrich Isaac, 1490
Arr. F. Melius Christiansen, 1907

1. E - ter - nal God, our Fa - ther, In Je - sus' name we gath - er
2. Thy grace in Christ con - fess - ing, We come to seek the bless - ing
3. Thy Son, our ris - en Sav - ior, Hath gained for us Thy fa - vor,
4. Heirs of Thy free sal - va - tion, May we bring con - so - la - tion
5. Thy word our hearts sus - tain - eth: Its shin - ing light re - main - eth

To praise and wor - ship Thee. Let hymns of ad - o - ra - tion And
Thy ho - ly word im - parts. Grant us through Thy blest Spir - it In
The curse of law He bore. In Shep - herd love He sought us, With
To those in need and pain. True to our Lord and Sav - ior, May
Our guide to realms a - bove. There we shall praise and bless Thee, With

pray'rs of sup - pli - ca - tion Like in - cense sweet a - rise to Thee.
fer - vent love to hear it, And keep it in be - lieve - ing hearts.
His own blood He bought us, To grant us life for - ev - er - more.
we as Chris - tians ev - er Un - spot - ted from the world re - main.
an - gel hosts con - fess Thee, And ev - er - more ex - tol Thy love.

49 Father, Source of Life and Light

ALMA MATER 7 7 6L

H N Hendrickson

H. N. Hendrickson
Harm. H. P. Opseth

1. Fa - ther, source of life and light, Who has kept us through the night,
2. Sav - ior, Mas - ter, in Thy way Guide our err - ing steps to - day
3. Ho - ly Spir - it, ev - er near, Keep our hearts from guilt - y fear.

42

Shel-tered 'neath Thy might-y wing, Thee our morn-ing praise we bring.
In temp-ta-tions try-ing hour Touch us with Thy quick-'ning pow'r.
Strengthen us for each our task More than we know how to ask.

Shine up-on us from a-bove With the ra-diance of Thy love.
Rich-est gift Thy grace can give, Teach us, Mas-ter, how to live.
Sanc-ti-fied, re-deemed, and free, Hum-bly let us walk with thee.

50 Now That the Sun Is Beaming Bright

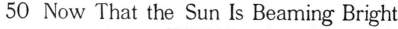

BELMONT C.M.

From the Latin

William Gardiner, 1812

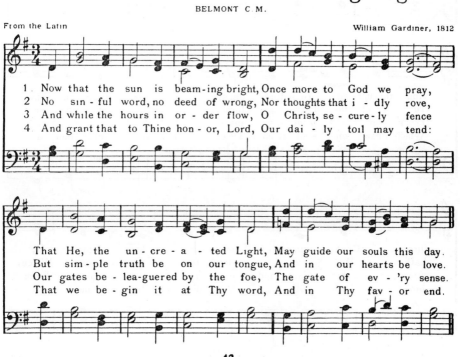

1. Now that the sun is beam-ing bright, Once more to God we pray,
2. No sin-ful word, no deed of wrong, Nor thoughts that i-dly rove,
3. And while the hours in or-der flow, O Christ, se-cure-ly fence
4. And grant that to Thine hon-or, Lord, Our dai-ly toil may tend:

That He, the un-cre-a-ted Light, May guide our souls this day.
But sim-ple truth be on our tongue, And in our hearts be love.
Our gates be-lea-guered by the foe, The gate of ev-'ry sense.
That we be-gin it at Thy word, And in Thy fav-or end.

43

51 My Heart Its Incense Burning

MY HEART ITS INCENSE BURNING 76, 7 6, 6 7, 7 6

German, Anonymous, 1592
Tr. H. Mills, 1856, alt.

German, 1598

1. My heart its in - cense burn - ing, I'll of - fer thank and praise, Now, with re - turn of morn - ing, And through all fu - ture days; I'll praise Thee on Thy throne, Great source of ev - 'ry bless - ing, My

2. Thy mer - cy ne'er for - sakes me; It kept me through the night, And now from sleep it wakes me To greet the dawn - ing light. Thy mer - cy al - so hath My man - y sins for - giv - en, Which,

3. In mer - cy still di - rect me Through-out the com - ing day: From sa - tan's wiles pro - tect me, From sin, and from dis - may: De - fend from fire and storm, From want and ev - 'ry weak - ness, From

4. Let an - gels keep their sta - tions, Nor cease their guard of me, A - vert - ing all temp - ta - tions Which draw my soul from Thee. Thy shield hold Thou a - bove! Then noth - ing shall dis - tress me, To

44

song to Thee ad - dress - ing Through Christ, Thy on - ly Son.
in the face of heav - en, So oft pro - voked Thy wrath.
sor - row and from sick - ness, From sud - den death's a - larm.
du - ty I'll ad - dress me, Re - joic - ing in Thy love.

52 Dayspring of Eternity

DAYSPRING 7 8, 7 8, 7 3

Christian K von Rosenroth, 1684
Tr J R Hopkins, 1866

J. A Freylinghausen, 1704

1. Day-spring of e - ter - ni - ty, Bright-ness of the Fa-ther's glo - ry,
2. Let Thy grace, like morn-ing dew, Fall on hearts in Thee con - fid - ing;
3. Give the flame of love to burn Till the bands of sin it break - eth,
4. Light us to the gold-en shore, O Thou ris - ing Sun of morn - ing

Dawn on us that we may see Clouds and dark-ness flee be - fore Thee;
Thy sweet com-fort, ev - er new, Fill our souls with strength a - bid - ing,
Till, at each new day's re-turn, Pur - er light my soul a - wak - eth:
Lead where tears shall flow no more, Where all sighs to songs are turn - ing,

Drive a - far, with con - quering might, All our night.
And Thy quick - 'ning eyes be - hold Thy dear fold.
O ere twi - light come, let me Rise to Thee.
Where Thy glo - ry sheds al - way Per - fect day.

45

53 O Holy Spirit, Enter In

MORNING STAR 8 8 7, 8 8 7, 4 4 4 4 8

Michael Schirmer, 1640
Tr Catherine Winkworth, 1863

Philipp Nicolai, 1599
Arr. F. Melius Christiansen, 1907

1. O Ho-ly Spir-it, en-ter in, And in our hearts Thy work be-gin,
Thy tem-ple deign to make us; Sun of the soul, Thou Light di-vine,
A-round and in us bright-ly shine, To joy and glad-ness wake us.
That we to Thee tru-ly liv-ing, To Thee giv-ing
pray'r un-ceas-ing, Still may be in love in-creas-ing.

2. Give to Thy word im-pres-sive pow'r, That in our hearts from this good hour,
As fire it may be glow-ing; That we con-fess the Fa-ther, Son,
And Thee, the Spir-it, Three in One, Thy glo-ry ev-er show-ing.
O stay and sway our souls ev-er, That they nev-er
may for-sake Thee, But by faith their ref-uge make Thee.

3. Thou Fountain whence all wis-dom flows, Which God on pi-ous hearts be-stows,
Grant us Thy con-so-la-tion, That in our pure faith's u-ni-ty
We faith-ful wit-ness-es may be, Of grace that brings sal-va-tion.
Hear us, cheer us by Thy teach-ing; Let our preach-ing
and our la-bor Praise Thee, Lord, and bless our neigh-bor.

46

54 As the Sunflower Turns in the Morning

GIFT OF GRACE 10 9 4L.

Oscar R. Overby, 1931

Ludvig M. Lindeman, 1812-1887
Arr. Oscar R. Overby, 1931

Slowly

1. As the sun-flow-er turns in the morn-ing To com-mune with the bright-ness a - broad, So, my soul, to re-ceive His a - dorn - ing, Now a - wake and re - spond to your God.
2. Dark-est night may sub-due you with sad-ness, As the sun - flow-er clos - es her heart; But the Sav - ior re-stores you to glad - ness, Bid-ding sor - row and dark - ness de - part.
3. Wait no long-er though sins may con-found you, And your er - rors im-pel you to grieve; Full for - give-ness and mer - cy sur-round you: You need on - ly a - wake and re - ceive.
4. As the sun-light from heav-en is flow-ing, Yea, un - aid - ed by flow - ers that wake, So is God in His good-ness be-stow - ing His re - demp - tion on all who par - take.
5. Should I wait for the spir - it to crum-ble, Or for sad - ness to dark - en my ways! No, re - joic - ing with heart that is hum - ble, I re - spond to the sun of His grace.

Arrangement and Text Copyright by Oscar R. Overby

See also:

The Morning Star, 146
Come, Thou almighty King, 237
Heavenly Spirit, all others transcending, 229
Come, Holy Ghost, Creator blest, 227
Come, O come, Thou quickening Spirit, 231

Christ whose glory fills the sky, 150
Holy, holy, holy, 232
O Bread of life from heaven, 90
O Holy Ghost, Thou gift divine, 225
Still, still with Thee, 335

55 Lord, Dismiss Us with Thy Blessing

REGENT SQUARE 8 7 6L.

John Fawcett, 1773

Henry Smart, 1867

1. Lord, dis-miss us with Thy bless-ing, Fill our hearts with
2. Thanks we give and ad - o - ra - tion For Thy gos - pel's
3. So, when-e'er the sig - nal's giv - en Us from earth to

joy and peace! Let us each, Thy love pos-sess - ing,
joy - ful sound. May the fruits of Thy sal - va - tion
call a - way, Borne on an - gel's wings to heav - en,

Tri - umph in re - deem - ing grace. O re - fresh us,
In our hearts and lives a - bound. May Thy pres - ence,
Glad the sum - mons to o - bey, May we read - y,

O re - fresh us, Trav - 'ling through this wil - der - ness.
May Thy pres - ence With us ev - er - more be found.
May we read - y, Rise and reign in end - less day.

48

56 O Holy Spirit, Grant Us Grace

LUTHER'S HYMN 8 7, 8 7, 8 8 7

Batholomäus Ringwaldt, 1581
Sören Jonassön, 1693
Tr O H Smeby, 1909

Joseph Klug, 1535

1. O Ho - ly Spir - it, grant us grace That we our Lord and
Sav - ior In faith and fer - vent love em-brace, And tru - ly serve Him
ev - er, So that when death is draw - ing nigh, We
to His o - pen wounds may fly, And find in them sal - va - tion.

2. Help us that we Thy sav - ing word In faith - ful hearts may
treas - ure; Let e'er that bread of life af - ford New grace in rich - est
meas - ure; Yea, let us die to ev - 'ry sin, For
heav'n cre-ate us new with - in, That fruits of faith may flour-ish.

3. And when our earth - ly race is run, Death's bit - ter hour im-
pend - ing, Then may Thy work, in us be -gun, Con - tin - ue till life's
end - ing; Un - til we glad - ly may com - mend Our
souls in - to our Sav - ior's hand, To rest in peace e - ter - nal.

49

57 Abide in Grace, Lord Jesus

ABIDE IN GRACE 7 6 4L.

Josua Stegmann, 1627
Tr F. W Detterer, 1890

Melchior Vulpius, 1609

1. A - bide in grace, Lord Je - sus, A - mong us con-stant - ly,
2. A - bide, Lord, with the sto - ry Of Thy re-deem-ing love,
3. A - bide, our path-way bright-en With Thy cel - es - tial ray,
4. A - bide with us in bless-ing, Lord of the earth and sky;
5. A - bide, our on - ly safe - ty, Thy peo-ple's sure de - fense,

Lest Sa-tan's art de - ceive us And gain the vic - to - ry
May we the gos - pel's glo - ry And sav - ing vir - tue prove
Blest Light, our souls en - light - en, Show us the truth, the way.
Rich grace and strength pos - sess - ing, Do Thou our need sup - ply!
No pow - er can with - stand Thee, Di - vine Om-nip - o - tence!

58 Blest Be the Tie That Binds

DENNIS 6 6, 8 6

John Fawcett, 1740 - 1817

Hans G. Naegeli, 1768 - 1836

1. Blest be the tie that binds Our hearts in Chris-tian love
2. Be - fore our Fa - ther's throne We pour our ar - dent pray'rs;
3. We share our mu - tual woes, Our mu - tual bur - dens bear,
4. When we a - sun - der part, It gives us in - ward pain,

The fel - low - ship of kin-dred minds Is like to that a - bove.
Our fears, our hopes, our aims are one, Our com-forts and our cares.
And oft - en for each oth - er flows The sym - pa - thiz - ing tear.
But we shall still be joined in heart, And hope to meet a - gain.

50

59 How Blest Are They Who Hear God's Word

HOW BLEST ARE THEY 8 8 7, 8 8, 7 7

Johan Nordal Brun, 1786
Tr. O. H. Smeby, 1908

Hans Thomissön's Psalmebog, 1569

1. How blest are they who hear God's word, And keep and heed what
they have heard: They wis-dom dai-ly gath-er; Their
light shines bright-er day by day, And while they tread life's wea-ry way,
They have the oil of glad-ness To soothe their pain and sad-ness.

2. God's word a trea-sure is to me, Through sor-row's night my
sun shall be, The shield of faith in bat-tle; The
Fa-ther's hand hath writ-ten there My ti-tle as His child and heir,
The king-dom's thine for-ev-er; That prom-ise fail-eth nev-er.

3. To-day I was my Sav-ior's guest, My soul was here so
rich-ly blest, The bread of life re-ceiv-ing. O
may there-by my faith pre-vail, So that its fruit shall nev-er fail
Till my ac-count is giv-en Be-fore the throne in heav-en.

51

60 Savior, Again to Thy Dear Name We Raise

BENEDICTION 10 10 4L.

John Ellerton, 1866

Edward John Hopkins, 1867

1. Sav - ior, a - gain to Thy dear name we raise With one ac -
2. Grant us Thy peace up - on our home-ward way; With Thee be -
3. Grant us Thy peace, Lord, through the com - ing night, Turn Thou for
4. Grant us Thy peace through-out our earth - ly life, Our balm in

cord our part - ing hymn of praise; Once more we bless Thee
gan, with Thee shall end the day; Guard Thou the lips from
us its dark - ness in - to light; From harm and dan - ger
sor - row and our stay in strife; Then, when Thy voice shall

ere our wor - ship cease, Then, low - ly bend - ing, wait Thy word of peace.
sin, the hearts from shame, That in this house have called up - on Thy name.
keep Thy chil - dren free, For dark and light are - both a - like to Thee.
bid our con - flict cease, Call us, O Lord, to Thine e - ter - nal peace.

61 Father Almighty, Darkness Now Is Deepening

INTEGER VITÆ 11 11, 11 5

Sven O. Sigmond, 1916

Friedrich F. Flemming, 1778 - 1813

1 Fa - ther Al - might - y, dark - ness now is deep - 'ning,
2. Bless - ed Lord Je - sus, Thou whose side is riv - en,
3. O Ho - ly Spir - it, Christ the Son ex - plain - ing,
4. Fa - ther and Son and Ho - ly Spir - it, blend - ing.

And we com-mend us to Thy gra-cious keep-ing; O may Thine
Thou by whose wounds our sins are all for-giv-en: Draw us to
Who with the Fa-ther and the Son art reign-ing, And for us
All three in One in a-ges with-out end-ing: O let Thy

an-gels guard us in our sleep-ing, Pro-tect us through this night!
Thee, Lord Je-sus, in Thy heav-en, From ev-'ry sin re-lease!
all God's won-drous life art gain-ing: Di-rect us by Thy light!
bless-ing be on us de-scend-ing, Grant us Thy per-fect peace!

62 O Happy Day When We Shall Stand

O HAPPY DAY C.M.

Wilhelm Andreas Wexels, 1846
Tr. George Taylor Rygh, 1908

Nicolaus Hermann, 1560

1. O hap-py day when we shall stand A-mid the heav'n-ly throng, And sing with
2. O bless-ed day! From far and near The ser-vants of the Lord Shall meet the
3. O what a might-y, rush-ing flood Of love with-out sur-cease, Shall roll a-
4. God, may Thy bounteous grace inspire Our hearts so that we may All join the

hosts from ev-'ry land The new ce-les-tial song, The new ce-les-tial song.
ran-somed millions there Who heard God's saving word, Who heard God's saving word.
bout the throne of God In joy and end-less peace, In joy and end-less peace!
heav'nly, white-robed choir Up-on that glo-rious day, Up-on that glo-rious day.

53

63 And Now We Must Bid One Another Farewell

AND NOW WE MUST BID 11 9, 11 9, 5 5 9

Martha Clausen, ca. 1830
Tr. George Taylor Rygh, 1908

Ludvig M Lindeman, 1812-1887

1. And now we must bid one an-oth-er fare-well; The peace of our God keep you ev - er! God's peace in our bos-om, and all will be well, Or wheth-er we meet or we sev - er. May Christ, our dear Lord, Be our sure re-ward When we from this world pass for - ev - er!

2 O help us, dear Fa - ther, and Christ, Thou the Son, That glad - ly our course we may fin - ish! And Thou, Ho - ly Spir-it, Thou com-fort-ing One, Thy love in our hearts so re-plen - ish, That we by Thy might May fight the good fight, Till won is the crown ev - er - last - ing

64 Seal My Heart with Thine Impressure

O WHAT PRECIOUS BALM 8 7, 8 7, 7 7, 8 8

Thomas Kingo, 1689
Tr. Composite

Louis Bourgeois 1551

1. Seal my heart with Thine im-pres-sure, Je-sus, King and God of Grace,

That no pain or earth-born pleas-ure Shall Thine im-age there ef-face.

Let this im-print, Lord, a-bide: Je-sus Christ, the Cru-ci-fied,

Is my life, my firm foun-da-tion, All my glo-ry and sal-va-tion.

65 Lord, Bestow on Us Thy Blessing

O WHAT PRECIOUS BALM 87, 87, 77, 88

Jesper Swedberg, 1653-1735
Tr. V. E. Boe, 1932

Lord, bestow on us Thy blessing,
Let Thy face upon us shine;
May we all, Thy grace possessing,
Walk within Thy light divine.
Come and visit every heart
And Thy peace to us impart.
Father, Son, and Spirit hear us,
Be Thou now and ever near us.

66 Friends of Jesus in Their Parting

FRIENDS OF JESUS 8 7 6L.

Jens N.L. Schjörring, 1825
Tr. C.K. Solberg

Swedish Folk-Tune

1. "Friends of Je - sus in their part - ing On - ly part to meet a - gain;"
2. Though be - neath the star - ry heav - ens We may chance to meet no more,
3. Here we oft - en say with sad - ness To our friends a sad "fare - well,"
4. When the part - ing tears are flow - ing, Sing this glad and sweet re - frain:

When the part - ing tears are flow - ing, This shall be their sweet re - frain,
Still we know as saints in glo - ry We shall meet on yon - der shore.
Yon - der we shall meet with glad - ness, As our wel - come we shall tell.
"Friends of Je - sus in their part - ing On - ly part to meet a - gain.

"Friends of Je - sus in their part - ing On - ly part to meet a - gain."
Still we know as saints in glo - ry We shall meet on yon - der shore.
Yon - der we shall meet with glad - ness, As our wel - come we shall tell.
Friends of Je - sus in their part - ing On - ly part to meet a - gain."

67 Now the Day Is Over

MERRIAL 6 5 4L

Sabine Baring-Gould, 1865

Joseph Barnby, 1868

1. Now the day is o - ver, Night is draw - ing nigh;____
2. Je - sus, give the wea - ry Calm and sweet re - pose;____
3. Grant to lit - tle chil - dren Vi - sions bright of Thee;____
4. Com - fort ev - 'ry suf - f'rer Watch - ing late in pain;

Shad - ows of the ev - 'ning Steal a - cross the sky.
With Thy ten-d'rest bless - ing May our eye-lids close.
Guard the sail - ors toss - ing On the deep blue sea.
Those who plan some e - vil From their sins re - frain.

Ev 'ning steal a - cross the sky;

5. Through the long night-watches,
   May Thine angels spread
   Their white wings above me,
   Watching 'round my bed.

6. When the morning wakens,
   Then may I arise
   Pure, and fresh, and sinless
   In Thy holy eyes.

68 The Sun Is Sinking in the West

AT SUNSET 8 8, 6 6

Andreas Bersagel, 1914
Tr. and St. 3, V.E. Boe, 1931

V. E. Boe, 1914

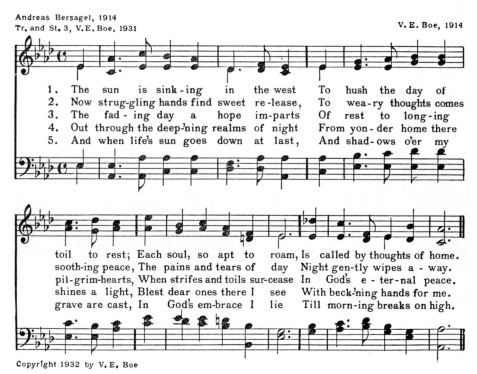

1. The sun is sink-ing in the west To hush the day of
2. Now strug-gling hands find sweet re-lease, To wea-ry thoughts comes
3. The fad - ing day a hope im-parts Of rest to long-ing
4. Out through the deep-'ning realms of night From yon - der home there
5. And when life's sun goes down at last, And shad-ows o'er my

toil to rest; Each soul, so apt to roam, Is called by thoughts of home.
sooth-ing peace, The pains and tears of day Night gen-tly wipes a - way.
pil-grim-hearts, When strifes and toils sur-cease In God's e - ter-nal peace.
shines a light, Blest dear ones there I see With beck-'ning hands for me.
grave are cast, In God's em-brace I lie Till morn-ing breaks on high.

Copyright 1932 by V. E. Boe

69 Brothers and Sisters, We Now Must Depart

PARTING HYMN 10 10 8

St. 1-2 Jens Larsen, ca. 1860
St. 3-4 Frederik Boye, ca. 1750
Tr. J.C. Aaberg

Danish Tune

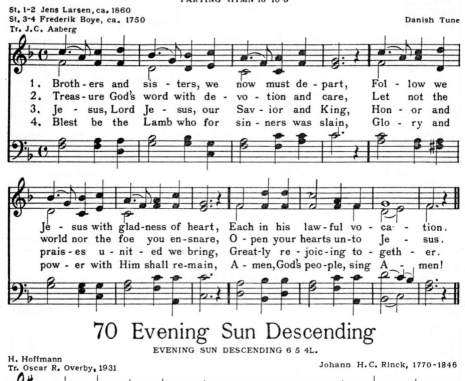

1. Broth-ers and sis-ters, we now must de-part, Fol-low we
2. Treas-ure God's word with de-vo-tion and care, Let not the
3. Je-sus, Lord Je-sus, our Sav-ior and King, Hon-or and
4. Blest be the Lamb who for sin-ners was slain, Glo-ry and

Je-sus with glad-ness of heart, Each in his law-ful vo-ca-tion.
world nor the foe you en-snare, O-pen your hearts un-to Je-sus.
prais-es u-nit-ed we bring, Great-ly re-joic-ing to-geth-er.
pow-er with Him shall re-main, A-men, God's peo-ple, sing A-men!

70 Evening Sun Descending

EVENING SUN DESCENDING 6 5 4L.

H. Hoffmann
Tr. Oscar R. Overby, 1931

Johann H.C. Rinck, 1770-1846

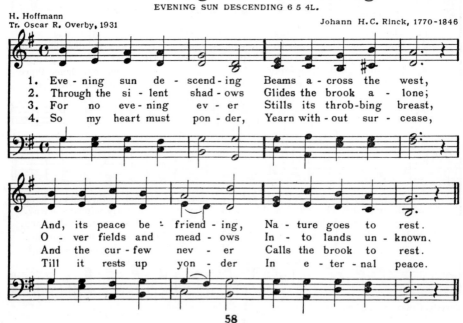

1. Eve-ning sun de-scend-ing Beams a-cross the west,
2. Through the si-lent shad-ows Glides the brook a-lone;
3. For no eve-ning ev-er Stills its throb-bing breast,
4. So my heart must pon-der, Yearn with-out sur-cease,

And, its peace be-friend-ing, Na-ture goes to rest.
O-ver fields and mead-ows In-to lands un-known.
And the cur-few nev-er Calls the brook to rest.
Till it rests up yon-der In e-ter-nal peace.

58

71 Softly Now the Light of Day

SEYMOUR 7 7 4L.

George W. Doane, 1827

Arr. fr. Carl M. von Weber, 1826

1. Soft - ly now the light of day Fades up - on my sight a - way;
2. Thou, whose all per - vad - ing eye Naught es - capes, with - out, with - in,
3. Soon for me the light of day Shall for - ev - er pass a - way;
4. Thou who, sin - less, yet hast known All of man's in - firm - i - ty,

Free from care, from la - bor free, Lord, I would com - mune with Thee.
Par - don each in - firm - i - ty, O - pen fault and se - cret sin
Then, from sin and sor - row free, Take me, Lord, to dwell with Thee
Then, from Thy e - ter - nal throne, Je - sus, look with pit - ying eye

72 Savior, Breathe an Evening Blessing

EVENING BLESSING 8 7 4L.

James Edmeston, 1820

Halfdan Kjerulf, 1815-1868
Arr. Oscar R Overby, 1932

1. Sav - ior, breathe an eve - ning bless - ing, Ere re - pose our spir - its seal; Sin and
2. Though de-struc-tion walk a - round us, Though the ar - row past us fly, An - gel-
3. Though the night be dark and drea - ry, Dark - ness can - not hide from Thee; Thou art
4. Should swift death this night o'er-take us, And our couch be-come our tomb, May the

want we come con - fess - ing; Thou can save, and Thou can heal. Thou can save, and Thou can heal.
guards from Thee sur-round us; We are safe if Thou art nigh. We are safe if Thou art nigh.
He who nev - er wea - ry, Watchest where Thy peo - ple be. Watchest where Thy peo - ple be.
morn in heav'n a - wake us, Clad in bright and death-less bloom. Clad in bright and death-less bloom.

73 God, That Madest Earth and Heaven

WELSH HYMN 8 4, 8 4, 8 8, 8 4

St. 1. Reginald Heber, 1783-1826
St 2-3. William Mercer, 1864

Welsh Traditional
Jones' Relics of the Welsh Bards, 1784

1. God, that mad-est earth and heav-en, Dark-ness and light;
2. And when morn a-gain shall call us To run life's way,
3. Ho-ly Fa-ther, throned in heav-en, All ho-ly Son,

Who the day for toil hath giv-en, For rest the night;
May we still, what-e'er be-fall us, Thy will o-bey.
Ho-ly Spir-it, free-ly giv-en, Blest Three in One!

May Thine ang-el-guard de-fend us, Slum-ber sweet Thy mer-cy send us,
From the pow'r of e-vil hide us, In the nar-row path-way guide us,
Grant Thy grace, we now im-plore Thee, Till we cast our crowns be-fore Thee,

Ho-ly dreams and hopes at-tend us, This live-long night.
Nor Thy smile be e'er de-nied us, The live-long day.
And in worth-ier strains a-dore Thee, While a-ges run.

74 The Sun Has Gone Down

THE SUN HAS GONE DOWN 5 11, 11 11, 11 5 5
(Or use   O LAND OF OUR KING, NO. 345)

Samuel O. Bruun, 1694
Tr O.T Sanden, 1908

Norwegian Folk-Tune

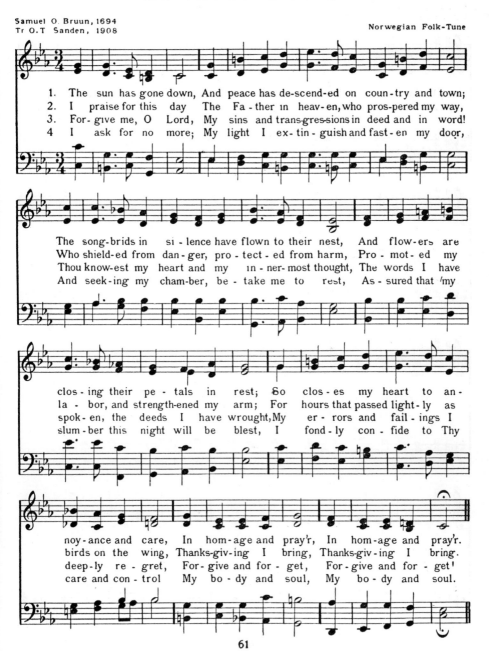

1. The sun has gone down, And peace has de-scend-ed on coun-try and town;
2. I praise for this day The Fa-ther in heav-en, who pros-pered my way,
3. For-give me, O Lord, My sins and trans-gres-sions in deed and in word!
4. I ask for no more; My light I ex-tin-guish and fast-en my door,

The song-brids in si-lence have flown to their nest, And flow-ers are
Who shield-ed from dan-ger, pro-tect-ed from harm, Pro-mot-ed my
Thou know-est my heart and my in-ner-most thought, The words I have
And seek-ing my cham-ber, be-take me to rest, As-sured that my

clos-ing their pe-tals in rest; So clos-es my heart to an-
la-bor, and strength-ened my arm; For hours that passed light-ly as
spok-en, the deeds I have wrought, My er-rors and fail-ings I
slum-ber this night will be blest, I fond-ly con-fide to Thy

noy-ance and care, In hom-age and pray'r, In hom-age and pray'r.
birds on the wing, Thanks-giv-ing I bring, Thanks-giv-ing I bring.
deep-ly re-gret, For-give and for-get, For-give and for-get!
care and con-trol My bo-dy and soul, My bo-dy and soul.

75 The Day Is Fast Declining

O LIVING BREAD 7 6 8L.

Hans J Himmerich, 1681-1735
Wilhelm Andreas Wexels, 1797-1866
Tr V. E. Boe, 1929

Zinck's Koralbog, 1801

1. The day is fast de - clin - ing And night is draw-ing near;
2. When dark-ness earth has blind - ed And day has passed from sight,

Thy mer - cy, Lord, is shin - ing, Dis - pel - ling all our fear.
We are, O Lord, re - mind - ed Of death's ap - proach-ing night.

Our sins for - give, O Fa - ther, Pro - tect us great and small,
Il - lum - ine Thou our pas - sage, O Je - sus, dear-est Friend,

Thy ho - ly ang - els gath - er To watch a - round us all.
Send us Thy glad-some mes - sage, Grant us a bless - ed end.

76 God Be with You Now and Ever

DECK THYSELF 8 8 8L.

Oscar R. Overby, 1932

Johann Crüger, 1649

1. God be with you now and ev - er, When we meet and when we
2. Fa - ther, mer - ci - ful and ten - der, All to Thee we now sur -

se - ver. He will keep you, He will guide you; In His
ren - der. Bless each part - ing joy and sor - row Till we

love se - cure - ly hide you Turn your heart from all af -
meet up - on the mor - row Peace di - vine, all peace tran -

flic - tion, And re - ceive His ben - e - dic - tion. God be
scend-ing, Keep each heart thro' days un - end - ing. God be

with you now and ev - er, When we meet and when we sev - er.
with you now and ev - er, When we meet and when we sev - er.

63

77 Sun of My Soul! Thou Savior Dear

HURSLEY L.M.

John Keble, 1827

Peter Ritter, 1792
Arr. William H. Monk

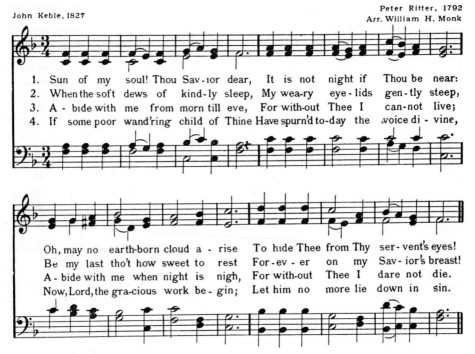

1. Sun of my soul! Thou Sav-ior dear, It is not night if Thou be near:
2. When the soft dews of kind-ly sleep, My wea-ry eye-lids gen-tly steep,
3. A - bide with me from morn till eve, For with-out Thee I can-not live;
4. If some poor wand'ring child of Thine Have spurn'd to-day the voice di - vine,

Oh, may no earth-born cloud a - rise To hide Thee from Thy ser-vent's eyes!
Be my last tho't how sweet to rest For-ev - er on my Sav-ior's breast!
A - bide with me when night is nigh, For with-out Thee I dare not die.
Now, Lord, the gra-cious work be - gin; Let him no more lie down in sin.

5. Watch by the sick; enrich the poor
With blessings from Thy boundless store;
Be every mourner's sleep tonight,
Like infants' slumbers, pure and light.

6. Come near and bless us when we wake,
Ere through the world our way we take,
Till in the ocean of Thy love
We lose ourselves in heaven above.

See also·
God's Word is our great heritage, 91
There is an eye that never sleeps, 25
Abide with me, 340
Gracious Spirit, Dove divine, 230
Now Jesus at the door is knocking, 119
O God, our help in ages past, 142
Jesus rule my thoughts, 365
Now thank we all our God, 242
From all that dwell, 35
Let me be Thine forever, 234
Peace to soothe our bitter woes, 210
Stay with us, Lord, 201
Alone with Thee, O Lord, 332

II. Church and Means of Grace

1. Church

2. Word of God

3. Baptism

4. Lord's Supper

5. Confirmation

6. Ministry

II. Church and Means of Grace

78 Glorious Things of Thee Are Spoken

AUSTRIA 8 7 8L.

John Newton, 1779

Franz Joseph Haydn, 1797

1. Glo - rious things of thee are spok- en, Zi - on, cit - y of our God;
2. See, the streams of liv - ing wa - ters Springing from e - ter - nal love,
3. Round each hab - i - ta - tion hov.'-ring, See the cloud and fire ap - pear
4. Sav - ior, if of Zi - on's cit - y I, thro' grace, a mem - ber am,

He whose word can - not be brok - en, Form'd thee for His own a - bode;
Well sup - ply thy sons and daugh-ters, And all fear of want re - move.
For a glo - ry and a cov -'ring, Show - ing that the Lord is near;
Let the world de - ride or pit - y, I will glo - ry in Thy name.

On the Rock of A - ges found - ed, What can shake thy sure re - pose?
Who can faint, while such a riv - er Ev - er flows their thirst t'assuage.
Thus they march, the pil - lar lead - ing, Light by night and shade by day;
Fad - ing is the world-ling's pleas-ure, All his boast-ed pomp and show;

With sal - va - tion's walls sur - round-ed, Thou may smile at all thy foes.
Grace which, like the Lord, the giv - er, Nev - er fails from age to age.
Dai - ly on the man - na feed - ing Which He gives them when they pray.
Sol - id joys and last - ing treas-ure None but Zi - on's chil - dren know.

79 How Fair the Church of Christ Shall Stand

HOW FAIR THE CHURCH L.M. 6L.

Thomas Kingo, 1699
Tr. O.T. Sanden, 1908

Schumann's Gesangbuch, 1539

1. How fair the Church of Christ shall stand, A bea-con-light in all the land, When love and faith all hearts in-spire, And all u-nite in one de-sire To be as broth-ers, and a-gree To live in peace and u-ni-ty.

2. 'Tis all in vain that you pro-fess The doc-trines of the Church, un-less You live ac-cord-ing to your creed, And show your faith by word and deed. Ob-serve the rule: To oth-ers do As you would have them do to you.

3. Re-sent-ment, hate, and cru-el jest, Must not be har-bored in the breast Where love and char-i-ty should dwell; Then, think and speak of oth-ers well, Re-frain from all that caus-es strife And mars a tru-ly Chris-tian life.

4. So let your tongue, your heart, and mind, A-gree to ban-ish ev-'ry kind Of ma-lice, false-hood, and dis-guise, And here on earth a par-a-dise Of peace and har-mon-y main-tain, Where con-cord and good will shall reign.

5. O gra-cious God, wilt Thou my heart So fash-ion in each se-cret part, That Thou be sanc-ti-fied in me, Till Thee in heav'n a-bove I see, Where ho-ly, ho-ly, ho-ly, Lord, We sing to Thee with sweet ac-cord.

80 The Church's One Foundation

AURELIA 7 6 8L.

Samuel J. Stone, 1839 - 1901

Samuel S. Wesley, 1864

1. The Church's one foun - da - tion, Is Je - sus Christ her Lord;
2. E - lect from ev - 'ry na - tion, Yet one o'er all the earth;
3. 'Mid toil and trib - u - la - tion, And tu - mult of her war,
4. Yet she on earth hath un - ion, With God, the Three in One,

She is His new cre - a - tion, By wa - ter and the word:
Her char - ter of sal - va - tion, One Lord, one Faith, one birth;
She waits the con - sum - ma - tion Of peace for ev - er - more;
And mys - tic sweet com - mun - ion With those whose rest is won:

From heav'n He came and sought her To be His ho - ly Bride;
One ho - ly Name she bless - es, Par - takes one ho - ly food;
Till with the vis - ion glo - rious Her long - ing eyes are blest,
Oh, hap - py ones and ho - ly! Lord, give us grace, that we,

With His own blood He bought her, And for her life He died.
And to one hope she press - es, With ev - 'ry grace en - dued.
And the great Church vic - to - rious, Shall be the Church at rest.
Like them, the meek and low - ly, On high may dwell with Thee.

81 Built on the Rock the Church Doth Stand

BUILT ON THE ROCK 8 8 7L.

Nicolai F. S. Grundtvig, 1837
Tr. Carl Doving, 1909

Ludvig M. Lindeman, 1812-1887

1. Built on the Rock the Church doth stand, Ev - en when stee - ples are
2. Sure - ly in tem - ples made with hands, God, the Most High, is not
3. We are God's house of liv - ing stones, Build - ed for His hab - i -
4. Still we our earth - ly tem - ples rear, That we may her - ald His
5. Here stands the font be - fore our eyes Tell - ing how God did re -

fall - ing; Crum - bled have spires in ev - 'ry land, Bells still are
dwell - ing, High a - bove earth His tem - ple stands, All earth - ly
ta - tion; He thro' bap - tis - mal grace us owns, Heirs of His
prais - es; They are the homes where He draws near And lit - tle
ceive us; Th' al - tar re - calls Christ's sac - ri - fice And what His

chim - ing and call - ing; Call - ing the young and old to rest,
tem - ples ex - cell - ing; Yet He whom heav'ns can - not con - tain
won - drous sal - va - tion; Were we but two His name to tell,
chil - dren em - brac - es, Beau - ti - ful things in them are said,
ta - ble doth give us; Here sounds the word that doth pro - claim

But a - bove all the soul dis - trest, Long - ing for rest ev - er - last - ing.
Chose to a - bide on earth with men, Built in our bod - ies His tem - ple.
Yet He would deign with us to dwell, With all His grace and His fav - or.
God there with us His cov - 'nant made, Mak - ing us heirs of His king - dom.
Christ yes - ter - day, to - day the same, Yea, and for aye our Re - deem - er.

82 Through the Night of Doubt and Sorrow

PILGRIM SONG 8 7 8L.

Bernhard S. Ingemann, 1843
Tr. Sabine Baring-Gould

Latin Hymn

1. Through the night of doubt and sor - row On-ward goes the pil - grim band
2. One the light of God's own pres-ence, O'er His ran-somed peo-ple shed,
3. One the strain the lips of thou-sands, Lift as from the heart of one;
4. On - ward there-fore, pil - grim broth-ers! On-ward, with the cross our aid!

Sing-ing songs of ex - pect - ta - tion, March-ing to the prom-ised Land.
Chas-ing far the gloom and ter - ror, Bright-ning all the path we tread:
One the con-flict, one the per - il, One the march in God be - gun:
Bear its shame, and fight its bat - tle, Till we rest be - neath its shade!

Clear be - fore us, thro' the dark-ness, Gleams and burns the guid-ing light.
One the ob - ject of our jour-ney, One the faith which nev - er tires,
One the glad-ness of re - joic-ing On the far e - ter-nal shore,
Soon shall come the great a - wak-ing, Soon, the rend-ing of the tomb,

Broth-er clasps the hand of broth-er, Step-ping fear-less thro' the night.
One the earn-est look-ing for-ward, One the hope our God in - spires.
Where the One Al - might-y Fath-er Reigns in love for ev - er - more.
Then the scat-t'ring of all sha-dows, And the end of toil and gloom.

83 I Love Thy Kingdom, Lord

ST. THOMAS S.M.

Timothy Dwight, 1800

Aaron Williams, Ca. 1760

1. I love Thy king - dom, Lord, The house of Thine a - bode,
2. I love Thy Church, O God! Her walls be - fore Thee stand,
3. For her my tears shall fall; For her my pray'rs as - cend;
4. Be-yond my high - est joy I prize her heav'n - ly ways,
5. Sure as Thy truth shall last, To Zi - on shall be giv'n.

The Church our blest Re - deem-er saved With His own pre - cious blood.
Dear as the ap - ple of Thine eye, And gra - ven on Thy hand.
To her my cares and toils be giv'n, Till toils and cares shall end.
Her sweet com-mun - ion, sol - emn vows, Her hymns of love and praise.
The bright-est glo - ries earth can yield, And bright - er bliss of heav'n.

See also:

84 Thy Word, O Lord, Like Gentle Dews

I SEE THEE STANDING, LAMB OF GOD C.M.D.

Karl B. Garve, 1825
Tr. Catherine Winkworth, 1855

Unknown

1. Thy Word, O Lord, like gen-tle dews, Falls soft on hearts that pine;
2. Thy Word is like a flam-ing sword, A wedge that cleav-eth stone;
3. Thy Word, a won-drous guid-ing star, On pil-grim hearts doth rise,

Lord, to Thy gar-den ne'er re-fuse This heav'n-ly balm of Thine.
Keen as a fire, so burns Thy word, And pierc-eth flesh and bone.
Leads those to God who dwell a-far, And makes the sim-ple wise.

Wa-tered by Thee, let ev-'ry tree Forth blos-som to Thy praise,
Let it go forth o'er all the earth, To cleanse our hearts with-in,
Let not its light e'er sink in night; In ev-'ry spir-it shine,

By grace of Thine bear fruit di-vine, Thro' all the com-ing days.
To show Thy pow'r in Sa-tan's hour And break the might of sin.
That none may miss heav'ns fi-nal bliss, Led by Thy light di-vine.

85 We Have a Sure, Prophetic Word

LORD JESUS CHRIST, BE PREST NOW L.M.

E. Cronemvett, 1880

Cantionale Sacrum, Gotha, 1651
Arr. F. Melius Christiansen, 1907

1. We have a sure, pro - phet - ic word, By in - spir - a - tion of the Lord; And though as - sailed on ev - 'ry hand, Je - ho - vah's word shall ev - er stand.
2. By pow'rs of em - pire banned and burned, By pa - gan pride re - ject - ed spured, The word still stands the Chris - tian's trust, While haugh - ty em - pires lie in dust.
3. Lo, what the word in times of old Of fu - ture days and deeds fore - told, Is all ful - filled, while ag - es roll, As traced on that pro - phet - ic scroll.
4. A - bid - ing, stead - fast, firm, and sure, The sta - tues of our God en - dure: Blest he who trusts this stead - fast word; His an - chor holds in Christ, the Lord.

86 Lord, Keep Us Steadfast in Thy Word

LORD KEEP US STEADFAST L.M.

Martin Luther, 1541
Tr. Catherine Winkworth, 1863

German, 1543

1. Lord, keep us stead-fast in Thy word: Curb those who fain by craft or sword
2. Lord Je - sus Christ, Thy pow'r make known; For Thou art Lord of lords a - lone:
3. O Com-fort - er, of price-less worth, Send peace and u - ni - ty on earth;

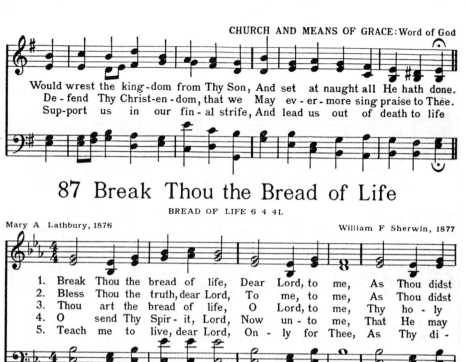

Would wrest the king-dom from Thy Son, And set at naught all He hath done.
De-fend Thy Christ-en-dom, that we May ev-er-more sing praise to Thee.
Sup-port us in our fin-al strife, And lead us out of death to life

87 Break Thou the Bread of Life

BREAD OF LIFE 6 4 4 L

Mary A Lathbury, 1876

William F Sherwin, 1877

1. Break Thou the bread of life, Dear Lord, to me, As Thou didst
2. Bless Thou the truth, dear Lord, To me, to me, As Thou didst
3. Thou art the bread of life, O Lord, to me, Thy ho - ly
4. O send Thy Spir - it, Lord, Now un - to me, That He may
5. Teach me to live, dear Lord, On - ly for Thee, As Thy di -

break the loaves Be - side the sea; Be - yond the sa - cred page
bless the bread By Gal - i - lee; Then shall all bond-age cease,
word the truth That sav - eth me; Give me to eat and live
touch my eyes, And make me see: Show me the truth con-cealed
sci - ples lived In Gal - i - lee; Then, all my strug-gles o'er,

I seek Thee, Lord; My spir - it pants for Thee, O liv-ing Word!
All fet - ters fall; And I shall find my peace, My All-in - all!
With Thee a - bove; Teach me to love Thy truth, For Thou art love.
With - in Thy word, And in Thy book re - veal'd I see the Lord.
Then vict - 'ry won, I shall be - hold Thee, Lord, The liv-ing One.

88 Thy Word Is Like a Garden, Lord

SERAPH 8 6 8L.

Thomas H. Gill, 1819-1906

Old Melody

1. Thy Word is like a gar - den, Lord, With flow-ers bright and fair;
2. Thy Word is like a star - ry host; A thou-sand rays of light
3. O may I love Thy pre - cious Word, May I ex - plore the mine,

And ev -'ry one who seeks may pluck A love - ly clus - ter there.
Are seen to guide the trav - el - er And make his path - way bright.
May I its fra - grant flow-ers glean, May light up - on me shine!

Thy Word is like a deep, deep mine; And jew - els rich and rare
Thy Word is like an ar - mor - y, Where sol - diers may re - pair,
O may I find my ar - mor there, Thy Word my trust - y sword;

Are hid - den in its might-y depths For ev - 'ry search - er there.
And find for life's long bat - tle - day, All need - full weap - ons there.
I'll learn to fight with ev - 'ry foe The bat - tle of the Lord.

76

89 O Word of God Incarnate

MÜNICH 7 6 8L.

William W. How, 1867 — Meiningisches Gesangbuch, 1693

1. O Word of God in - car - nate, O Wis - dom from on high,
   O Truth un-changed, un-chang-ing, O Light of our dark sky;
   We praise Thee for the ra - diance That from the hal - lowed page,
   A lamp un - to our foot-steps, Shines on from age to age.

2. The Church from her dear Mas - ter Re - ceived the gift di - vine,
   And still that light she lift - ed O'er all the earth to shine.
   It is the gold - en cask - et Where gems of truth are stored;
   It is the heav'n-drawn pic - ture Of Christ, the liv - ing Word.

3. It float - eth like a ban - ner Be - fore God's host un - furled;
   It shin - eth like a bea - con A - bove the dark-ling world;
   It is the chart and com - pass That o'er life's surg - ing sea,
   A - mid the rocks and quick-sands Still guides, O Christ, to Thee.

4. O make Thy Church, dear Sav - ior, A lamp of burn-ished gold,
   To bear be - fore the na - tions Thy true light as of old;
   O teach Thy wand'ring pil - grims By this their path to trace,
   Till, clouds and dark - ness end - ed, They see Thee face to face.

90 O Bread of Life from Heaven

O BREAD OF LIFE 7 7 6, 7 7 8

Latin, Anonymous, 1661
Tr. Philip Schaff, 1869

Heinrich Isaac, 1490
Arr. F. Melius Christiansen, 1907

1. O Bread of life from heav - en, To wea - ry pil - grims giv - en,
2. O Fount of grace re - deem-ing, O Riv - er ev - er stream - ing
3. O Lord, this feast re - ceiv - ing, Thy word of truth be - liev - ing,

O Man - na from a bove: The souls that hun-ger feed Thou, The
From Je - sus' ho - ly side: Come Thou, Thy-self be - stow - ing On
We Thee un - seen a - dore: Grant, when our race is end - ed, That

hearts that seek Thee lead Thou, With Thy most sweet and ten - der love.
thirst - ing souls, and flow - ing Till all their wants are sat - is - fied.
we, to heav'n as - cend - ed, May see Thy glo - ry ev - er - more.

91 God's Word Is Our Great Heritage

EIN FESTE BURG 8 7, 8 7, 6 6, 6 6 7

Nicolai E. S. Grundtvig, 1817
Tr. George Taylor Rygh, 1909

Martin Luther, 1529

God's word is our great her - it - age, And shall be ours for-

ev - er; To spread its light from age to age Shall

be our chief en-deav - or; Through life it guides our way,

In death it is our stay; Lord grant, while worlds en - dure,

We keep its teach-ings pure, Through-out all gen-er-a - tions.

92 Father of Mercies, in Thy Word

EVAN C.M.

Anna Steele, 1760

William H. Havergal, 1846

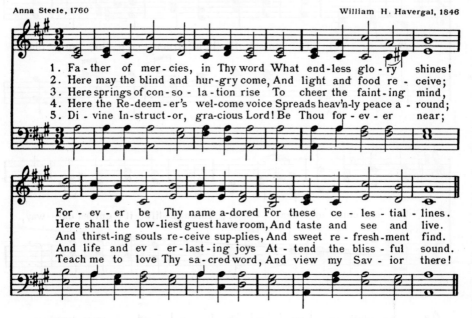

1. Fa - ther of mer - cies, in Thy word What end - less glo - ry shines!
2. Here may the blind and hur - gry come, And light and food re - ceive;
3. Here springs of con - so - la - tion rise To cheer the faint - ing mind,
4. Here the Re - deem - er's wel - come voice Spreads heav'n - ly peace a - round;
5. Di - vine In - struct - or, gra - cious Lord! Be Thou for - ev - er near;

For - ev - er be Thy name a - dored For these ce - les - tial - lines.
Here shall the low - liest guest have room, And taste and see and live.
And thirst - ing souls re - ceive sup - plies, And sweet re - fresh - ment find.
And life and ev - er - last - ing joys At - tend the bliss - ful sound.
Teach me to love Thy sa - cred word, And view my Sav - ior there!

93 How Precious Is the Book Divine

ST. PETER C.M.

John Fawcett, 1782

Alexander Robert Reinagle, 1826

1. How pre - cious is the Book di - vine, By in - spi - ra - tion giv'n!
2. It sweet - ly cheers our droop - ing hearts In this dark vale of tears;
3. This lamp thro' all the te - dious night Of life shall guide our way,

Bright as a lamp its doc - trines shine, To guide our souls to heav'n.
Life, light, and joy it still im - parts, And quells our ris - ing fears.
Till we be - hold the clear - er light Of an e - ter - nal day.

See also:
Deep and glorious, 160

94 He That Believes and Is Baptized

HE THAT BELIEVES 8 7, 8 7, 8 8 7

Thomas Kingo, 1689
Tr. George Taylor Rygh, 1909·

German, 1529

1. He that be - lieves and is bap-tized Shall see the Lord's sal -
va - tion; Bap - tized in - to the death of Christ, He is a new cre -
a - tion; Through Christ's re - demp - tion he shall stand A -
mong the glo-rious heav'n-ly band Of ev - 'ry tribe and na - tion.

2. With one ac - cord, O God, we pray: Grant us Thy Ho - ly
Spir - it; Look Thou on our in - fir - mi - ty Through Je-sus' blood and
mer - it! Grant us to grow in grace each day By
ho - ly bap-tism that we may E - ter-nal life in - her - it!

81

95 Abide among Us, We Implore Thee

ABIDE AMONG US 9 8 4L.

Nicolai F. S. Grundtvig, 1837
Tr. Carl Doving, 1909

Ludvig M. Lindeman, 1812-1887

1. A - bide a - mong us, we im - plore Thee,
2. Lord, aft - er Thee we Chris - tians call them,
3. If Thou their earth - ly race shouldst length - en,
4. O write Thy bless - ed name, dear Sav - ior,

Lord Je - sus Christ, Thy Spir - it breathe! And let the babes we
O let them in Thy name a - rise! And keep them Thine what-
Thy faith - ful ser - vants let them prove; If few their days, their
Up - on their hearts, we Thee im - plore; And on Thy palms en -

bring be - fore Thee Now be bap - tized in - to Thy death.
e'er be - fall them, That they may reach Thy Par - a - dise.
weak - ness strength - en, That they may share Thy dy - ing love.
grave this fa - vor, That they are Thine for - ev - er - more.

96 Savior, Who Thy Flock Art Feeding

BROCKLESBURY 8 7 4L.

William A. Muhlenberg, 1826

Charlotte A. Barnard, 1868

1. Sav - ior, who Thy flock art feed - ing With the shep-herd's kind-est care;
2. Now, these lit - tle ones re - ceiv - ing, Fold them in Thy gra-cious arm;
3. Nev - er, from Thy pres-ence rov - ing, Let them be the li - on's prey;
4. Then, with - in Thy fold e - ter - nal, Let them find a rest-ing-place,

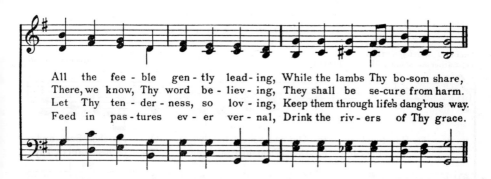

All the fee - ble gen - tly lead- ing, While the lambs Thy bo-som share,
There, we know, Thy word be - liev - ing, They shall be se-cure from harm.
Let Thy ten - der - ness, so lov - ing, Keep them through life's dang'rous way.
Feed in pas - tures ev - er ver - nal, Drink the riv - ers of Thy grace.

97 O Lord, Our Little Ones to Thee

O LORD, OUR LITTLE ONES C.M

William Whiting, 1872

Ludwig van Beethoven, 1770-1827

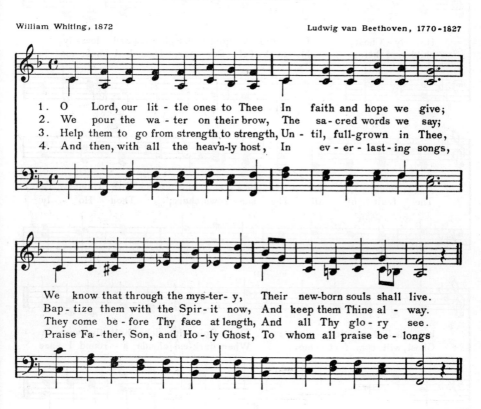

1. O Lord, our lit - tle ones to Thee In faith and hope we give;
2. We pour the wa - ter on their brow, The sa - cred words we say;
3. Help them to go from strength to strength, Un - til, full-grown in Thee,
4. And then, with all the heav'n-ly host, In ev - er - last-ing songs,

We know that through the mys-ter- y, Their new-born souls shall live.
Bap - tize them with the Spir- it now, And keep them Thine al - way.
They come be - fore Thy face at length, And all Thy glo - ry see.
Praise Fa - ther, Son, and Ho - ly Ghost, To whom all praise be - longs

98 Baptized into Thy Name Most Holy

WHO KNOWS HOW NEAR 9 8, 9 8, 8 8

Johann J Rambach, 1735
Tr. Catherine Winkworth, 1829-1879

German, 1690

1 Bap-tized in - to Thy name most ho - ly,   O   Fa - ther, Son, and
2 My   lov - ing   Fa - ther, Thou dost take me   To   be hence-forth Thy

Ho   ly Ghost,   I   claim a   place, though weak and   low - ly,
child and heir;   My   faith - ful   Sav - ior, Thou dost   make me

A - mong Thy   seed, Thy   chos - en   host;   With   Christ   I'm
The   fruit   of   all   Thy   sor - rows share;   Thou   Ho - ly

bur - ied, dead   to   sin,   Thy   Spir - it   now shall   live with-in
Ghost, wilt com - fort   me,   When dark-est clouds a - round I   see

99 Lamb of God Most Holy

LAMB OF GOD 6 7, 6 7, 7 7 8

Nicolaus Decius, 1531
Tr. Arthur T. Russel, 1848

German, 1540
Arr. F. Melius Christiansen, 1907

1. Lamb of God most ho - ly! Who on the cross didst suf-fer,
2. Lamb of God most ho - ly! Who on the cross didst suf-fer,
3. Lamb of God most ho - ly! Who on the cross didst suf-fer,

Pa - tient still and low - ly, Thy - self to scorn didst of - fer;
Pa - tient still and low - ly, Thy - self to scorn didst of - fer;
Pa - tient still and low - ly, Thy - self to scorn didst of - fer;

Our sins by Thee were tak - en, Or hope had us for -
Our sins by Thee were tak - en, Or hope had us for -
Our sins by Thee were tak - en, Or hope had us for -

sak - en: Have mer - cy on us, O Je - sus!
sak - en: Have mer - cy on us, O Je - sus!
sak - en: Thy peace be with us, O Je - sus!

100 Deck Thyself, My Soul, with Gladness

DECK THYSELF 8 8 8L.

Johann Franck, 1649
Tr. Catherine Winkworth, 1863

Johann Crüger, 1649

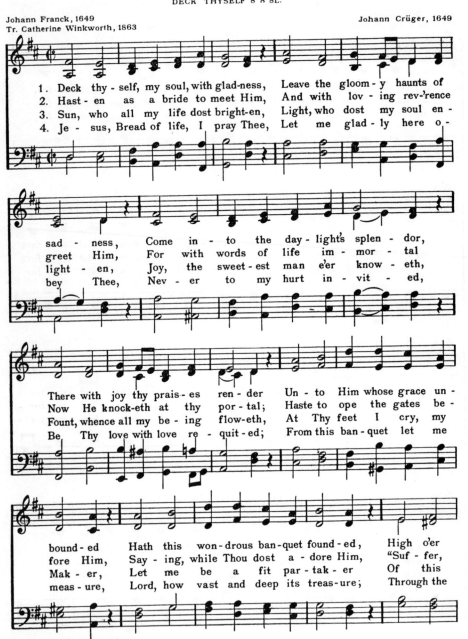

1. Deck thy - self, my soul, with glad-ness, Leave the gloom - y haunts of sad - ness, Come in - to the day - light's splen - dor, There with joy thy prais - es ren - der Un - to Him whose grace un - bound - ed Hath this won - drous ban-quet found - ed, High o'er

2. Hast - en as a bride to meet Him, And with lov - ing rev - 'rence greet Him, For with words of life im - mor - tal Now He knock-eth at thy por - tal; Haste to ope the gates be - fore Him, Say - ing, while Thou dost a - dore Him, "Suf - fer,

3. Sun, who all my life dost bright-en, Light, who dost my soul en - light - en, Joy, the sweet - est man e'er know - eth, Fount, whence all my be - ing flow-eth, At Thy feet I cry, my Mak - er, Let me be a fit par - tak - er Of this

4. Je - sus, Bread of life, I pray Thee, Let me glad - ly here o - bey Thee, Nev - er to my hurt in - vit - ed, Be Thy love with love re - quit - ed; From this ban - quet let me meas - ure, Lord, how vast and deep its treas - ure; Through the

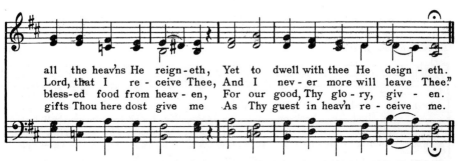

all the heav'ns He reign-eth, Yet to dwell with thee He deign-eth.
Lord, that I re-ceive Thee, And I nev-er more will leave Thee."
bless-ed food from heav-en, For our good, Thy glo-ry, giv-en.
gifts Thou here dost give me As Thy guest in heav'n re-ceive me.

101 The Thought of Jesus, O How Sweet

COMMUNION HYMN L. M.

Bernard of Clairvaux, ca. 1150
Tr. Joseph M. Neale, 1852, alt.

German, 1605

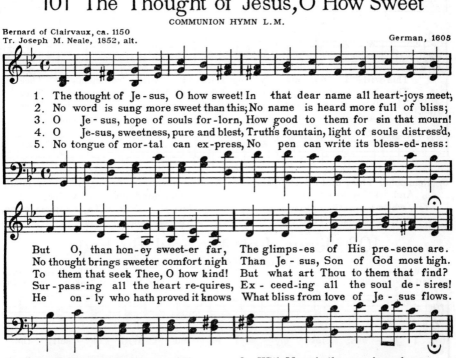

1. The thought of Je-sus, O how sweet! In that dear name all heart-joys meet;
2. No word is sung more sweet than this; No name is heard more full of bliss;
3. O Je-sus, hope of souls for-lorn, How good to them for sin that mourn!
4. O Je-sus, sweetness, pure and blest, Truth's fountain, light of souls distress'd,
5. No tongue of mor-tal can ex-press, No pen can write its bless-ed-ness:

But O, than hon-ey sweet-er far, The glimps-es of His pre-sence are.
No thought brings sweeter comfort nigh Than Je-sus, Son of God most high.
To them that seek Thee, O how kind! But what art Thou to them that find?
Sur-pass-ing all the heart re-quires, Ex-ceed-ing all the soul de-sires!
He on-ly who hath proved it knows What bliss from love of Je-sus flows.

6. O Jesus, King of wondrous might!
O Victor, glorious from the fight!
O sweetness, ne'er to be expressed,
And altogether loveliest!

7. Remain with us, O Lord, today!
In every heart Thy grace display:
That now the shades of night are fled,
On Thee our spirits may be fed.

8. I seek for Jesus in repose,
When round my heart its chambers close;
Abroad, and when I shut the door,
I long for Jesus evermore

9. With Mary in the morning gloom
I seek for Jesus at the tomb;
For Him, with love's most earnest cry,
I seek with heart and not with eye.

10. Now Jesus, to the Father gone,
Is seated on the heavenly throne:
My heart and spirit long to be,
With Him through all eternity.

11. We follow Jesus now, and raise
The voice of prayer, the hymn of praise,
That he at last may make us meet
With Him to gain the heavenly seat.

102 According to Thy Gracious Word
DUNDEE C M

James Montgomery, 1825

Scottish Psalter, 1615

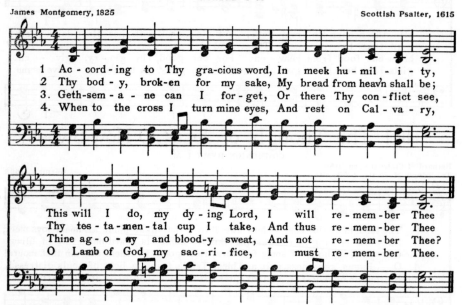

1 Ac - cord - ing to Thy gra-cious word, In meek hu - mil - i - ty,
2 Thy bod - y, brok-en for my sake, My bread from heav'n shall be;
3. Geth-sem - a - ne can I for - get, Or there Thy con - flict see,
4. When to the cross I turn mine eyes, And rest on Cal - va - ry,

This will I do, my dy - ing Lord, I will re - mem - ber Thee
Thy tes - ta - men - tal cup I take, And thus re - mem - ber Thee
Thine ag - o - ny and blood-y sweat, And not re - mem - ber Thee?
O Lamb of God, my sac - ri - fice, I must re - mem - ber Thee.

5. Remember Thee, and all Thy pains,
   And all Thy love to me;
   Yes, while a breath, a pulse remains,
   Will I remember Thee

6. And when these failing lips grow dumb,
   And mind and mem'ry flee,
   When Thou shalt in Thy kingdom come,
   Jesus, remember me

103 Jesus, Let My Soul Be Fed
FEAR, MY CHILD, THY GOD 7 7 8L

Bertel Pedersen, 1608
Tr. Carl Doving, 1909

German, 1544
Arr. Ludvig M. Lindeman, 1812-1887

1 Je - sus, let my soul be fed With Thy - self, the

liv-ing bread, For Thy flesh is meat in-deed, And Thy cleans-ing

blood I need; Let it cleanse from sin and shame,

That Thy death I may pro-claim, And for - ev - er bless Thy name.

104 I Come to Thee, O Blessed Lord

WHEN IN THE HOUR OF UTMOST NEED L.M.

Magnus Brostrup Landstad, 1861
Tr. Carl Doving, 1910

Louis Bourgeois, 1547

1. I come to Thee, O bless-ed Lord, In - vit - ed by Thy gra-cious word,
2. I come to Thee with sin and grief, For Thou a-lone canst give re - lief,
3. Shouldst Thou a strict ac-count de-mand, Who could, O Lord, be-fore Thee stand?
4. O Je - sus Lamb of God a - lone, Who didst for all our sins a - tone,
5 O Je - sus Lamb of God a - lone, Who didst for all our sins a - tone,

To this Thy feast to sup with Thee, Grant that a wor-thy guest I be
Thy death for me, dear Lord, I plead: O Je - sus, help me in my need!
Purge all my se - cret sins a-way: Be Thou, O Christ, the sin-ner's stay!
Though I have sinned and gone a-stray, Turn not, O Lord, Thy guest a-way!
Be mer - ci - ful, I Thee im-plore, Have mer - cy, Lord, for ev - er-more!

105 O Living Bread from Heaven

O LIVING BREAD 7 6 8L

Johann Rist, 1651
Tr. Catherine Winkworth, 1558, alt

Zinck's Koralbog, 1801

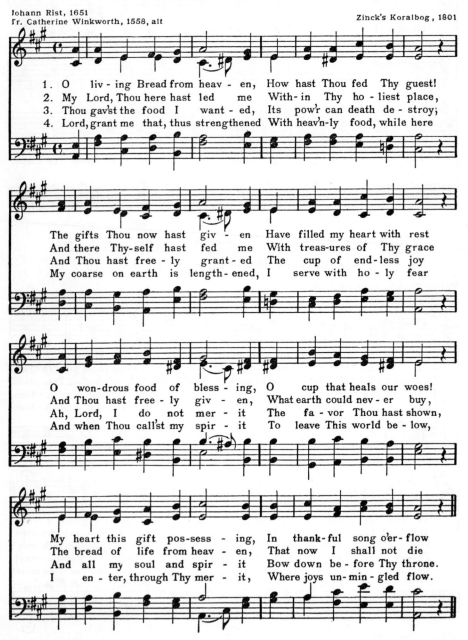

1. O liv-ing Bread from heav-en, How hast Thou fed Thy guest!
2. My Lord, Thou here hast led me With-in Thy ho-liest place,
3. Thou gav'st the food I want-ed, Its pow'r can death de-stroy;
4. Lord, grant me that, thus strengthened With heav'n-ly food, while here

The gifts Thou now hast giv-en Have filled my heart with rest
And there Thy-self hast fed me With treas-ures of Thy grace
And Thou hast free-ly grant-ed The cup of end-less joy
My coarse on earth is length-ened, I serve with ho-ly fear

O won-drous food of bless-ing, O cup that heals our woes!
And Thou hast free-ly giv-en, What earth could nev-er buy,
Ah, Lord, I do not mer-it The fa-vor Thou hast shown,
And when Thou call'st my spir-it To leave This world be-low,

My heart this gift pos-sess-ing, In thank-ful song o'er-flow
The bread of life from heav-en, That now I shall not die
And all my soul and spir-it Bow down be-fore Thy throne.
I en-ter, through Thy mer-it, Where joys un-min-gled flow.

106 O Jesus, Blessed Lord, to Thee

FROM HEAVEN ABOVE L. M.

Thomas Kingo, 1689
Tr. A. J. Mason, 1889

Valentin Schumann's
Geistliche Lieder, 1539

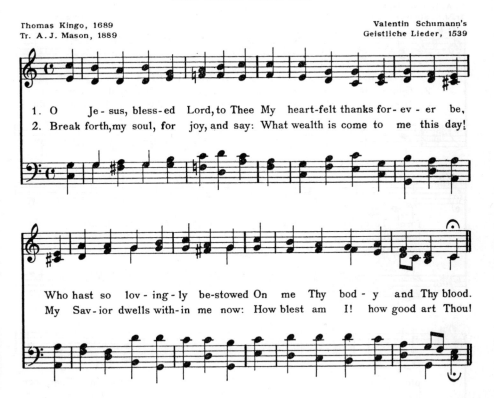

1. O   Je - sus, bless - ed   Lord, to Thee   My   heart-felt thanks for- ev - er   be,
2. Break forth, my soul, for   joy, and say: What wealth is come to   me   this day!

Who hast so   lov - ing - ly   be-stowed On   me   Thy   bod - y   and Thy blood.
My   Sav - ior dwells with-in   me   now: How blest am   I!   how good art Thou!

See also:

Just as I am, 248
Jesus, for Thee and Thy blessed communion, 315
Zion to thy Savior singing, 172
O Bread of life from heaven, 90

107 Father, Son, and Holy Ghost

CONFIRMATION 7 6, 7 6, 3 3, 6 6

C. A. Döring, 1821
Tr. J.S. Stallybrass, 1859

Johann Rosenmüller, 1655
Arr. F. Melius Christiansen, 1907

1. Fa - ther, Son, and Ho - ly Ghost, Bless the young be - fore Thee; Thou their wants and dan-gers know'st, Watch them, we im - plore Thee. Here they stand, Hope - ful band, Faith in Thee con - fess - ing, Wait - ing for Thy bless - ing.

2. Gen - tle Sav - ior, they are Thine, Thou wilt nev - er lose them; May Thy life and love di - vine Melt their ten - der bo - som. Lord, we pray That they may All, like Thee, be ho - ly, Lov - ing, meek, and low - ly,

3. Giv - er Thou of gifts to all, No good thing de - ny them: Hear, O hear our ear-nest call, Life and light sup - ply them. Strength re - new, Keep them true, All that stand be - fore Thee, Bless them, we im - plore Thee.

92

108 O Jesus, I Have Promised

MUNICH 7 6 8L.

John E. Bode, 1869   Meiningisches Gesangbuch, 1693

1. O Je - sus, I have prom - ised To serve Thee to the end;
2. O let me feel Thee near me, The world is ev - er near;
3. O let me hear Thee speak - ing In ac - cents clear and still,
4. O Je - sus, Thou hast prom - ised To all who fol - low Thee
5. O let me see Thy foot - marks, And in them plant my own;

Be Thou for - ev - er near me, My Mas - ter and my Friend!
I see the sights that daz - zle, The tempt - ing sounds I hear.
A - bove the storms of pas - sion, The mur - murs of self - will.
That where Thou art in glo - ry There shall Thy ser - vant be;
My hope to fol - low du - ly Is in Thy strength a - lone.

I shall not fear the bat - tle If Thou art by my side,
My foes are ev - er near me, A - round me and with - in;
O speak to re - as - sure me, To hast - en or con - trol:
And, Je - sus, I have prom - ised To serve Thee to the end;
O guide me, call me, draw me, Up - hold me to the end;

Nor wan - der from the path - way If Thou wilt be my guide.
But, Je - sus, draw Thou near - er, And shield my soul from sin.
O speak and make me lis - ten, Thou Guard-ian of my soul!
O give me grace to fol - low, My Mas - ter and my Friend!
And then in heav'n re - ceive me, My Sav - ior and my Friend!

109 Blessed Savior, Who Hast Taught Me

RIPLEY 8 7 8L.

John Mason Neale, 1842

Gregorian Chant
Arr. Lowell Mason, 1839

1. Bless-ed Sav-ior, who hast taught me I should live to Thee a - lone;
2. I would trust in Thy pro-tect - ing, Whol-ly rest up - on Thine arm;
3. So that, might and firm-ness gain-ing, Hope in dan-ger, joy in grief,

All these years Thy hand hath brought me, Since I first was made Thine own.
Fol - low whol-ly Thy di - rect - ing, O my on - ly guard from harm!
Now and ev - er-more re-main-ing Steadfast in the true be - lief;

At the font my vows were spok-en By my par-ents in the Lord,
Meet me now with Thy sal - va - tion, In the Church's or-dered way;
Rest-ing in my Sav-ior's mer - it, Strengthened, with the Spir-it's strength,

That my vows shall be un - bro - ken, At the al - tar I re - cord.
Let me feel Thy con - fir - ma - tion In Thy truth and fear to - day;
With Thy Church I may in - her - it All my Fa-ther's joy at length.

See also:

My God, accept my heart, 257
How shall the young secure their hearts, 379

I ought to love my Savior, 372
I would gather treasures in heaven, 378
Savior, while my heart is tender, 377

110 Lord of the Church, We Humbly Pray

BE NOT DISMAYED 8 8 7 6L.

Edward Osler, 1836

German, 1530

1. Lord of the Church, we hum-bly pray For those who guide us in the way, And speak Thy ho-ly word: With love di-vine their hearts in-spire, And touch their lips with hal-lowed fire, And need-ful grace af-ford.

2. Help them to preach the truth of God, Re-demp-tion through the Sav-ior's blood: Nor let the Spir-it cease On all the Church His gifts to show'r; To them a mes-sen-ger of pow'r, To us, of life and peace.

3. So may they live to Thee a-lone: Then hear the wel-come word,"Well done!" And take their crown a-bove: En-ter in-to their Mas-ter's joy, And all e-ter-ni-ty em-ploy In praise, and bliss, and love.

95

111 Lord, Pour Thy Spirit from On High

COME HOLY GHOST L.M.

James Montgomery, 1833, alt.   German, 1524

1. Lord, pour Thy Spir - it from on high, And
2. With - in Thy tem - ple when they stand To
3. Faith, wis - dom, zeal, do Thou im - part, Give
4. To watch, and pray, and nev - er faint; By
5. And when their work is fin - ished here, Let

Thine ap - point - ed ser - vants bless; Thy prom - ised pow'r to
teach the truth as taught by Thee, Like stars, O Sav - ior,
firm - ness and hu - mil - i - ty, To bear Thy peo - ple
day and night their watch to keep; To warn the sin - ner,
them in hope their charge re - sign; Be - fore the throne with

each sup - ply, And clothe Thy priests with right - eous - ness
in Thy hand Let all Thy Church's pas - tors be
on their heart, And love the souls with love from Thee
cheer the saint, Pro - tect Thy lambs, and feed Thy sheep.
joy ap - pear, And there with end - less glo - ry shine

See also:

Come, Holy Ghost, Creator blest, 227
Built on the Rock, 81
Father of mercies, in Thy word, 92

III. The Church Year

1. Advent

2. Christmas

3. New Year

4. Epiphany

5. Lent and Passion

6. Easter and Ascension

7. Pentecost

8. Trinity

9. Reformation

10. Thanksgiving

112 O How Shall I Receive Thee

ST. THEODULPH 7 6 8L

Paul Gerhardt, 1653
Tr. Arthur T. Russell, 1851, alt.

Melchior Teschner, 1615

1. O how shall I re - ceive Thee, How greet Thee, Lord, a - right?
2. Thy Zi - on palms is strew-ing, And branch-es fresh and fair;
3. I lay in fet - ters groan-ing, Thou came to set me free!
4. Love caused Thy In - car - na - tion, Love brought Thee down to me,
5. Re - joice then, ye sad - heart-ed, Who sit in deep-est gloom,

All na - tions long to see Thee, My hope, my heart's de - light!
My heart, its pow'rs re - new - ing, An an - them shall pre - pare.
I stood, my shame be - moan - ing, Thou came to hon - or me!
Thy thirst for my sal - va - tion Pro - cured my lib - er - ty.
Who mourn o'er joys de - part - ed, And trem-ble at your doom;

O kin - dle, Lord, most ho - ly, Thy lamp with - in my breast,
My soul puts off her sad - ness Thy glo - ries to pro - claim;
A glo - ry Thou dost give me, A treas-ure safe on high,
O love be - yond all tell - ing, That led Thee to em - brace,
He who a - lone can cheer you Is stand-ing at the door;

To do in spir - it low - ly All that may please Thee best.
With all her strength and glad - ness She fain would serve Thy name.
That will not fail nor leave me As earth - ly rich - es fly.
In love all love ex - cel - ling, Our lost and fall - en race!
He brings His pit - y near you, And bids you weep no more.

99

113 Rejoice, All Ye Believers

IN HEAVEN IS JOY 7 6 8L.

Laurentius Laurentii, 1700
Tr. Sarah Findlater, 1854

Norwegian Folk-Tune

1. Re - joice, all ye be - liev - ers, And let your lights ap - pear!
2. The watch-ers on the moun-tain Pro - claim the Bride-groom near;
3. Ye saints, who here in pa - tience Your cross and suf - f'rings bore,
4. Our Hope and Ex - pec - ta - tion, O Je - sus, now ap - pear;

The eve - ning is ad - vanc-ing, And dark - er night is near.
Go meet Him as He com - eth, With hal - le - lu - jahs clear.
Shall live and reign for - ev - er, Where sor - row is no more.
A - rise, Thou Sun so longed for, O'er this be - night-ed sphere!

The Bride-groom is a - ris - ing, And soon He draw-eth nigh.
The mar - riage feast is wait - ing, The gates wide o - pen stand;
A - round the throne of glo - ry The Lamb ye shall be - hold,
With hearts and hands up - lift - ed, We plead, O Lord, to see

Up, watch, and pray, and wres-tle, At mid - night comes the cry!
Up, up, ye heirs of glo - ry, The Bride-groom is at hand!
In tri - umph cast be - fore Him Your di - a - dems of gold!
The day of earth's re - demp-tion, That brings us un - to Thee!

114 The Only Son from Heaven

THE ONLY SON FROM HEAVEN 7 6, 7 6, 7 7 6

Elisabeth Cruciger, 1524
Tr. Arthur T. Russell, 1851

German, 1524

1. The on - ly Son from heav - en, Fore - told by an - cient
2. O time of God ap - point - ed, O bright and ho - ly
3. O Lord, our hearts a - wak - en, To know and love Thee

seers, By God, the Fa - ther, giv - en, In hu - man shape ap -
morn! He comes, the King a - noint - ed, The Christ, the vir - gin -
more, In faith to stand un - shak - en, In Spir - it to a -

pears; No sphere His light con - fin - ing, No
born; His home on earth He mak - eth, And
dore, That we still heav'n - ward hast - ing, Yet

star so bright - ly shin - ing As He, our Morn - ing Star.
man of heav'n par - tak - eth, Of life a - gain an heir.
here Thy joy fore - tast - ing, May reap its ful - ness there.

115 Make Wide the Door, Unbar the Gate

FROM HEAVEN ABOVE L. M.

Georg Weissel, 1642
Tr. P. A. Sveeggen, 1919

Valentin Schumann's
Geistliche Lieder, 1539

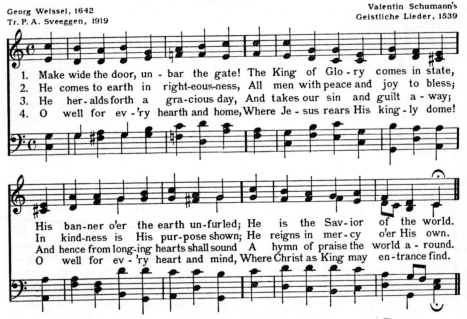

1. Make wide the door, un - bar the gate! The King of Glo - ry comes in state,
2. He comes to earth in right-eous-ness, All men with peace and joy to bless;
3. He her - alds forth a gra - cious day, And takes our sin and guilt a - way;
4. O well for ev - 'ry hearth and home, Where Je - sus rears His king - ly dome!

His ban - ner o'er the earth un-furled; He is the Sav - ior of the world.
In kind-ness is His pur-pose shown; He reigns in mer - cy o'er His own.
And hence from long-ing hearts shall sound A hymn of praise the world a - round.
O well for ev - 'ry heart and mind, Where Christ as King may en - trance find.

5. For then a heavenly joy will greet
Our souls from God's own mercy-seat;
In Him, the Son of God, is light
That makes our deepest darkness bright.

6. Make wide the door, remove all bars;
Give room to Him who rules the stars;
For then the King of Glory will
The wondrous work of God fulfill.

7. My heart I open now to Thee;
Come, Jesus, and abide with me;
And in Thy mercy make it so,
That I Thy depths of love may know.

8. O let Thy Spirit more and more,
From day to day make wide the door,
That Christ alone our King may be,
And Savior through eternity!

116 Repent, the Kingdom Draweth Nigh

WHEN IN THE HOUR OF UTMOST NEED L.M.

Anna Hoppe, 1921

Louis Bourgeois, 1547

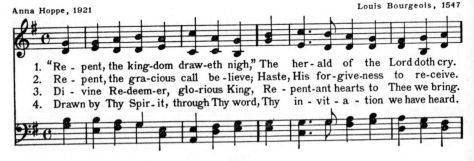

1. "Re - pent, the king-dom draw-eth nigh," The her - ald of the Lord doth cry.
2. Re - pent, the gra-cious call be - lieve; Haste, His for-give-ness to re-ceive.
3. Di - vine Re-deem-er, glo-rious King, Re - pent-ant hearts to Thee we bring.
4. Drawn by Thy Spir-it, through Thy word, Thy in - vit - a - tion we have heard.

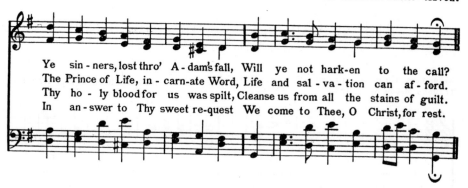

Ye sin-ners, lost thro' A-dam's fall, Will ye not hark-en to the call?
The Prince of Life, in-carn-ate Word, Life and sal-va-tion can af-ford.
Thy ho-ly blood for us was spilt, Cleanse us from all the stains of guilt.
In an-swer to Thy sweet re-quest We come to Thee, O Christ, for rest.

117 I Know a Kingdom without End

I KNOW A KINGDOM 8 7 4L.

German Origin
Danish, Hans Chr. Sthen, ca. 1578
Tr. P. A. Sveeggen, 1919

German, 16th Century

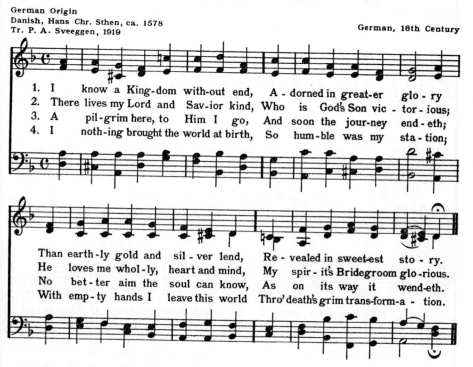

1. I know a King-dom with-out end, A-dorned in great-er glo-ry
2. There lives my Lord and Sav-ior kind, Who is God's Son vic-tor-ious;
3. A pil-grim here, to Him I go, And soon the jour-ney end-eth;
4. I noth-ing brought the world at birth, So hum-ble was my sta-tion;

Than earth-ly gold and sil-ver lend, Re-vealed in sweet-est sto-ry.
He loves me whol-ly, heart and mind, My spir-it's Bridegroom glo-rious.
No bet-ter aim the soul can know, As on its way it wend-eth.
With emp-ty hands I leave this world Thro' death's grim trans-form-a-tion.

5. Still, I am sure that this my frame
   From death again shall sever,
   And rise to life in Jesus' name,
   To dwell in bliss forever.

6. Then I shall reach, as I believe,
   The end of tribulation
   And, free from all that made me grieve,
   Eternal jubilation.

118 O Come, O Come, Immanuel

ST. PETERSBURG L.M.6L.

Anonymous, Latin, ca. 12th Century
Tr. John Mason Neale, 1852

Dimitri S. Bortniansky, 1752-1828

1. O come, O come, Im - man - u - el, And ran-som cap-tive Is - ra - el,
2. O come, Thou Rod of Jes - se, free Thine own from Sa - tan's ty - ran - ny;
3. O come, Thou Dayspring, come and cheer Our spir-its by Thine ad - vent here:
4. O come, Thou Key of Da - vid, come, And o - pen wide our heav'n-ly home:
5. O come, O come, Thou Lord of might, Who to Thy tribes, on Sin - ai's height,

That mourns in lone - ly ex - ile here Un - til the Son of God ap - pear.
From depths of hell Thy peo - ple save And give them vic - t'ry o'er the grave.
And drive a - way the shades of night, And pierce the clouds and bring us light!
Make safe the way that leads on high, And close the path to mis - er - y.
In an - cient times didst give the law In cloud, and maj - es - ty, and awe.

Re - joice! re - joice! Im - man - u - el Shall come to thee, O Is - ra - el!
Re - joice! re - joice! Im - man - u - el Shall come to thee, O Is - ra - el!
Re - joice! re - joice! Im - man - u - el Shall come to thee, O Is - ra - el!
Re - joice! re - joice! Im - man - u - el Shall come to thee, O Is - ra - el!
Re - joice! re - joice! Im - man - u - el Shall come to thee, O Is - ra - el!

119 Now Jesus at the Door Is Knocking

WHO KNOWS HOW NEAR 9 8, 9 8, 8 8

Magnus Brostrup Landstad, 1863
Tr. O.H. Smeby, C.K. Solberg, C. Doving, 1909

German, 1690

1. Now Je-sus at the door is knock-ing! Hark, how He pleads our
2. Be-hold, He at the door is call-ing, O heed, my soul, what
3. Come Thou who spread-est joy and glad-ness, For-ev-er bide with

souls to win! Who hears His voice, the door un-lock-ing,
He doth say; De-ny Him not, O thought ap-pall-ing,
me and mine, And bring to those who sit in sad-ness

To sup with him He en-ters in! How blest the
And turn Him not from thee a-way. My soul gives
And gloom of death Thy light di-vine; A voice comes

day, my soul, how blest! When Je-sus comes to be thy guest!
an-swer deep with-in: Thou bless-ed of the Lord, come in!
from my soul with-in: Thou bless-ed of the Lord, come in!

120 Come, Thou Long Expected Jesus

LORD VICTORIOUS 8 7 8L.

Charles Wesley, 1744

J. A. Freylinghausen's Gesangbuch, 1704

1. Come, Thou long ex - pect - ed Je - sus, Born to set Thy peo - ple free;
2. Born Thy peo - ple to de - liv - er; Born a child, and yet a king;

From our fears and sins re - lease us, Let us find our rest in Thee.
Born to reign in us for - ev - er, Now Thy gra - cious king - dom bring,

Is - rael's strength and con - so - la - tion, Hope of all the earth Thou art;
By Thine own e - ter - nal Spir - it, Rule Thou in our hearts a - lone;

Dear de - sire of ev - 'ry na - tion, Joy of ev - 'ry long - ing heart.
By Thine all - suf - fic - ient mer - it, Raise us to Thy glo - rious throne.

121 The Way That unto Jesus Leads

LUTHER'S HYMN 8 7, 8 7, 8 8 7

Thomas Kingo, 1634 - 1703
Tr. P. A. Sveeggen

Joseph Klug, 1535

1. The way that un - to Je - sus leads, It bless - ed is to
2. The blind can see, the lame can walk, The lep - rous now have
3. O bless - ed Je - sus, he who can At Thee be - come of -

wan - der; Ful - fil - ment there of all its needs The soul in joy shall
heal - ing; The dead a - rise, the dumb can talk, His won - drous pow'r re-
fend - ed, Be - cause Thou bear'st the form of man, He meets the doom in-

pon - der. His words and deeds of heav'n - ly worth, All
veal - ing. And now the gos - pels bless - ed cheer The
tend - ed. Through faith in Thee I find re - lease, My

prove He came, thro' hu - man birth, Our God, from heav - en yon - der.
hum-blest-heart-ed poor may hear; His truth brooks no con - ceal - ing.
Life, my Bliss, my Hope, my Peace, Thro' Thee my griefs are end - ed.

107

122 Now Hail We Our Redeemer

THE ONLY SON FROM HEAVEN 7 6, 7 6, 7 7 6

Aurelius Ambrose, 340-397
Olavus Petri, 1536
Tr. E. W. Olson

German, 1524

1. Now hail we our Re - deem - er, E - ter - nal Son of
2. A man, of God be - got - ten, Brought in the age of
3. O Je - sus, grant us mer - cy, And grace on us be -
4. In - to Thy hand the Fa - ther Gave all, that we might

God, Born in the flesh to save us, And cleanse us in His
grace; Lo, all the earth is ra - diant With light, and hope, and
stow, To walk by Thine own guid-ance, Thy sav - ing truth to
be In bonds of faith u - nit - ed; And ded - i - cate to

blood. The Morn - ing Star a - scend - eth, Light
peace. Our pris - on He de - mol - ished, Death's
know. For Thee our hearts are yearn - ing, From
Thee A peo - ple through Thy mer - it En -

to the world He lend - eth, Our Guide in grief and gloom.
pow - er He a - bol - ished, And o - pened heav - en's gate.
world-ly pleas-ures turn - ing Un - to Thy right-eous - ness.
ti - tled to in - her - it Thy realm e - ter - nal - ly.

123 Come, Thou Savior of Our Race

HENDON 7 7 4L.

Aurelius Ambrose, 340-397
Martin Luther, 1524
Tr. William Reynolds, 1850

Henri Abraham Cesar Malan, 1827

1. Come, Thou Sav - ior of our race, Choic-est Gift of heav'n-ly
2. Not of mor - tal blood or birth, He de - scends from heav'n to
3. Won-drous birth! O won-drous Child Of the vir - gin un - de -
4. From the Fa - ther forth He came, And re - turn-eth to the

grace! O Thou bless - ed Vir-gin's Son, Be Thy race on
earth: By The Ho - ly Ghost con - ceived, God and man by
filed! Tho' by all the world dis - owned, Still to be in
same; Cap - tive lead - ing death and hell,— High the song of

earth be - gun, Be Thy race on earth be - gun.
us be - lieved, God and man by us be - lieved.
heav'n en - throned, Still to be in heav'n en - throned.
tri - umph swell! High the song of tri - umph swell!

5. Equal to the Father now,
Though to dust Thou once didst bow,
Boundless shall Thy kingdom be;
When shall we its glories see?

6. Brightly doth Thy manger shine!
Glorious in its light divine:
Let not sin o'ercloud this light,
Ever be our faith thus bright.

See also:
Thy little ones, dear Lord, are we, 366
Jesus, Jesus, come to me, 341
Also hymns under CHRISTIAN LIFE, 246-348

124 Ring, O Ye Bells, O Ring Out

PRAISE TO THE LORD 14 14, 4 7 8

Nicolai F. S. Grundtvig, 1783-1872
Tr P. A. Sveeggen, 1919

German, 1668
Arr. F. Melius Christiansen, 1907

1. Ring, O ye bells, O ring out ere the day-light ad - vanc - es! Gleam, O ye stars, send-ing forth like the an - gels your glanc - es! Peace up-on earth Her-alds the won-der-ful birth; Glo - ry to God in the high - est!

2. Christ-mas has come, with its sun-light our fears all dis - pel - ling, Come with the Child of whom voic - es an - gel - ic are tell - ing, Come from a - bove, Bring-ing glad tid - ings of love; Glo - ry to God in the high - est!

3. Sing, O ye chil - dren of men to the ut - ter-most na - tion; Min - gle sweet mu - sic and sing in your rapt ju - bi - la - tion! Born is the Child, Pledge of God's Fa - ther-hood mild; Glo - ry to God in the high - est!

125 Come Hither, Ye Faithful, Triumphantly Sing

ADESTE FIDELES 11 11 4L.

Anonymous, Latin, 17th or 18th Century
Tr. Edward Caswall

J. F. Wade's Cantus Diversi, 1751

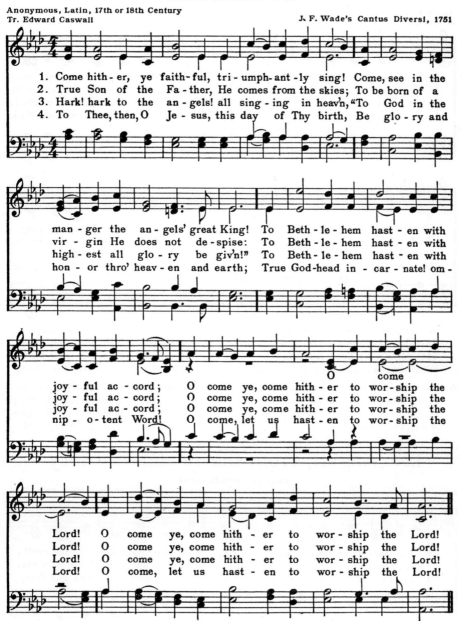

1. Come hith - er, ye faith- ful, tri - umph- ant -ly sing! Come, see in the
2. True Son of the Fa - ther, He comes from the skies; To be born of a
3. Hark! hark to the an - gels! all sing - ing in heav'n, "To God in the
4. To Thee, then, O Je - sus, this day of Thy birth, Be glo - ry and

man - ger the an - gels' great King! To Beth - le - hem hast - en with
vir - gin He does not de - spise: To Beth - le - hem hast - en with
high - est all glo - ry be giv'n!" To Beth - le - hem hast - en with
hon - or thro' heav - en and earth; True God-head in - car - nate! om -

joy - ful ac - cord; O come ye, come hith - er to wor - ship the
joy - ful ac - cord; O come ye, come hith - er to wor - ship the
joy - ful ac - cord; O come ye, come hith - er to wor - ship the
nip - o - tent Word! O come, let us hast - en to wor - ship the

Lord! O come ye, come hith - er to wor - ship the Lord!
Lord! O come ye, come hith - er to wor - ship the Lord!
Lord! O come ye, come hith - er to wor - ship the Lord!
Lord! O come, let us hast - en to wor - ship the Lord!

126 From Heaven Above to Earth I Come

FROM HEAVEN ABOVE L. M.

Martin Luther, 1535
Tr. Composite

Martin Luther's
Geistliche Lieder, 1539

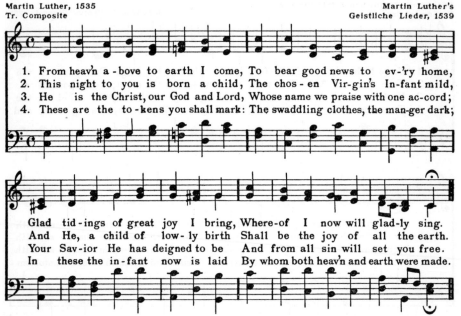

1. From heav'n a-bove to earth I come, To bear good news to ev-'ry home,
2. This night to you is born a child, The chos-en Vir-gin's In-fant mild,
3. He is the Christ, our God and Lord, Whose name we praise with one ac-cord;
4. These are the to-kens you shall mark: The swaddling clothes, the man-ger dark;

Glad tid-ings of great joy I bring, Where-of I now will glad-ly sing.
And He, a child of low-ly birth Shall be the joy of all the earth.
Your Sav-ior He has deigned to be And from all sin will set you free.
In these the in-fant now is laid By whom both heav'n and earth were made.

5 We welcome Thee, most noble Guest,
Through whom this sinful world is blest
Thy coming is a boon for me;
What thanks shall I return to Thee?

6 Were earth a thousand times as fair,
Beset with gold and jewels rare,
It still were far too poor to be
A narrow cradle, Lord, for Thee.

7. Ah, dearest Jesus, holy Child,
Make Thee a bed, soft, undefiled,
Within my heart, and let it be
A quiet chamber, kept for Thee.

8. Praise be to God upon His throne
Who gave the world His only Son;
For this His hosts, on joyful wing,
A blest New Year of mercy sing.

127 Angels, from the Realms of Glory

REGENT SQUARE 8 7 6L.

James Montgomery, 1819

Henry Smart, 1813-1879

1. An-gels, from the realms of glo-ry, Wing your flight o'er all the earth;
2. Shep-herds, in the field a-bid-ing, Watch-ing o'er your flocks by night,
3. Saints, be-fore the al-tar bend-ing, Watch-ing long in hope and fear,

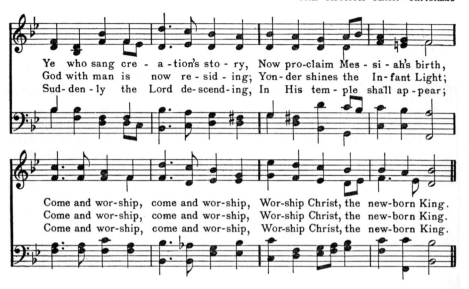

Ye who sang cre - a -tion's sto - ry, Now pro-claim Mes - si - ah's birth,
God with man is now re - sid - ing; Yon-der shines the In - fant Light;
Sud- den - ly the Lord de-scend-ing, In His tem - ple shall ap -pear;

Come and wor-ship, come and wor-ship, Wor-ship Christ, the new-born King.
Come and wor-ship, come and wor-ship, Wor-ship Christ, the new-born King.
Come and wor-ship, come and wor-ship, Wor-ship Christ, the new-born King.

128 A Great and Mighty Wonder

ABIDE IN GRACE 7 6 4L.

St. Germannus, 634-734
Tr. Joseph M. Neale, 1862

Melchior Vulpius, 1609

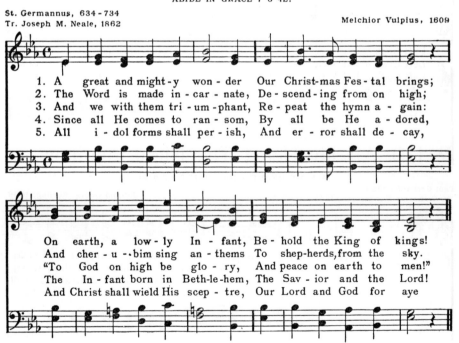

1. A   great and might - y won - der   Our Christ-mas Fes - tal brings;
2. The   Word is made in - car - nate,   De - scend-ing from on high;
3. And   we with them tri - um -phant,   Re - peat the hymn a - gain:
4. Since all He comes to ran - som,   By all be He a - dored,
5. All   i - dol forms shall per - ish, And er - ror shall de - cay,

On   earth, a   low - ly   In - fant, Be - hold the King of kings!
And cher - u - •bim sing an - thems To shep-herds, from the sky.
"To God on high be glo - ry,   And peace on earth to men!"
The In - fant born in Beth-le-hem, The Sav - ior and the Lord!
And Christ shall wield His scep - tre, Our Lord and God for aye

129 Be Ye Joyful, Earth and Sky

BE YE JOYFUL 7 4, 7 4, 7 7 8

Anonymous
Tr. H. Brueckner

Bohemian Folk-Tune

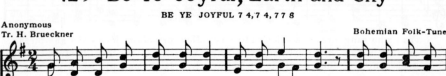

1. Be ye joy-ful, earth and sky, Hal-le-lu - jah! Un - to us God's
2. Here the fair-est Rose we see, Hal-le-lu - jah! Blooming forth from
3. He, the great in - car-nate Word, Hal-le-lu - jah! Je-sus Christ doth

Son came nigh, Hal-le-lu - jah! He for our sal - va - tion
Jes-se's tree, Hal-le-lu - jah! He for our sal - va - tion
help af - ford, Hal-le-lu - jah! He for our sal - va - tion

Left God's hab-i-ta - tion, Yes, He left God's hab-i-ta - tion.
Left God's hab-i-ta - tion, Yes, He left God's hab-i-ta - tion
Left God's hab-i-ta - tion, Yes, He left God's hab-i-ta - tion.

130 All My Heart This Night Rejoices

ALL MY HEART THIS NIGHT 8 3 3 6 8L.

Paul Gerhardt, 1656
Tr. Catherine Winkworth, 1858

Johann Georg Ebeling, 1666

1. All my heart this night re-joic - es, As I hear, Far and near,
2. Hark, a voice from yon-der man - ger, Soft and sweet, Doth en-treat,
3. Come then, let us hast-en yon - der, Here let all, Great and small,
4. Ye who pine in wea-ry sad - ness, Weep no more, For the door

Sweet-est an-gel voic - es; "Christ is born," their choirs are sing - ing,
"Flee from woe and dan - ger; Breth-ren, come; from all that grieves you
Kneel in awe and won - der; Love Him who with love is yearn - ing;
Now is found of glad - ness: Cling to Him, for He will guide you

ing, Till the air Ev - 'ry-where Now with joy is ring - ing.
you You are freed; All you need I will sure - ly give you."
ing; Hail the Star That from far Bright with hope is burn - ing.
you Where no cross, Pain or loss Can a - gain be - tide you.

131 While Shepherds Watched Their Flocks

CRÜGER C.M.

Nahum Tate, 1702   Johann Crüger, 1657

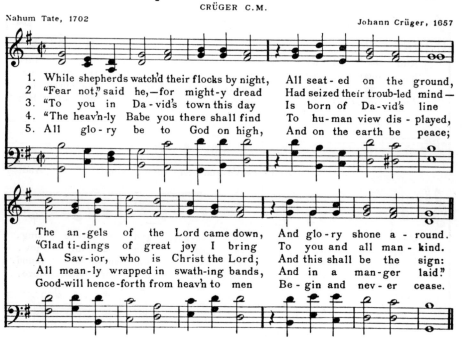

1. While shepherds watch'd their flocks by night, All seat - ed on the ground,
2. "Fear not," said he,—for might-y dread Had seized their troub-led mind—
3. "To you in Da - vid's town this day Is born of Da - vid's line
4. "The heav'n-ly Babe you there shall find To hu-man view dis - played,
5. All glo - ry be to God on high, And on the earth be peace;

The an - gels of the Lord came down, And glo - ry shone a - round.
"Glad ti-dings of great joy I bring To you and all man - kind.
A Sav-ior, who is Christ the Lord; And this shall be the sign:
All mean-ly wrapped in swath-ing bands, And in a man-ger laid."
Good-will hence-forth from heav'n to men Be - gin and nev - er cease.

132 Joy to the World! The Lord Is Come

ANTIOCH C.M.

Isaac Watts, 1719

George Frederick Händel, 1742
Arr. Lowell Mason, 1830

1. Joy to the world! The Lord is come: Let earth re -
2. Joy to the world! The Sav - ior reigns: Let men their
3. No more let sin and sor - row grow, Nor thorns in -
4. He rules the world with truth and grace And makes the

ceive her King; Let ev - 'ry heart pre - pare Him room,
songs em - ploy, While fields and floods, rocks, hills, and plains,
fest the ground; He comes to make His bless - ings flow
na - tions prove The glo - ries of His right-eous - ness

And heav'n and na - ture sing, And heav'n and na - ture
Re - peat the sound - ing joy, Re - peat the sound - ing
Far as the curse is found, Far as the curse is
And won - ders of His love, And won - ders of His

And heav'n and na - ture sing,

And heav'n and na - ture sing, And

sing, And heav'n, and heav'n and na - ture sing.
joy, Re - peat, re - peat the sound-ing joy.
found, Far as, far as the curse is found.
love, And won - ders, won - ders of His love.

heav'n and na - ture sing.

116

133 O Little Town of Bethlehem

ST. LOUIS 8 6, 8 6, 7 6, 8 6

Phillips Brooks, 1868   Lewis H. Redner, 1868

1. O lit - tle town of Beth - le - hem, How still we see Thee lie;
2. For Christ is born of Ma - ry; And gath-ered all a - bove,
3. How si - lent - ly, how si - lent - ly The won-drous gift is giv'n!
4. O ho - ly Child of Beth - le - hem, De - scend to us, we pray;

A - bove thy deep and dream-less sleep The si - lent stars go by·
While mor-tals sleep, the an - gels keep Their watch of won-d'ring love.
So God im-parts to hu - man hearts The bless-ings of His heav'n
Cast out our sin, and en - ter in, Be born in us to - day

Yet in thy dark streets shin - eth The ev - er - last - ing Light;
O morn-ing stars, to - geth - er Pro - claim the ho - ly birth;
No ear may hear His com - ing, But in this world of sin,
We hear the Christ-mas an - gels The great glad tid - ings tell;

The hopes and fears of all the years Are met in thee to - night.
And prais - es sing to God our King, And peace to men on earth
Where meek souls will re - ceive Him still, The dear Christ en - ters in.
O come to us, a - bide with us, Our Lord Im - man - u - el

134 Now Sing We, Now Rejoice

IN DULCI JUBILO 6 6, 7 6, 7 6, 5 5

Latin and German, 15th Century
Tr. Arthur T. Russell, 1851

14th Century, J. Klug, 1535

Two slow beats per measure.

1. Now sing we, now re - joice,   Now raise to heav'n our voice;
2. Come from on high to   me,   I   can - not rise   to Thee:
3. Now thro' His Son doth shine   The Fa - ther's grace di - vine:
4. O   where shall joy be found?   Where but on heav'n -ly ground?

Lo! He from whom joy stream-eth, Poor in the man - ger lies;
O   cheer my wea - ried spir - it: O   pure and ho - ly Child,
Death o - ver us hath reign-ed   Thro' sin and van - i - ty:
Where now the an - gels sing-ing   With all His saints u - nite,

Yet   not   so bright-ly beam-eth The sun   in yon-der skies!
Thro' all Thy grace and mer - it, Blest Je - sus! Lord most mild,
The   Son for us ob - tain - ed   E - ter -nal joy on high.
Their sweet-est prais-es bring-ing In heav'n - ly joy and light:

Thou my Sav - ior art!   Thou my Sav - ior art!
Draw me af - ter Thee!   Draw me af - ter Thee!
May   we praise Him there! May   we praise Him there!
May   we praise Him there! May   we praise Him there!

118

135 It Came upon the Midnight Clear

CAROL C. M. D.

Edmund H. Sears, 1850   Richard S. Willis, 1850

1. It came up-on the mid-night clear, That glo-rious song of old,
2. Still through the clo-ven skies they come, With peace-ful wings un-furled;
3. And ye, be-neath life's crush-ing load, Whose forms are bend-ing low,
4. For lo! the days are hast'ning on, By proph-et-bards fore-told,

From an-gels bend-ing near the earth, To touch their harps of gold:
And still their heav'n-ly mu-sic floats O'er all the wea-ry world:
Who toil a-long the climb-ing way, With pain-ful steps and slow,—
When, with the ev-er-cir-cling years, Comes round the age of gold;

"Peace on the earth, good-will to men, From heav'n's all-gra-cious King";
A-bove its sad and low-ly plains They bend on heav'n-ly wing,
Look now, for glad and gold-en hours Come swift-ly on the wing;
When peace shall o-ver all the earth Its an-cient splen-dors fling,

The world in sol-emn still-ness lay To hear the an-gels sing.
And ev-er o'er its Ba-bel sounds The bless-ed an-gels sing.
O rest be-side the wea-ry road, And hear the an-gels sing.
And the whole world give back the song Which now the an-gels sing.

136 Hark! The Herald Angels Sing

MENDELSSOHN 7 7 8L.

Charles Wesley, 1739, alt.

Felix Bartholdy Mendelssohn, 1840
Arr. William H. Cummings, 1855

1. Hark! The her-ald an-gels sing, "Glo-ry to the new-born King;
2. Christ, by high-est heav'n a-dored, Christ, the ev-er-last-ing Lord;
3. Hail, the heav'n-born Prince of Peace! Hail, the Sun of Right-eous-ness!

Peace on earth, and mer-cy mild, God and sin-ners rec-on-ciled."
Come, De-sire of na-tions, come, Fix in us Thy hum-ble home.
Light and life to all He brings, Ris'n with heal-ing in His wings.

Joy-ful all ye na-tions, rise, Join the tri-umph of the skies;
Veiled in flesh the God-head see; Hail th' In-car-nate De-i-ty,
Mild He lays His glo-ry by, Born that man no more may die,

With th' an-gel-ic host pro-claim, "Christ is born in Beth-le-hem."
Pleased as man with man to dwell; Je-sus, our Im-man-u-el.
Born to raise the sons of earth, Born to give them sec-ond birth.

Hark! The her-ald an-gels sing, "Glo-ry to the new-born King."
Hark! The her-ald an-gels sing, "Glo-ry to the new-born King."
Hark! The her-ald an-gels sing, "Glo-ry to the new-born King."

137 Precious Child, So Sweetly Sleeping

PRECIOUS CHILD 8 7, 8 7, 7 7

Anna Hoppe, 1928

Norwegian Folk-Tune
Arr. Oscar R. Overby, 1931

1. Pre-cious Child, so sweet-ly sleep-ing In a vir-gin's fond em-brace,
2. An-thems joy-ous now are ring-ing In the skies of Beth-le-hem;
3. Thou hast come to bring sal-va-tion To this sin-cursed world be-low,
4. Take my hum-ble ad-o-ra-tion While on earth be-low I dwell.

Heav'n-ly hosts their watch are keep-ing O'er Thy hum-ble dwell-ing place.
An-gels their sweet song are sing-ing, "Peace on earth, good will to men."
That Thy blood re-deemed cre-a-tion Thine a-bound-ing love might know.
Let my songs in ex-ul-ta-tion Of Thy bound-less good-ness tell,

Blest Mes-si-ah, new-born King, Let my heart its trib-ute bring.
Pre-cious Je-sus, at Thy birth Heav-en's peace is brought to earth.
En-ter each be-liev-ing heart; Par-don, grace, and peace im-part.
Till in heav'n a-bove, my King, End-less hymns of praise I sing.

121

138 Behold, a Branch Is Growing

BEHOLD A BRANCH 7 6, 7 6, 6 7 6

Traditional Rhenish Folksong, 16th Century
Tr. St. 1-4, Harriet R. Krauth, 1875
St. 5, John Caspar Mattes, 1914

Rhenish Folk-Tune
Alte Kath. Kirchengesang, Köln, 1599

1. Be - hold, a Branch is grow - ing Of love - liest form and grace; As proph-ets sung, fore - know - ing, It springs from Jes - se's race, And bears one lit - tle Flow'r In midst of cold - est win - ter, At deep - est mid - night hour.

2. I - sai - ah hath fore - told it In words of prom - ise sure, And Ma - ry's, arms en - fold it, A Vir - gin meek and pure. Through God's e - ter - nal will This Child to her is giv - en, At mid - night calm and still.

3. The shep - herds heard the sto - ry Pro - claimed by an - gels bright, How Christ, the Lord of glo - ry, Was born on earth this night. To Beth - le - hem they sped; And in the man - ger found Him, As an - gel her - alds said.

4. This Flow'r, whose fra - grance ten - der With sweet - ness fills the air, Dis - pels with glo - rious splen - dor The dark - ness ev - 'ry - where. True Man, yet ver - y God, From sin and death He saves us And light - ens ev - 'ry load.

5. O Sav - ior, Child of Ma - ry, Who felt our hu - man woe; O Sav - ior, King of Glo - ry, Who dost our weak - ness know, Bring us at length, we pray, To the bright courts of heav - en, And to the end - less day.

122

139 Rejoice, Rejoice This Happy Morn

MORNING STAR 8 8 7, 8 8 7, 4 4 4 4 8

Birgitte C. Boye, 1778
Tr. Carl Doving, 1911

Philipp Nicolai, 1599

1. Re-joice, re-joice this hap-py morn, A Sav-ior un-to us is born.

The Christ, the Lord of Glo - ry; His low-ly birth in Beth - le-hem

The an-gels from on high pro-claim, And sing re-demp-tion's sto - ry.

My soul, ex - tol God's great fa - vor, Bless Him ev - er

for sal - va - tion, Give Him praise and ad - o - ra - tion!

140 Silent Night! Holy Night

SILENT NIGHT Irregular

Joseph Mohr, 1818   Franz Gruber, 1818

1. Si - lent night! Ho - ly night! Through the dark-ness beams a light,
2. Si - lent night! Ho - ly night! Dark - ness flies, and all is light!
3. Si - lent night! Ho - ly night! Guid - ing Star, O lend thy light!
4. Si - lent night! Ho - ly night! Won-drous Star, O lend thy light!

Yon-der, where they sweet vig - ils keep O'er the Babe who, in si - lent sleep,
Shep-herds hear the an - gels sing: "Hal - le - lu - jah! hail the King!
See the east - ern wise men bring Gifts and hom - age to our King!
With the an - gels let us sing Hal - le - lu - jah to our King!

Rests in heav - en - ly peace, Rests in heav - en - ly peace.
Je-sus the Sav - ior is here! Je - sus the Sav - ior is here!"
Je-sus the Sav - ior is here! Je - sus the Sav - ior is here!
Je-sus our Sav - ior is here! Je - sus our Sav - ior is here!

See also:

I know not how that Bethlehem's Babe, 206
O day full of grace, 226
The Morning Star, 146
All glory be to Thee, 1
Away in a manger, 363
How glad I am each Christmas Eve, 369
Now found is the Fairest of Roses, 153
Beautiful Savior, 6
I love to hear the story, 364

141 A Year Again Is Now Descending

IF THOU BUT SUFFER GOD 9 8, 9 8, 8 8

Johann J. Rambach, 1693-1735
Tr. P. A. Sveeggen, 1919

Georg Neumark, 1640
Arr. F. Melius Christiansen

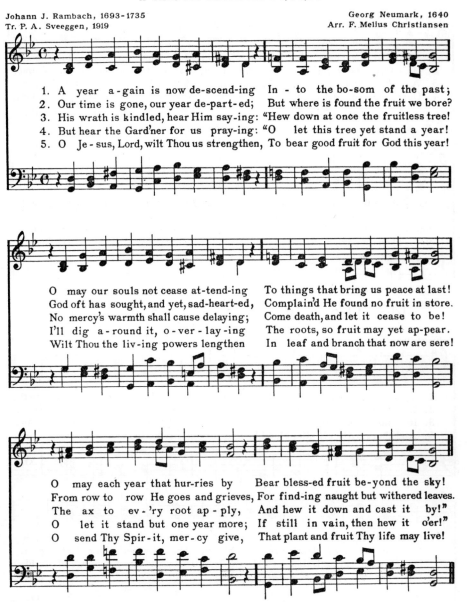

1. A year a-gain is now de-scend-ing In - to the bo-som of the past;
2. Our time is gone, our year de-part-ed; But where is found the fruit we bore?
3. His wrath is kindled, hear Him say-ing: "Hew down at once the fruitless tree!
4. But hear the Gard'ner for us pray-ing: "O let this tree yet stand a year!
5. O Je-sus, Lord, wilt Thou us strengthen, To bear good fruit for God this year!

O may our souls not cease at-tend-ing To things that bring us peace at last!
God oft has sought, and yet, sad-heart-ed, Complain'd He found no fruit in store.
No mercy's warmth shall cause delaying; Come death, and let it cease to be!
I'll dig a-round it, o-ver-lay-ing The roots, so fruit may yet ap-pear.
Wilt Thou the liv-ing powers lengthen In leaf and branch that now are sere!

O may each year that hur-ries by Bear bless-ed fruit be-yond the sky!
From row to row He goes and grieves, For find-ing naught but withered leaves.
The ax to ev-'ry root ap-ply, And hew it down and cast it by!"
O let it stand but one year more; If still in vain, then hew it o'er."
O send Thy Spir-it, mer-cy give, That plant and fruit Thy life may live!

142 O God, Our Help in Ages Past

ST. ANNE C.M.

Isaac Watts, 1719

William Croft, 1708

1. O God, our help in a-ges past, Our hope for years to come,
2. Be - fore the hills in or-der stood, Or earth re-ceived her frame,
3. A thou-sand a - ges in Thy sight Are like an ev-'ning gone;
4. Our God, our help in a-ges past, Our hope for years to come,

Our shel-ter from the storm-y blast, And our e-ter-nal home!
From ev - er-last-ing Thou art God, To end-less years the same.
Short as the watch that ends the night Be - fore the ris-ing sun
Be Thou our guard while life shall last, And our e-ter-nal home.

143 There Is a Name I Love to Hear

CRÜGER C.M.

Frederick Whitfield, 1829-1904

Johann Crüger, 1657

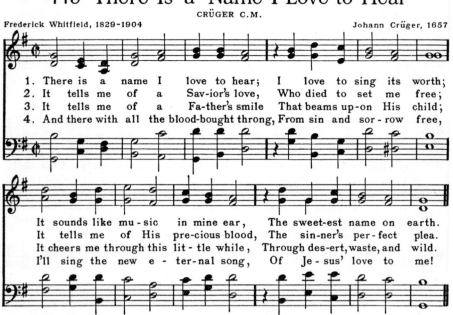

1. There is a name I love to hear; I love to sing its worth;
2. It tells me of a Sav-ior's love, Who died to set me free;
3. It tells me of a Fa-ther's smile That beams up-on His child;
4. And there with all the blood-bought throng, From sin and sor - row free,

It sounds like mu-sic in mine ear, The sweet-est name on earth.
It tells me of His pre-cious blood, The sin-ner's per-fect plea.
It cheers me through this lit - tle while, Through des-ert, waste, and wild.
I'll sing the new e - ter-nal song, Of Je - sus' love to me!

126

144 Jesus, Name of Wondrous Love

William W. How, 1854

VIENNA 7 7 4L.

J. H. Knecht, 1793

1. Je - sus, name of won - drous love, Name all oth - er names a - bove!
2. Je - sus, name of price - less worth To the fall - en sons of earth,
3. Je - sus, on - ly name that's giv'n Un - der all the might - y heav'n,
4. Je - sus, name of won - drous love, Hu - man name of God a - bove:

Un - to which must ev - 'ry knee Bow in deep hu - mil - i - ty.
For the prom - ise that it gave, "Je - sus shall His peo - ple save."
Where - by man, to sin en - slaved, Bursts his fet - ters, and is saved.
Plead - ing on - ly this we flee, Help - less, O our God, to Thee.

145 The Old Year Now Hath Passed Away

WHEN IN THE HOUR OF UTMOST NEED L.M.

Jacob Tapp? 1588
Tr. Catherine Winkworth, 1863

Arr. Ludvig M. Lindeman, 1812 - 1887

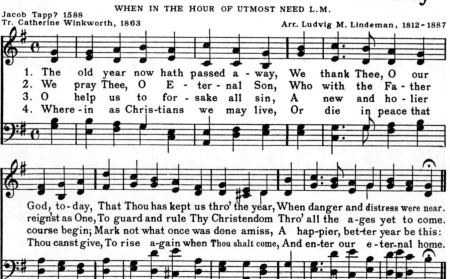

1. The old year now hath passed a - way, We thank Thee, O our
2. We pray Thee, O E - ter - nal Son, Who with the Fa - ther
3. O help us to for - sake all sin, A new and ho - lier
4. Where - in as Chris - tians we may live, Or die in peace that

God, to - day, That Thou has kept us thro' the year, When danger and distress were near.
reign'st as One, To guard and rule Thy Christendom Thro' all the a - ges yet to come.
course begin; Mark not what once was done amiss, A hap - pier, bet - ter year be this:
Thou canst give, To rise a - gain when Thou shalt come, And en - ter our e - ter - nal home.

See also:

How sweet the name of Jesus sounds, 278
The church's one foundation, 80
We have a sure, prophetic word, 85

Praise to the Lord, 3
Give praise to God our King, 5
My soul, now bless thy Maker, 9

146 The Morning Star upon Us Gleams

MORNING STAR 8 8 7, 8 8 7, 4 4 4 4 8

Philipp Nicolai, 1599
Tr. E. J. Palmer, 1892

Philipp Nicolai, 1599

1. The Morn-ing Star up - on us gleams; How full of grace and truth His beams,
2. Strike deep in - to this heart of mine Thy rays of love, Thou Star di - vine,
3. Thou, might-y Fa-ther, in Thy Son Didst love me, ere Thou hadst be-gun
4. Lift up the voice and strike the string, Let all glad sounds of mu - sic ring

How pass-ing fair His splen-dor! Good Shep-herd, Da-vid's pro - per heir,
And fire its dy - ing em - bers: And grant that naught have pow'r to part
This an-cient world's foun-da - tion. Thy Son hath made a friend of me,
In God's high prais-es blend - ed. Christ will be with me all the way,

My King in heav'n, Thou dost me bear Up - on Thy bo - som ten - der
Me from Thy bod - y, Lord, who art The life of all Thy mem - bers
And when in spir - it Him I see I've done with trib - u - la - tion.
To - day, to-mor - row, ev - 'ry day, Till trav-'ling days be end - ed.

Near - est, Dear - est, High - est, bright-est, Thou de - light - est
I stand, Thy hand Ev - er tak - ing, Ne'er for - sak - ing:
What bliss Is this! Where He liv - eth Me He giv - eth
Sing out, Ring out Tri - umph glo-rious, O vic - to - rious,

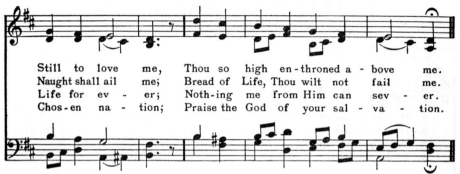

Still to love me, Thou so high en-throned a - bove me.
Naught shall ail me; Bread of Life, Thou wilt not fail me.
Life for ev - er; Noth-ing me from Him can sev - er.
Chos-en na - tion; Praise the God of your sal - va - tion.

147 O Christ, Our True and Only Light

LORD, KEEP US STEADFAST L.M.

Johann Heermann, 1630
Tr. Catherine Winkworth, 1858, alt.

German, 1543

1. O Christ, our true and on - ly light, Il - lu-mine those who sit in night;
2. Fill with the ra-diance of Thy grace The souls now lost in er-ror's maze,
3. And all who else have stray'd from Thee Do Thou re-claim, that they may be
4. O cause the deaf to hear Thy word, And teach the mute to speak, O Lord,

Let those a - far now hear Thy voice, And in Thy fold with us re-joice.
And all whom in their se-cret minds, Some dark de - lu-sion haunts and blinds.
In conscience cleansed, in heart made whole, And fill with heav'n-ly bliss their soul.
Who dare not yet the faith a - vow, Though se-cret-ly they hold it now.

5. Shine on the darkened and the cold,
Recall the wanderers from Thy fold,
Unite all those who walk apart,
Confirm the weak and doubting heart.

6. So they with us may evermore
Such grace with wondering thanks adore,
And endless praise to Thee be given
By all Thy Church in earth and heav'n.

148 O How Beautiful the Sky

O HOW BEAUTIFUL THE SKY 7 7, 8 8, 7 7

Nicolai F. S. Grundtvig, 1783-1872
Tr I. Dorrum, 1929

Danish, Anonymous

1. O   how beau - ti - ful   the   sky,   With the spark-ling stars on   high,
2. In   the midst of Christ-mas night, While the stars were shin-ing bright,
3. Long a - go   it   was fore-told   By God's chos - en   men   of   old
4. Wise men by this star were led   To the Christ-child's low - ly   bed.

How they glit-ter, bright-ly gleam-ing, How they twin-kle, glad-some, beam-ing,
Of   a sud-den, clear and ra-diant, One ap-pear'd and shone re-splend-ent
When at mid-night such a won-der Did ap-pear in heav'n up yon-der,
Guid-ing star, O   may we heed thee, May we know we   ev - er need thee,

As   they draw our hearts to heav'n, As they draw our hearts to   heav'n.
With the lus - tre of the sun, With the lus - tre of the sun.
Born should be a   Sa - vior King, Born should be a   Sa - vior King.
Lead us to our heav'n-ly King, Lead us to our heav'n - ly King.

5. In His word did God provide
   Such a star to be our guide.
   Holy writ, the Gospel story,
   Doth reveal to us the glory,
   Leading onward, on to Christ,
   Leading onward, on to Christ.

149 O Jesus, King of Glory

ST. THEODULPH 7 6 8L.

Martin Behm, 1606

Melchior Teschner, 1615

1. O Jesus, King of glo - ry! Both Da-vid's Lord and Son!
2. The east-ern sag - es, bring-ing Their trib-ute gifts to Thee,
3. Thou art a might-y mon - arch, As by the word we're told,
4. Yet art Thou deck'd with beau - ty, With rays of glo-rious light;
5. And bid Thy word a - mong us Shine as the fair-est star;

Thy realm en-dures for - ev - er, In heav'n is fixed Thy throne;
Bear wit-ness to Thy king - dom, And hum-bly bow the knee;
Yet car - est Thou but lit - tle For earth-ly goods or gold;
Thy heart is filled with good-ness, And all Thy ways are right;
Keep sin and all false doc - trine For - ev - er from us far;

Help, that in earth's do - min - ions, Through-out from pole to pole,
To Thee the star is point - ing, To Thee, th' in-car-nate Word;
On no proud steed Thou rid - est, Thou wear'st no jew-elled crown,
Vouch-safe to shield Thy peo - ple With Thine al-might- y arm,
Help us con-fess Thee tru - ly, And with Thy Chris-ten - dom

Thy realm may spread sal - va - tion To each be-night-ed soul.
Hence joy-ous-ly we hail Thee: Our Sav-ior and our Lord!
Nor dwell'st in lord - ly cas - tle, But bear-est scoff and frown.
That they may dwell in safe - ty From those who mean them harm.
Here own Thee King and Sav - ior And in the world to come.

131

150 Christ, Whose Glory Fills the Skies

JESUS, SUN OF RIGHTEOUSNESS 7 7 6L.

Charles Wesley, 1740

Ludvig M. Lindeman, 1812-1887

1. Christ, whose glo - ry fills the skies, Christ, the true, the on - ly light,
2. Dark and cheer - less is the morn, Un - ac - com - pa - nied by Thee;
3. Vis - it, then, this soul of mine; Pierce the gloom of sin and grief;

Sun of right - eous - ness, a - rise, Tri - umph o'er the shades of night:
Joy - less is the day's re - turn, Till Thy mer - cy's beams I see;
Fill me, ra - dian - cy di - vine; Scat - ter all my un - be - lief:

Day - spring from on high, be near; Day - star, in my heart ap - pear.
Till Thou in - ward light im - part, Glad my eyes and warm my heart.
More and more Thy - self dis - play, Shin - ing to the per - fect day.

151 Brightest and Best

EASTWELL 11 10 4L.

Reginald Heber, 1811

Herbert S. Oakeley, 1830-1903

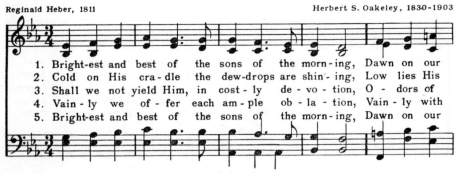

1. Bright - est and best of the sons of the morn - ing, Dawn on our
2. Cold on His cra - dle the dew - drops are shin - ing, Low lies His
3. Shall we not yield Him, in cost - ly de - vo - tion, O - dors of
4. Vain - ly we of - fer each am - ple ob - la - tion, Vain - ly with
5. Bright - est and best of the sons of the morn - ing, Dawn on our

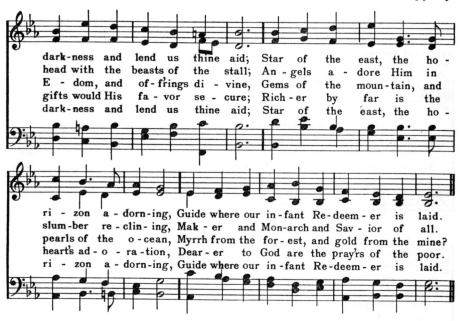

dark-ness and lend us thine aid; Star of the ho - ri - zon a - dorn-ing, Guide where our in-fant Re-deem - er is laid.
head with the beasts of the stall; An - gels a - dore Him in slum-ber re - clin- ing, Mak - er and Mon-arch and Sav - ior of all.
E - dom, and of- frings di - vine, Gems of the moun-tain, and pearls of the o - cean, Myrrh from the for-est, and gold from the mine?
gifts would His fa - vor se - cure; Rich - er by far is the heart's ad - o - ra - tion, Dear - er to God are the pray'rs of the poor.
dark-ness and lend us thine aid; Star of the east, the ho - ri - zon a - dorn-ing, Guide where our in-fant Re-deem - er is laid.

152 Immortal Love, Forever Full

SERENITY C. M.

John G. Whittier, 1866

Arr. from William V. Wallace, 1856

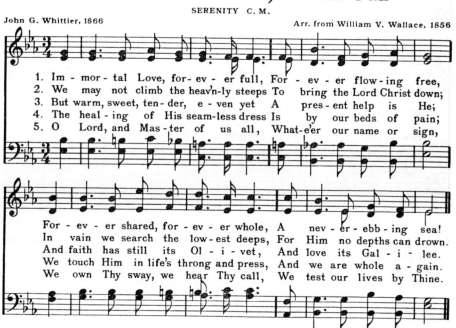

1. Im - mor - tal Love, for- ev - er full, For - ev - er flow-ing free, For - ev - er shared, for - ev - er whole, A nev - er - ebb - ing sea!
2. We may not climb the heav'n-ly steeps To bring the Lord Christ down; In vain we search the low-est deeps, For Him no depths can drown.
3. But warm, sweet, ten-der, e - ven yet A pres-ent help is He; And faith has still its Ol - i - vet, And love its Gal - i - lee.
4. The heal - ing of His seam-less dress Is by our beds of pain; We touch Him in life's throng and press, And we are whole a - gain.
5. O Lord, and Mas-ter of us all, What-e'er our name or sign, We own Thy sway, we hear Thy call, We test our lives by Thine.

133

153 Now Found Is the Fairest of Roses

DESPAIR NOT, O HEART 9 9 4L.

Hans Adolf Brorson, 1694-1764
Tr. J.C. Aaberg

4th Century? 1542

1. Now found is the fair-est of ros - es, 'Mongst bri-ars it
2. Since man his Cre - a - tor de - sert - ed And whol - ly His
3. But God, as His prom-ise had grant-ed, A Rose in the
4. All men should with glad-ness for - ev - er Give prais - es to

sweet-ly re - pos - es; My Je - sus so pre-cious and
im - age per - vert - ed, The world like a des - ert was
des - ert has plant-ed, Which now is with sweet-ness en -
God for His fa - vor, But man - y have ne'er com-pre -

ho - ly A - bode a - mong sin - ners so low - ly.
ly - ing, And all in trans-gres-sion were dy - ing.
dow - ing The race that in e - vil was grow-ing.
hend - ed The Rose to the world has de - scend-ed.

5. My Jesus, Thou ever remainest
My glory and crown, who sustainest
My heart in the fullness of pleasure;
Thy sweetness alone I will treasure.

6. The world may of all things bereave me,
Its thorns may annoy and aggrieve me,
The foe may affliction engender,
My rose I will never surrender.

154 Jesus, Lover of My Soul

MARTYN 7 7 8L.

Charles Wesley, 1740   Simeon B. Marsh, 1834

1. Je - sus, lov - er of my soul, Let me to Thy bo - som fly,
2. Oth - er ref - uge have I none; Hangs my help-less soul on Thee;
3. Thou, O Christ, art all I want; More than all in Thee I find;
4. Plen-teous grace with Thee is found, Grace to cov - er all my sin;

While the near - er wa - ters flow, While the tem-pest still is high;
Leave, ah, leave me not a - lone, Still sup-port and com-fort me!
Raise the fall - en, cheer the faint, Heal the sick, and lead the blind!
Let the heal-ing streams a - bound, Make and keep me pure with - in;

Hide me, O my Sav - ior, hide, Till the storm of life is past;
All my trust on Thee is stayed; All my help from Thee I bring;
Just and ho - ly is Thy Name, I am all un - right-eous - ness;
Thou of life the foun-tain art, Free-ly let me take of Thee;

Safe in - to the ha - ven guide, O re - ceive my soul at last!
Cov - er my de - fense-less head With the shad - ow of Thy wing.
False and full of sin I am, Thou art full of truth and grace.
Spring Thou up with - in my heart! Rise to all e - ter - ni - ty!

155 I Need Thee, Precious Jesus

PASSION CHORALE 7 6 8L.

Frederick Whitfield, 1855   Hans Leo Hassler, 1601

1. I need Thee, pre-cious Je-sus, For I am full of sin;
2. I need Thee, bless-ed Je-sus, For I am ver-y poor;
3. I need Thee, bless-ed Je-sus; I need a friend like Thee,
4. I need Thee, bless-ed Je-sus, And hope to see Thee soon,

My soul is dark and guilt-y, My heart is dead with-in;
A stran-ger and a pil-grim, I have no earth-ly store.
A friend to soothe and pit-y, A friend to care for me.
En-cir-cled with the rain-bow And seat-ed on Thy throne:

I need the cleans-ing foun-tain Where I can al-ways flee,
I need the love of Je-sus To cheer me on my way,
I need the heart of Je-sus To feel each anx-ious care,
There, with Thy blood-bought chil-dren, My joy shall ev-er be

The blood of Christ most pre-cious, The sin-ner's per-fect plea.
To guide my doubt-ing foot-steps, To be my strength and stay.
To tell my ev-'ry tri-al, And all my sor-rows share.
To sing Thy praise, Lord Je-sus, To gaze, my Lord, on Thee.

156 My Jesus, As Thou Wilt

JEWETT 6 6 8L.

Benjamin Schmolck, 1709
Tr Jane Borthwick, 1854

Carl M. von Weber, 1821

1. My Je - sus, as Thou wilt! O may Thy will be mine;
2. My Je - sus, as Thou wilt! Though seen through man - y a tear,
3. My Je - sus, as Thou wilt! All shall be well for me;

In - to Thy hand of love I would my all re - sign
Let not my star of hope Grow dim or dis - ap - pear;
Each chang-ing fu - ture scene I glad - ly trust with Thee,

Through sor - row, or through joy, Con-duct me as Thine own,
Since Thou on earth hast wept, And sor - rowed oft a - lone,
Thus to my home a - bove I trav - el calm - ly on,

And help me still to say, My Lord, Thy will be done
If I must weep with Thee, My Lord, Thy will be done
And sing in life or death, My Lord, Thy will be done

157 There Many Shall Come

THERE MANY SHALL COME 11 9, 11 9 9
(See No. 158)

Magnus Brostrup Landstad, 1861
Tr. P. O. Stromme, 1909

Swedish, 1695

1. There man-y shall come from the east and the west And sit at the
2. But they who have al-ways re-sist-ed His grace And on their own
3. O may we all hear when our Shep-herd doth call, In ac-cents per -
4. God grant that I may of His in-fi-nite love Re-main in His
5 All tri-als are then like the dreams that are past, For-got-ten all

feast of sal - va - tion, With A - bra - ham, I - saac, and
vir - tue de - pend - ed, Shall then be con-demned and cast
sua-sive and ten - der, That while there is time we make
mer-ci - ful keep - ing; And sit with the King at His
troub-le and sor - row: All ques-tions and doubts have been

Ja - cob, the blest, O - bey - ing the Lord's in - vi -
out from His face, E - ter - nal - ly lost and un -
haste one and all And find Him, our might-y de -
ta - ble a - bove, When here in the grave I am
an - swered at last; Then dawn-eth e - ter - ni - ty's

ta - tion. Have mer - cy up - on us, O Je - sus!
friend - ed Have mer - cy up - on us, O Je - sus!
fend - er Have mer - cy up - on us, O Je - sus!
sleep - ing. Have mer - cy up - on us, O Je - sus!
mor - row Have mer - cy up - on us, O Je - sus!

158 There Many Shall Come

AHNFELT 11 9, 11 9 9
(See No. 157)

Magnus Brostrup Landstad, 1861
Tr. P. O. Stromme, 1909

Oscar Ahnfelt, 1813-1882
Arr. A. Lindström

1. There man - y shall come from the east and the west And sit at the feast of sal - va - tion, With A - bra-ham, I - saac, and Ja - cob, the blest, O - bey-ing the Lord's in - vi - ta - tion.
2. But they who have al - ways re - sist - ed His grace And on their own vir - tue de - pend-ed, Shall then be con-demned and cast out from His face, E - ter - nal - ly lost and un - friend- ed.
3. O may we all hear when our Shep - herd doth call, In ac - cents per-sua-sive and ten - der, That while there is time we make haste one and all And find Him, our might - y de - fend - er.
4. God grant that I may of His in - fi - nite love Re - main in His mer - ci - ful keep-ing; And sit with the King at His ta - ble a - bove, When here in the grave I am sleep - ing.
5. All tri - als are then like the dreams that are past, For - got - ten all troub-le and sor - row; All ques-tions and doubts have been an - swered at last; Then dawn-eth e - ter - ni - ty's mor - row.

Have mer - cy up - on us, O Je - sus!

159 O Father, May Thy Word Prevail

O FATHER, MAY THY WORD PREVAIL. 8.6, 8 6, 6 6, 8 6

Hans Adolf Brorson, ca. 1760
Tr. George Taylor Rygh, 1908

Ludvig M. Lindeman, 1812-1887

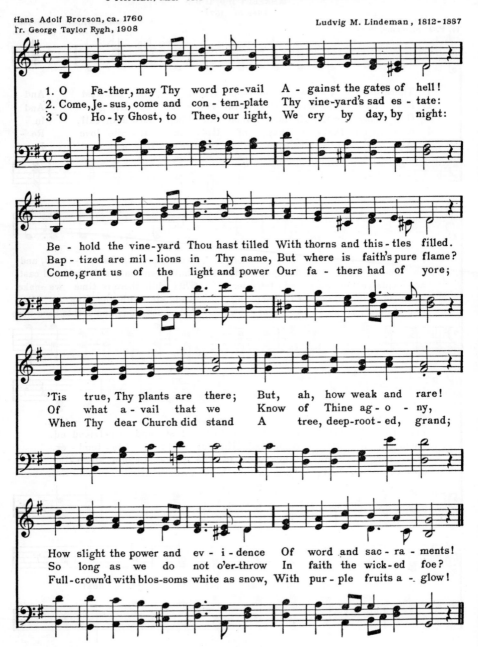

1. O Fa-ther, may Thy word pre-vail A - gainst the gates of hell!
2. Come, Je-sus, come and con - tem-plate Thy vine-yard's sad es - tate:
3. O Ho - ly Ghost, to Thee, our light, We cry by day, by night:

Be - hold the vine-yard Thou hast tilled With thorns and this - tles filled.
Bap - tized are mil - lions in Thy name, But where is faith's pure flame?
Come, grant us of the light and power Our fa - thers had of yore;

'Tis true, Thy plants are there; But, ah, how weak and rare!
Of what a - vail that we Know of Thine ag - o - ny,
When Thy dear Church did stand A tree, deep-root - ed, grand;

How slight the power and ev - i - dence Of word and sac - ra - ments!
So long as we do not o'er-throw In faith the wick - ed foe?
Full - crown'd with blos-soms white as snow, With pur - ple fruits a - glow!

160 Deep and Glorious, Word Victorious

DEEP AND GLORIOUS 8 7, 8 7, 8 8

T. V. Oldenburg, 1840
Tr. Carl Doving, 1909

Johann Crüger, 1649

1. Deep and glo-rious, word vic-to-rious, Word di-vine that ev-er lives! Call thou sin-ners to be win-ners Of the life that Je-sus gives; Tell a-broad what God hath giv-en; Je-sus is our way to heav-en.

2. Sav-ior ten-der, thanks we ren-der For the grace Thou dost af-ford; Time is fly-ing, time is dy-ing, Yet e-ter-nal stands Thy word; With Thy word Thy grace en-dur-eth, And a ref-uge us se-cur-eth.

3. By Thy Spir-it, thro' Thy mer-it, Draw all wea-ry souls to Thee! End their sigh-ing, end their dy-ing, Let them Thy sal-va-tion see! Lead us in life's path-way tend-ing, To the life and bliss un-end-ing.

161 Jesus, Savior, Pilot Me

PILOT 7 7 6L.

Edward Hopper, 1871   John E. Gould, 1871

1. Je - sus, Sav - ior, pi - lot me O - ver life's tem - pes - tuous sea; Un - known waves be - fore me roll, Hid - ing rock and treach -'rous shoal; Chart and com - pass came from Thee; Je - sus, Sav - ior, pi - lot me.

2. As a moth - er stills her child, Thou canst hush the o - cean wild; Bois -t'rous waves o - bey Thy will, When Thou say'st to them, "Be still." Won - drous Sov -'reign of the sea, Je - sus, Sav - ior, pi - lot me.

3. When at last I near the shore, And the fear - ful break - ers roar 'Twixt me and the peace - ful rest, Then, while lean - ing on Thy breast, May I hear Thee say to me, "Fear not, I will pi - lot thee."

162 We Saw Thee Not When Thou Didst Come

ST. PETERSBURG L.M.

J.H. Gurney, 1802-1862

Dimitri S. Bortniansky, 1752-1828

1. We saw Thee not when Thou didst come To this poor world of sin and death; Nor yet beheld Thy cottage home In that despised Nazareth; But we believe Thy footsteps trod Its streets and plains, Thou Son of God.

2. We saw Thee not when lifted high Amid that wild and savage crew; Nor heard we that imploring cry, "Forgive, they know not what they do!" But we believe the deed was done, That shook the earth and veiled the sun.

3. We gazed not in the open tomb Where once Thy mangled body lay; Nor saw Thee in that "upper room," Nor met Thee on the open way; But we believe that angels said, "Why seek the living with the dead?"

4. We walked not with the chosen few Who saw Thee from the earth ascend; Who raised to heav'n their won-d'ring view, Then low to earth all prostrate bend; But we believe that human eyes Beheld that journey to the skies.

143

163 Jesus, Priceless Treasure

JESUS, PRICELESS TREASURE 6 6 5, 6 6 5, 7 8 6

Johann Frank, 1655
Tr. Catherine Winkworth, 1863

Ludvig M. Lindeman, 1812-1887

1. Je - sus, price - less treas - ure, Source of pur - est pleas - ure, Tru - est friend to me: Ah, how long I've pant - ed And my heart hath faint - ed, Thirst-ing, Lord, for Thee. Thine I am, O spot - less Lamb! I will suf - fer naught to hide Thee, Naught I ask be - side Thee.

2. In Thine arms I rest me, Foes who would mo - lest me Can - not reach me here; Tho' the earth be shak - ing, Ev - 'ry heart be quak - ing, Je - sus calms my fear; Fires may flash and thun - der crash, Yea, and sin and hell as - sail me, Je - sus will not fail me.

3. Hence with earth - ly treas - ure! Thou art all my pleas - ure, Je - sus, all my choice; Hence, thou emp - ty glo - ry! Naught to me thy sto - ry, Told with tempt - ing voice; Pain or loss, or shame, or cross, Shall not from my Sav - ior move me, Since He deigns to love me.

4. Fare thee well that err - est, Thou that earth pre - fer - est, Thou wilt tempt in vain; Fare thee well, trans - gres - sion, Hence, ab - horred pos - ses - sion, Come not forth a - gain. Past your hour, O pride and pow'r, World - ly life, thy bonds I sev - er, Fare thee well for - ev - er!

5. Hence, all fear and sad - ness! For the Lord of glad - ness, Je - sus, en - ters in; Those who love the Fa - ther, Though the storms may gath - er, Still have peace with - in; Yea, what-e'er I here must bear, Thou art still my pur - est pleas-ure, Je - sus, price - less treas - ure.

164 Jesus Shall Reign Where'er the Sun

DUKE STREET L.M.

Isaac Watts, 1719   John Hatton, d. 1793

1. Je - sus shall reign wher - e'er the sun Does his suc -
2. To Him shall end - less prayer be made, And prais - es
3. Peo - ple and realms of ev - 'ry tongue Dwell on His
4. Bless-ings a - bound wher - e'er He reigns; The cap - tive
5. Let ev - 'ry crea - ture rise and bring Pe - cu - liar

ces - sive jour - neys run; His king - dom stretch from
throng to crown His head; His name, like sweet per -
love with sweet - est song; And in - fant voic - es
leaps to burst his chains, The wea - ry find e -
hon - ors to our King: An - gels de - scend with

shore to shore, Till moons shall wax and wane no more.
fume, shall rise With ev - 'ry morn - ing sac - ri - fice.
shall pro - claim Their ear - ly bless - ings on His name.
ter - nal rest, And all the sons of want are blest.
songs a - gain, And earth re - peat the loud A - men.

See also:

Behold, the branch is growing, 138   Now hail we our Redeemer, 122
Come, Thou long expected Jesus, 120   Also hymns under CHRISTIAN LIFE, 246-348

165 A Lamb Goes Forth Our Griefs to Share

TO US IS BORN 8 7, 8 7, 8 8 7, 8 8 7

Paul Gerhardt, 1648
Tr. H. Brueckner, 1925

German, 14th Century

1. A Lamb goes forth our griefs to share, In spir - it meek and low - ly;
2. Sus - pend - ed on the tree of shame, He suf - fers mor - tal an - guish;
3. As long as I my breath re-tain, Thy ten - der love be - hold - ing,
4. When I at last Thy king-dom see, With all its bound-less treas - ure,

He deigns our sin and guilt to bear, This Lamb of God most ho - ly.
For all our sins He takes the blame, In grief His soul must lan-guish.
I faith - ful shall to Thee re-main And rest in Thine en - fold - ing.
Thy blood my pur - ple robe shall be, My source of joy and pleas-ure.

He goes His way, grows weak and faint, To death is led with - out com-plaint,
His sighs are proof of mor - tal pain, And o - pen'd up is ev - 'ry vein,
Thy love with - in my heart shall shine, And I shall prize that light di - vine
It shall be - come my roy - al crown When I be - fore God's throne kneel down,

His pre - cious life to of - fer. He glad - ly suf - fers pain and death,
His blood in mer - cy flow - ing. O gen - tle Lamb, what shall it be
Till death mine eye-lids clos - eth; Thou shalt my ver - y be - ing own,
In deep - est hom-age bend - ing. Then He will place me at Thy side,

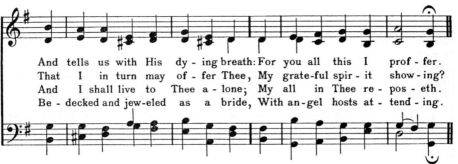

And tells us with His dy - ing breath: For you all this I prof - fer.
That I in turn may of - fer Thee, My grate-ful spir - it show - ing?
And I shall live to Thee a - lone; My all in Thee re - pos - eth.
Be - decked and jew-eled as a bride, With an-gel hosts at - tend - ing.

166 Upon the Cross the Robber Prayed

COME, HOLY GHOST L.M.

Hallgrim Petursson, 1614-1674
Tr. C. V. Pilcher
Skaparinn Stjarna, Herra hreinn

German, 1524

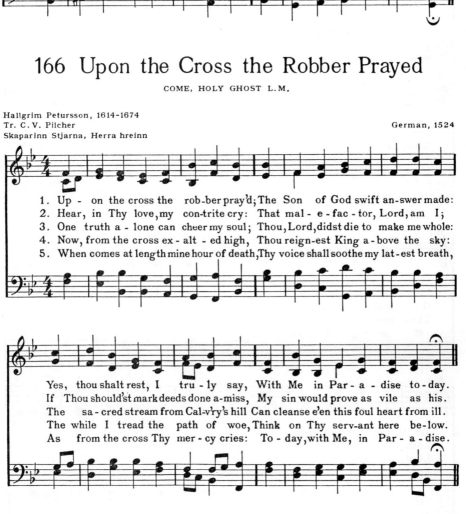

1. Up - on the cross the rob-ber pray'd; The Son of God swift an-swer made:
2. Hear, in Thy love, my con-trite cry: That mal - e - fac - tor, Lord, am I;
3. One truth a - lone can cheer my soul; Thou, Lord, didst die to make me whole:
4. Now, from the cross ex - alt - ed high, Thou reign-est King a - bove the sky:
5. When comes at length mine hour of death, Thy voice shall soothe my lat - est breath,

Yes, thou shalt rest, I tru - ly say, With Me in Par - a - dise to-day.
If Thou should'st mark deeds done a-miss, My sin would prove as vile as his.
The sa - cred stream from Cal-v'ry's hill Can cleanse e'en this foul heart from ill.
The while I tread the path of woe, Think on Thy serv-ant here be-low.
As from the cross Thy mer - cy cries: To - day, with Me, in Par - a - dise.

167 O Sacred Head, Now Wounded

PASSION CHORALE 7 6 8L

Bernard of Clairvaux, 1091-1153
Paul Gerhardt, 1656
Tr. James W. Alexander, 1830, alt.

Hans Leo Hassler, 1601
Arr. F. Melius Christiansen, 1907

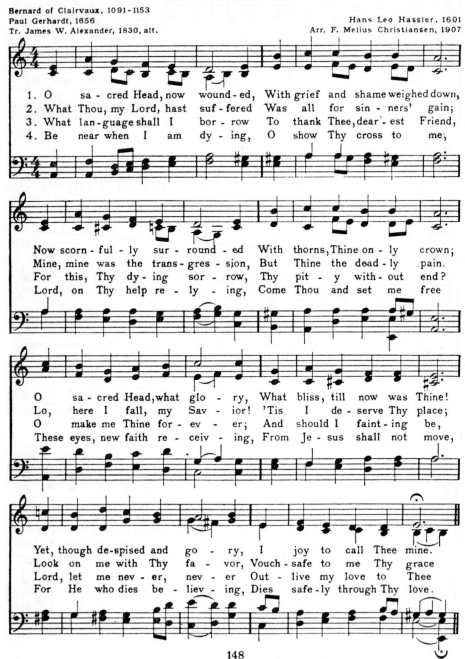

1. O sa - cred Head, now wound - ed, With grief and shame weighed down,
2. What Thou, my Lord, hast suf - fered Was all for sin - ners' gain;
3. What lan - guage shall I bor - row To thank Thee, dear - est Friend,
4. Be near when I am dy - ing, O show Thy cross to me;

Now scorn - ful - ly sur - round - ed With thorns, Thine on - ly crown;
Mine, mine was the trans - gres - sion, But Thine the dead - ly pain.
For this, Thy dy - ing sor - row, Thy pit - y with - out end?
Lord, on Thy help re - ly - ing, Come Thou and set me free

O sa - cred Head, what glo - ry, What bliss, till now was Thine!
Lo, here I fall, my Sav - ior! 'Tis I de - serve Thy place;
O make me Thine for - ev - er; And should I faint - ing be,
These eyes, new faith re - ceiv - ing, From Je - sus shall not move,

Yet, though de - spised and go - ry, I joy to call Thee mine.
Look on me with Thy fa - vor, Vouch - safe to me Thy grace
Lord, let me nev - er, nev - er Out - live my love to Thee
For He who dies be - liev - ing, Dies safe - ly through Thy love.

168 Anxious Heart, Be Rid of Sadness

ANXIOUS HEART 8 6 8L.
(Or use LORD VICTORIOUS, No. 120)

Hans Adolf Brorson, 1694-1764
Tr. Olav Lee

Norwegian Folk-Tune
Arr. Oscar R. Overby, 1931

1. Anx-ious heart, be rid of sad-ness, Let us haste to Cal-va-ry;
2. Thou, O gen-tle, lov-ing, ho-ly Lamb of God, for me hast died;

There re-ceive the peace and glad-ness Which His pas-sion of-fers thee.
For my sin and shame Thou sole-ly Here hast ful-ly sat-is-fied.

For the wea-ry, vexed and need-y Free sal-va-tion here a-bounds;
Hence I, trust-ing in Thy fa-vor, Safe thro' life and death shall go,

To the fount of sol-ace speed thee In the bless-ed Sav-ior's wounds.
Mind-ful of Thy suf-f'ring ev-er I shall van-quish all my woe.

149

169 In the Hour of Trial

PENITENCE 6 5 8L.

James Montgomery, 1834

Spencer Lane, 1878

1. In the hour of tri - al, Je - sus, plead for me, Lest, by base de-
2. Should Thy mer-cy send me Sor-row, toil, or woe; Or should pain at -
3. When, in dust and ash - es, To the grave I sink, While heaven's glo-ry

ni - al, I de - part from Thee; When Thou seest me wav - er,
tend me On my path be - low; Grant that I may nev - er
flash - es O'er the shelv - ing brink, On Thy truth re - ly - ing

With a look re - call; Nor for fear or fa - vor, Suf - fer me to fall.
Fail Thy hand to see; Grant that I may ev - er Cast my care on Thee.
Thro' that mor-tal strife, Lord, re-ceive me, dy - ing, To e - ter-nal life.

170 Go to Dark Gethsemane

GETHSEMANE 7 7 6L.

(Or use TOPLADY, No. 284)

James Montgomery, 1825

Richard Redhead, 1853

1. Go to dark Geth-sem - a - ne, Ye that feel the temp-ter's power;
2. Fol - low to the judg-ment-hall, View the Lord of life ar-raigned;
3. Cal - v'ry's mourn-ful moun-tain climb, There, a - dor - ing at His feet,
4. Ear - ly hast - en to the tomb Where they laid His breath-less clay;

150

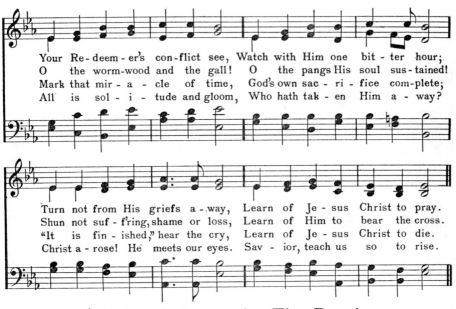

Your Re-deem-er's con-flict see, Watch with Him one bit-ter hour;
O the worm-wood and the gall! O the pangs His soul sus-tained!
Mark that mir-a-cle of time, God's own sac-ri-fice com-plete;
All is sol-i-tude and gloom, Who hath tak-en Him a-way?

Turn not from His griefs a-way, Learn of Je-sus Christ to pray.
Shun not suf-f'ring, shame or loss, Learn of Him to bear the cross.
"It is fin-ished," hear the cry, Learn of Je-sus Christ to die.
Christ a-rose! He meets our eyes. Sav-ior, teach us so to rise.

171 Lord Jesus, by Thy Passion

LORD JESUS, BY THY PASSION 7 6 4L.

Richard E. Littledale, 1864

Kingo's Gradual, 1699
Arr. F. Melius Christiansen, 1907

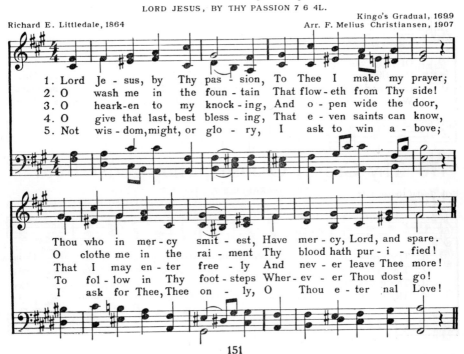

1. Lord Je-sus, by Thy pas-sion, To Thee I make my prayer;
2. O wash me in the foun-tain That flow-eth from Thy side!
3. O heark-en to my knock-ing, And o-pen wide the door,
4. O give that last, best bless-ing, That e-ven saints can know,
5. Not wis-dom, might, or glo-ry, I ask to win a-bove;

Thou who in mer-cy smit-est, Have mer-cy, Lord, and spare.
O clothe me in the rai-ment Thy blood hath pur-i-fied!
That I may en-ter free-ly And nev-er leave Thee more!
To fol-low in Thy foot-steps Wher-ev-er Thou dost go!
I ask for Thee, Thee on-ly, O Thou e-ter-nal Love!

172 Zion, to Thy Savior Singing

CRUCIFIXION 8 8 7 6L.

Thomas Aquinas, ca. 1260
Tr. A.R. Thompson, 1883

Zinck's Koralbog, 1801
Arr. Ludvig M. Lindeman, 1812-1887

1. Zi - on, to thy Sav-ior sing-ing, To thy prince and shep-herd bring-ing
2. Of all won-ders that can thrill thee, And with ad-o-ra-tion fill thee,
3. Here the King hath spread His ta-ble, Where-on eyes of faith are a-ble
4. O Good Shep-herd, bread life-giv-ing, Us, Thy grace and life re-ceiv-ing,

Sweet-est hymns of love and praise, Thou wilt nev-er reach the meas-ure
What than this can great-er be, That Him-self to thee He giv-eth?
Christ our Pass-o-ver to trace: Shad-ows of the law are go-ing,
Feed and shel-ter ev-er-more; Thou on earth our weak-ness guid-ing,

Of His worth, by all the treas-ure Of thy most ec-stat-ic lays.
He that eat-eth ev-er liv-eth, For the Bread of Life is He.
Light and life and truth in-flow-ing, Night to day is giv-ing place.
We in heav'n with Thee a-bid-ing, With all saints will Thee a-dore.

173 Thy Cross, O Jesus, Thou Didst Bear

CROSS-BEARER 8 7, 8 7, 4 4 7

Erik Gustaf Geijer, 1812
Tr. E.A. Edlen

Casper Friedrich Nachtenhöfer, 1651

1. Thy cross, O Je-sus, Thou didst bear And yield Thy-self an of-f'ring;
2. Thy cross, Re-deem-er, Thou didst bear, When all had Thee for-sak-en;
3. Thy cross, O Sav-ior, Thou didst bear: Thy bound-less might and glo-ry,
4. Thy cross to vic-t'ry Thou didst bear; O grant that I, dear Sav-ior,

152

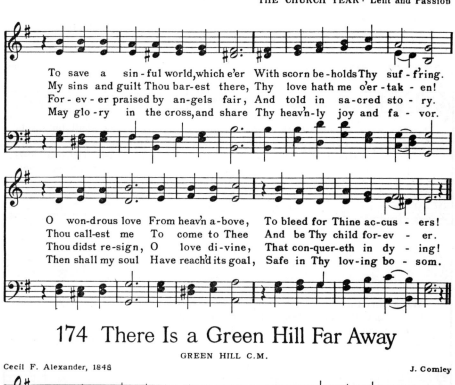

To save a sin-ful world, which e'er With scorn be-holds Thy suf-f'ring.
My sins and guilt Thou bar-est there, Thy love hath me o'er-tak-en!
For-ev-er praised by an-gels fair, And told in sa-cred sto-ry.
May glo-ry in the cross, and share Thy heav'n-ly joy and fa-vor.

O won-drous love From heav'n a-bove, To bleed for Thine ac-cus-ers!
Thou call-est me To come to Thee And be Thy child for-ev-er.
Thou didst re-sign, O love di-vine, That con-quer-eth in dy-ing!
Then shall my soul Have reach'd its goal, Safe in Thy lov-ing bo-som.

174 There Is a Green Hill Far Away

GREEN HILL C.M.

Cecil F. Alexander, 1848

J. Comley

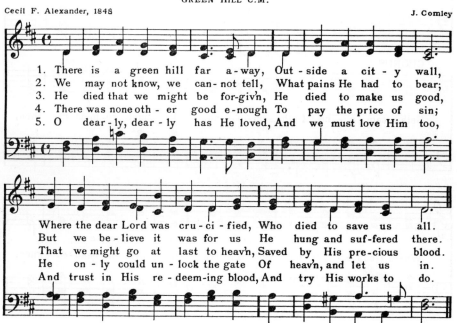

1. There is a green hill far a-way, Out-side a cit-y wall,
2. We may not know, we can-not tell, What pains He had to bear;
3. He died that we might be for-giv'n, He died to make us good,
4. There was none oth-er good e-nough To pay the price of sin;
5. O dear-ly, dear-ly has He loved, And we must love Him too,

Where the dear Lord was cru-ci-fied, Who died to save us all.
But we be-lieve it was for us He hung and suf-fered there.
That we might go at last to heav'n, Saved by His pre-cious blood.
He on-ly could un-lock the gate Of heav'n, and let us in.
And trust in His re-deem-ing blood, And try His works to do.

153

175 The Hour in Dark Gethsemane

IN DARK GETHSEMANE (Hull) C.M.

Norwegian, Anonymous
Tr. T. O Burntvedt, 1931

Asa Hull

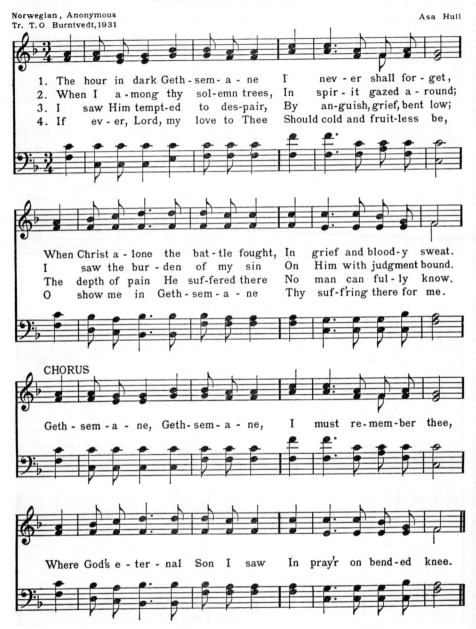

1. The hour in dark Geth-sem-a-ne   I   nev-er shall for-get,
2. When I   a-mong thy   sol-emn trees, In   spir-it gazed a-round;
3. I   saw Him tempt-ed   to des-pair, By   an-guish, grief, bent low;
4. If   ev-er, Lord, my   love to Thee Should cold and fruit-less be,

When Christ a-lone the bat-tle fought, In   grief and blood-y   sweat.
I   saw the bur-den of my sin On   Him with judgment bound.
The   depth of pain He suf-fered there No   man can ful-ly   know.
O   show me in Geth-sem-a-ne Thy   suf-f'ring there for me.

CHORUS

Geth-sem-a-ne, Geth-sem-a-ne,   I   must re-mem-ber thee,

Where God's e-ter-nal Son I saw   In pray'r on bend-ed knee.

176 A Way to Calvary Leadeth

VIA DOLOROSA 7 6 4L. and Chorus

C. G. Liander
Tr. Olav Lee

C. G. Liander

1. A - way to cal - v'ry lead - eth   From dark Geth-sem - a - ne,   May
2. In name-less woe our Sav-ior   Here pass'd with troub-led breath,   His
3. Be - hold Him in   the gar - den   All down with sor - row weighed, When
4. My soul, in nights of sor - row   Learn here what you must do,   Then
5. With nails and spear-point wounded   He down to death must go,   But

ev - 'ry one be - hold Him   Who   wea - ry walks that way.
heart of ten - der mer - cy   That   day was pierced to death.
in   that hour of   dark - ness   He   sweat - ed blood and prayed.
at   the cross your treas - ure   Will be   re-vealed to you:
from those wounds a - bund - ant   The streams of life will flow.

CHORUS

1-6. The way doth lead to   per - fect bliss,   But a way of pain it is.
7. And thus that pain - ful way of His   Has be-come our way to bliss.

6. What bliss to be permitted
One's soul to bathe therein
And thus be cleansed forever
From every taint of sin!

7. Thus only we are learning
That song forever new,
Which to our Savior's glory
Shall ring all ages thru.

177 Savior, When We Call, O Hear Us

CRUCIFIXION 8 8 7 6L.

Thomas Kelly, ca. 1845

Zinck's Koralbog, 1801
Arr. Ludvig M. Lindeman, 1812-1887

1. Sav-ior, when we call, O hear us; In the try-ing hour be near us,
2. Oth-er help than Thine we have not; Oth-er help than Thine we crave not;
3. Keep us on Thy strength re-ly-ing, In Thy name the foe de-fy-ing;

Lest the foe should prove too strong. To Thy mer-cy we be-take us:
'Tis e-nough if we have this: This from ev-'ry ill se-cures us;
Till Thy com-ing bring us peace. O how sweet the thought and cheer-ing,

Nev-er leave us, ne'er for-sake us; Pow'r and grace to Thee be-long.
Ev-'ry bless-ing this en-sures us; More than life Thy fa-vor is.
In the day of Thine ap-pear-ing Troub-le shall for-ev-er cease.

178 When I Survey the Wondrous Cross

ROCKINGHAM L.M.
(See No. 183)

Isaac Watts, 1707

Edward Miller, 1735-1807

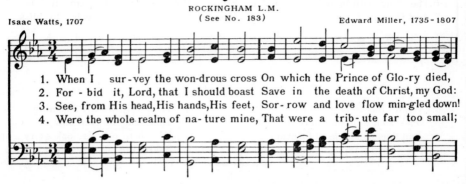

1. When I sur-vey the won-drous cross On which the Prince of Glo-ry died,
2. For-bid it, Lord, that I should boast Save in the death of Christ, my God:
3. See, from His head, His hands, His feet, Sor-row and love flow min-gled down!
4. Were the whole realm of na-ture mine, That were a trib-ute far too small;

My rich-est gain I count but loss, And pour con-tempt on all my pride.
All the vain things that charm me most, I sac - ri - fice them to His blood.
Did e'er such love and sor-row meet, Or thorns com-pose so rich a crown?
Love so a-maz - ing, so di - vine, De-mands my soul, my life, my all.

179 O World, See Here Suspended

O BREAD OF LIFE 7 7 6, 7 7 8

Paul Gerhardt, 1606-1676
Tr. Anna Hoppe, alt.

Heinrich Isaac, 1490
Arr. F. Melius Christiansen, 1907

1. O world, see here sus - pend - ed, His lov - ing arms ex - tend - ed,
2. O Thou, who hearts dost quick - en, Why art Thou sor-row-strick - en,
3. 'Tis I who sins en - cum - ber, Whose mis-deeds far out - num - ber
4. Death for a time must hold Thee, The grave too must en - fold Thee,

Thy Sav - ior on the cross! The Prince of life is will - ing, All
Why all this name-less pain? While we must make con-fes - sion Of
The sands up - on the shore; I caused Thy con-dem-na - tion, Thy
Lest I should be its prey; Death, who for me had tar - ried, Death

right-eous-ness ful - fill - ing, To suf - fer an-guish, scorn, and loss.
sin and dire trans - gres-sion, No sin on Thee hath left a stain.
deep hu - mil - i - a - tion, And all the wounds that pain Thee sore.
now him-self lies bur - ied, And I shall live with Thee for aye.

157

180 Beneath the Cross of Jesus

ST. CHRISTOPHER 7 6, 8 6, 8 6, 8 6

Elizabeth C. Clephane, 1872   Frederick C. Maker, 1881

1. Be - neath the cross of Je - sus I fain would take my stand,
2. Up - on the cross of Je - sus, Mine eye at times can see
3. I take, O cross, thy shad - ow For my a - bid - ing place;

The shad - ow of a might - y rock With - in a wea - ry land;
The ver - y dy - ing form of One Who suf - fered there for me.
I ask no oth - er sun - shine than The sun - shine of His face;

A home with - in the wil - der - ness, A rest up - on the way,
And from my smit - ten heart with tears, These won - ders I con - fess,—
Con - tent to let the world go by, To know no gain or loss,

From the burn - ing of the noon - tide heat, And the bur - den of the day.
The won - der of His glo - rious love, And my own worth - less - ness.
My sin - ful self my on - ly shame, My glo - ry all the cross.

181 O What Precious Balm and Healing

O WHAT PRECIOUS BALM 8 7, 8 7, 7 7, 8 8

Bernard of Clairvaux, 1091 - 1153
Johann Heermann, 1644
Tr. Richard Massie, 1857

Louis Bourgeois, 1551

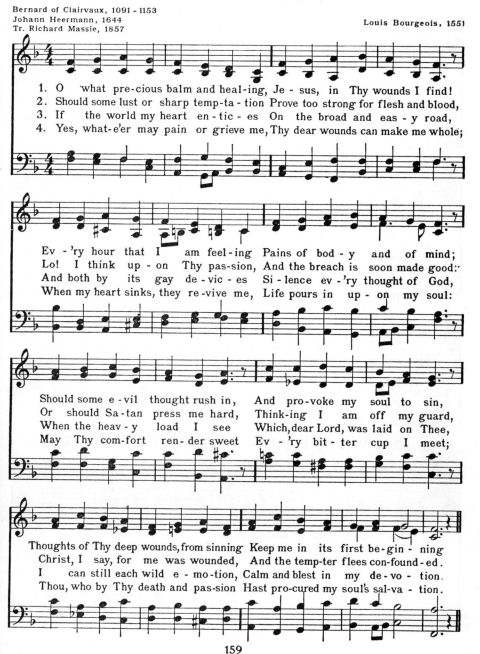

1. O what pre-cious balm and heal-ing, Je - sus, in Thy wounds I find!
2. Should some lust or sharp temp-ta - tion Prove too strong for flesh and blood,
3. If the world my heart en - tic - es On the broad and eas - y road,
4. Yes, what-e'er may pain or grieve me, Thy dear wounds can make me whole;

Ev - 'ry hour that I am feel-ing Pains of bod - y and of mind;
Lo! I think up - on Thy pas-sion, And the breach is soon made good:
And both by its gay de - vic - es Si - lence ev - 'ry thought of God,
When my heart sinks, they re -vive me, Life pours in up - on my soul:

Should some e - vil thought rush in, And pro-voke my soul to sin,
Or should Sa -tan press me hard, Think-ing I am off my guard,
When the heav - y load I see Which, dear Lord, was laid on Thee,
May Thy com-fort ren- der sweet Ev - 'ry bit - ter cup I meet;

Thoughts of Thy deep wounds, from sinning Keep me in its first be -gin - ning
Christ, I say, for me was wounded, And the temp-ter flees con-found - ed.
I can still each wild e - mo-tion, Calm and blest in my de - vo - tion.
Thou, who by Thy death and pas-sion Hast pro-cured my soul's sal-va - tion.

159

182 Jesus, Keep Me Near the Cross

NEAR THE CROSS 7 6 4L. and Chorus

Fanny J. Crosby, 1820-1915   William Howard Doane, 1838-1915

1. Je - sus, keep me near the Cross, There a pre-cious fountain Free to all— a
2. Near the Cross, a trembling soul, Love and mer-cy found me; There the bright and
3. Near the Cross! O Lamb of God, Bring its scenes before me; Help me walk from
4. Near the Cross I'll watch and wait, Hop-ing, trust-ing ev - er, Till I reach the

CHORUS

heal-ing stream, Flows from Calv'ry's mountain.
morn-ing star   Shed its beams a-round me.   In the Cross, in the Cross, Be my
day to day,   With its shad-ows o'er me.
gold-en strand, Just be-yond the riv - er.

glo-ry ev - er; Till my rap-tured soul shall find Rest be-yond the riv - er

Copyright property of W.H. Doane. Used by permission

183 When I Survey the Wondrous Cross

HAMBURG L.M.
Isaac Watts, 1707   (See No. 178)   Gregorian Chant
Arr. Lowell Mason, 1824

1. When I sur - vey the won-drous cross   On which the Prince of Glo-ry   died,
2. For-bid it, Lord, that   I should boast, Save in the cross of Christ, my   God:
3. See, from His head, His hands, His feet, Sor-row and love flow min-gled down!
4. Were the whole realm of na-ture mine, That were a trib-ute far too small;

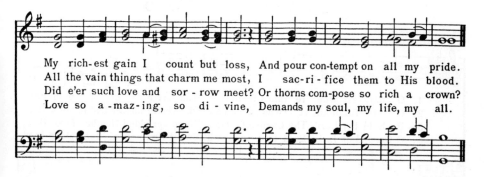

My rich-est gain I count but loss, And pour con-tempt on all my pride.
All the vain things that charm me most, I sac-ri-fice them to His blood.
Did e'er such love and sor-row meet? Or thorns com-pose so rich a crown?
Love so a-maz-ing, so di-vine, Demands my soul, my life, my all.

184 Alas! and Did My Savior Bleed

MARTYRDOM C.M.

Isaac Watts, 1707

Hugh Wilson, 1764-1824

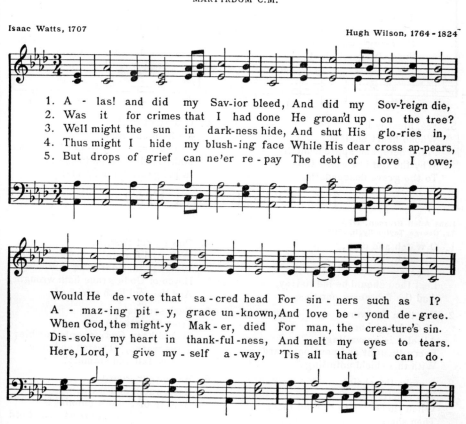

1. A - las! and did my Sav-ior bleed, And did my Sov-'reign die,
2. Was it for crimes that I had done He groan'd up - on the tree?
3. Well might the sun in dark-ness hide, And shut His glo-ries in,
4. Thus might I hide my blush-ing face While His dear cross ap-pears,
5. But drops of grief can ne'er re-pay The debt of love I owe;

Would He de-vote that sa-cred head For sin-ners such as I?
A - maz-ing pit-y, grace un-known, And love be-yond de-gree.
When God, the might-y Mak-er, died For man, the crea-ture's sin.
Dis-solve my heart in thank-ful-ness, And melt my eyes to tears.
Here, Lord, I give my-self a-way, 'Tis all that I can do.

185 O Darkest Woe

O DARKEST WOE 4 4 7, 7 6

Johann Rist, 1641
Tr. Catherine Winkworth, 1863

German, 1628

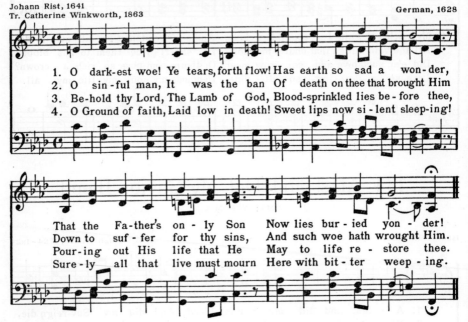

1. O dark-est woe! Ye tears, forth flow! Has earth so sad a won-der,
2. O sin-ful man, It was the ban Of death on thee that brought Him
3. Be-hold thy Lord, The Lamb of God, Blood-sprinkled lies be-fore thee,
4. O Ground of faith, Laid low in death! Sweet lips now si-lent sleep-ing!

That the Fa-ther's on-ly Son Now lies bur-ied yon-der!
Down to suf-fer for thy sins, And such woe hath wrought Him.
Pour-ing out His life that He May to life re-store thee.
Sure-ly all that live must mourn Here with bit-ter weep-ing.

5. Yea, blest is he
Whose heart shall be
Fixed here, and apprehendeth
Why the Lord of glory thus
To the grave descendeth.

6. O Jesus blest!
My help and rest!
With tears I pray — Lord, hear me;
Make me love Thee to the last,
In the grave be near me!

186 O Watch and Pray

O DARKEST WOE

Hans Adolf Brorson, 1735
Tr. George Taylor Rygh, 1908

1. O watch and pray,
My soul, the way
Of safety lies before thee;
Lest thou should be led astray,
And the foe come o'er thee.

2. Use thou the word
Of God, thy Lord;
All else is unavailing;
Every thought and passion guard
With this shield unfailing.

3. O make thy choice
The spirit's voice
When He comes to remind thee;
Then shall thy heart rejoice,
Satan get behind thee.

4. One secret thought
With evil fraught,
Which in the heart was cherished,
Havoc of God's grace hath wrought,
And the soul hath perished.

5. Each soul astray
From Christ, the way,
Should keep God's people humble;
Jesus warns, "O watch and pray
Lest ye fall and stumble".

6. Be on your guard,
Keep watch and ward,
Beware of Satan's cunning.
Watch and pray and trust your Lord
Till ye see Him coming.

162

187 Ride On, Ride On, O Savior-King

ALL SAINTS C.M.D.

C. K. Solberg   Henry S. Cutler, 1872

1. Ride on, ride on, O Sav-ior-King, To set the sin-ner free!
2. Ride on, ride on, O Sav-ior-King, To claim the hearts of men!
3. Ride on, ride on, O Sav-ior-King! Ride on o'er land and sea,

To sin-cursed souls sal-va-tion bring And peace e-ter-nal-ly!
Now death has lost its dread-ful sting And hope is born a-gain.
For Thou a-lone to man can bring E-ter-nal lib-er-ty;

Ride on to dark Geth-sem-a-ne, To un-told ag-o-ny,
O come, in hu-man hearts to reign, Sup-press the pow'r of sin!
Ride on to sin-bound na-tions, Lord, Un-til each heart shall own

And on the Cross of Cal-va-ry Pro-cure our vic-to-ry!
Our own en-deav-or is in vain, Lord, Thou must help us win!
Thy sav-ing, sanc-ti-fy-ing word And bow be-fore Thy throne!

188 Wide Open Are Thy Loving Hands

I SEE THEE STANDING, LAMB OF GOD C.M.D.

Bernard of Clairvaux ? 1091–1153
Tr. Charles Porterfield Krauth, 1870, alt.

Unknown

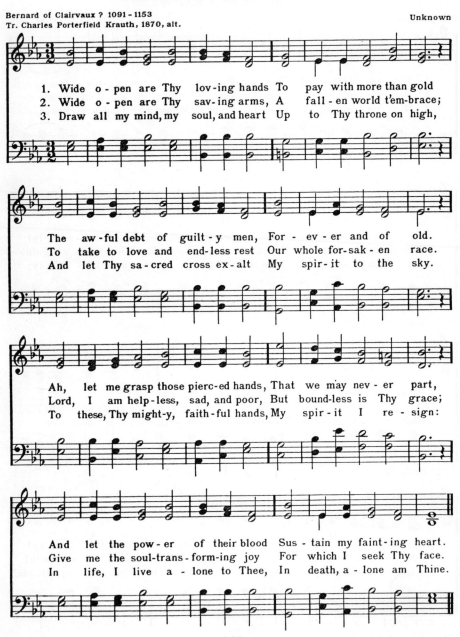

1. Wide o-pen are Thy lov-ing hands To pay with more than gold
2. Wide o-pen are Thy sav-ing arms, A fall-en world t'em-brace;
3. Draw all my mind, my soul, and heart Up to Thy throne on high,

The aw-ful debt of guilt-y men, For-ev-er and of old.
To take to love and end-less rest Our whole for-sak-en race.
And let Thy sa-cred cross ex-alt My spir-it to the sky.

Ah, let me grasp those pierc-ed hands, That we may nev-er part,
Lord, I am help-less, sad, and poor, But bound-less is Thy grace;
To these, Thy might-y, faith-ful hands, My spir-it I re-sign:

And let the pow-er of their blood Sus-tain my faint-ing heart.
Give me the soul-trans-form-ing joy For which I seek Thy face.
In life, I live a-lone to Thee, In death, a-lone am Thine.

189 'Tis Finished! So the Savior Cried

COMMUNION HYMN L.M.

Samuel Stennett, 1787

German, 1605

1. 'Tis fin-ished! so the Sav-ior cried; And meek-ly bowed His head and died:
2. 'Tis fin-ished! all that heav'n de-creed And all the an-cient proph-ets said
3. 'Tis fin-ished! this my dy-ing groan Shall sins of ev-'ry-kind a-tone
4. 'Tis fin-ished! let the joy-ful sound Be heard thro' all the na-tions round;

'Tis fin-ished! yes, the race is run, The bat-tle fought, the vic-'try won.
Is now ful-filled, as was de-signed, In me, the Sav-ior of man-kind.
And mil-lions are re-deem'd from death, By this my last ex-pir-ing breath.
'Tis fin-ished! let the ech-o fly Thro' heav'n and hell, thro' earth and sky.

190 Stricken, Smitten, and Afflicted

STRICKEN, SMITTEN 8 7 4L.

Thomas Kelly, 1804

Ludvig M. Lindeman, 1812-1887

1. Strick-en, smit-ten, and af-flict-ed, See Him dy-ing on the tree!
2. Mark the sac-ri-fice ap-point-ed! See who bears the aw-ful load;
3. Here we have a firm foun-da-tion; Here the ref-uge of the lost:
4. Lamb of God for sin-ners wounded! Sac-ri-fice to can-cel guilt!

'Tis the Christ by man re-ject-ed; Yes, my soul, 'tis He, 'tis He!
'Tis the Word, the Lord's A-noint-ed, Son of man, and Son of God!
Christ, the Rock of our sal-va-tion: His the name of which we boast.
None shall ev-er be con-found-ed Who on Thee their hope have built.

165

191 Sweet the Moments, Rich in Blessing

BROCKLESBURY 8 7 4L.

Walter Shirley, 1774, alt.   Charlotte A. Barnard, 1830-1869

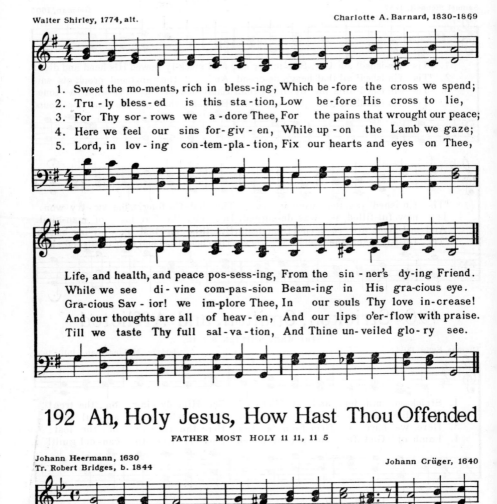

1. Sweet the mo-ments, rich in bless-ing, Which be-fore the cross we spend;
2. Tru-ly bless-ed is this sta-tion, Low be-fore His cross to lie,
3. For Thy sor-rows we a-dore Thee, For the pains that wrought our peace;
4. Here we feel our sins for-giv-en, While up-on the Lamb we gaze;
5. Lord, in lov-ing con-tem-pla-tion, Fix our hearts and eyes on Thee,

Life, and health, and peace pos-sess-ing, From the sin-ner's dy-ing Friend.
While we see di-vine com-pas-sion Beam-ing in His gra-cious eye.
Gra-cious Sav-ior! we im-plore Thee, In our souls Thy love in-crease!
And our thoughts are all of heav-en, And our lips o'er-flow with praise.
Till we taste Thy full sal-va-tion, And Thine un-veiled glo-ry see.

192 Ah, Holy Jesus, How Hast Thou Offended

FATHER MOST HOLY 11 11, 11 5

Johann Heermann, 1630
Tr. Robert Bridges, b. 1844   Johann Crüger, 1640

1. Ah, ho-ly Je-sus, how hast Thou of-fend-ed, That man to
2. For me, kind Je-sus, was Thine in-car-na-tion, Thy mor-tal
3. There-fore, kind Je-sus, since I can-not pay Thee, I do a-

judge Thee hath in hate pre - tend - ed?   By foes de - rid - ed,
sor - row, and Thy life's ob - la - tion;   Thy death of an - guish
dore Thee, and will ev - er pray Thee: Think on Thy pit - y

by Thine own re - ject - ed,   O most af - flict - ed!
and Thy bit - ter pas - sion,   For my sal - va - tion.
and Thy love un - swerv - ing,   Not my de - serv - ing.

193 In the Cross of Christ I Glory

RATHBUN 8 7 4L.

John Bowring, 1825

Ithamar Conkey, 1851

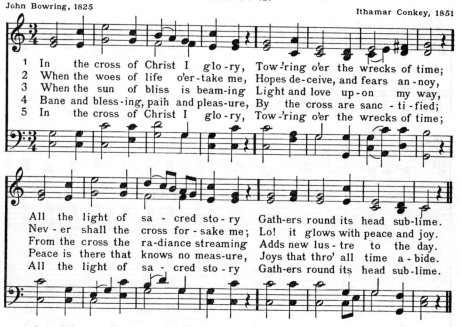

1 In   the cross of Christ I glo - ry, Tow-'ring o'er the wrecks of time;
2 When the woes of life o'er-take me, Hopes de-ceive, and fears an-noy,
3 When the sun of bliss is beam-ing Light and love up-on   my way,
4 Bane and bless-ing, pain and pleas-ure, By the cross are sanc - ti - fied;
5 In   the cross of Christ I glo - ry, Tow-'ring o'er the wrecks of time;

All the light of sa - cred sto - ry Gath-ers round its head sub-lime.
Nev - er shall the cross for-sake me; Lo! it glows with peace and joy.
From the cross the ra-diance streaming Adds new lus - tre to the day.
Peace is there that knows no meas-ure, Joys that thro' all time a - bide.
All the light of sa - cred sto - ry Gath-ers round its head sub-lime.

See also:

Thy life was given for me, 329
We would see Jesus, 342
Lamb of God most holy, 99

My faith looks up to Thee, 269
O how shall I receive Thee, 112
Rock of ages, 284

194 He Is Arisen! Glorious Word

MORNING STAR 8 8 7, 8 8 7, 4 4 4 4 8

Birgitte C. Boye, 1778
Tr. George Taylor Rygh, 1909

Philipp Nicolai, 1599
Arr. F. Melius Christiansen, 1907

He is a - ris - en! Glo-rious word! Now rec - on - ciled is God, my Lord; The gates of heav'n are o - pen. My Je - sus died tri - um-phant-ly, And Sa - tan's ar - rows bro - ken lie, De - stroyed hell's dir - est weap - on. O hear What cheer! Christ vic-to-rious Ris-eth glo-rious, Life He giv - eth — He was dead, but see, He liv - eth!

168

195 Come, Ye Faithful, Raise the Strain

CARE FOR ME 7 6 8L.

John of Damascus, 8th Century
Tr. John Mason Neale, 1859

Ludvig M. Lindeman, 1812-1887

1. Come, ye faith-ful, raise the strain Of tri-um-phant glad-ness,
2. 'Tis the spring of souls to-day, Christ hath burst His pris-on,
3. Now the queen of sea-sons, bright With the day of splen-dor,
4. Nei-ther might the gates of death Nor the tomb's dark por-tal,

God hath brought His Is-ra-el In-to joy from sad-ness;
And from three days' sleep in death As a sun hath ris-en;
With the roy-al feast of feasts, Comes its joy to ren-der;
Nor the watch-ers, nor the seal, Hold Thee as a mor-tal;

Loosed from Phar-aoh's bit-ter yoke Ja-cob's sons and daugh-ters,
All the win-ter of our sins, Long and dark, is fly-ing
Comes to glad Je-ru-sa-lem, Who with true af-fec-tion
But to-day a-midst Thine own Thou didst stand, be-stow-ing

Led them with un-moist-ened foot Thro' the Red Sea wa-ters.
From His light, to whom we give Laud and praise un-dy-ing.
Wel-comes, in un-wea-ried strains, Je-sus' res-ur-rec-tion.
This: Thy peace, which ev-er-more Pass-eth hu-man know-ing.

169

196 Easter Morrow Stills Our Sorrow

EASTER MORROW 8 8, 10 9, 8 8

Nicolai F. S. Grundtvig, 1783-1872
Tr. Oscar R. Overby, 1931

Ludvig M. Lindeman, 1812-1887

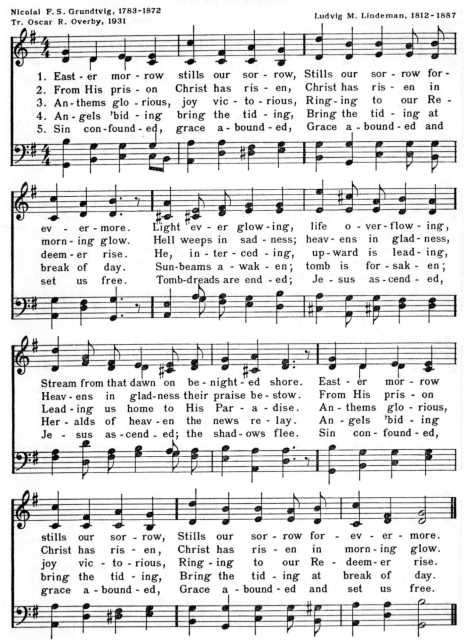

1. East-er mor-row stills our sor-row, Stills our sor-row for-
2. From His pris-on Christ has ris-en, Christ has ris-en in
3. An-thems glo-rious, joy vic-to-rious, Ring-ing to our Re-
4. An-gels 'bid-ing bring the tid-ing, Bring the tid-ing at
5. Sin con-found-ed, grace a-bound-ed, Grace a-bound-ed and

ev-er-more. Light ev-er glow-ing, life o-ver-flow-ing,
morn-ing glow. Hell weeps in sad-ness; heav-ens in glad-ness,
deem-er rise. He, in-ter-ced-ing, up-ward is lead-ing,
break of day. Sun-beams a-wak-en; tomb is for-sak-en;
set us free. Tomb-dreads are end-ed; Je-sus as-cend-ed,

Stream from that dawn on be-night-ed shore. East-er mor-row
Heav-ens in glad-ness their praise be-stow. From His pris-on
Lead-ing us home to His Par-a-dise. An-thems glo-rious,
Her-alds of heav-en the news re-lay. An-gels 'bid-ing
Je-sus as-cend-ed; the shad-ows flee. Sin con-found-ed,

stills our sor-row, Stills our sor-row for-ev-er-more.
Christ has ris-en, Christ has ris-en in morn-ing glow.
joy vic-to-rious, Ring-ing to our Re-deem-er rise.
bring the tid-ing, Bring the tid-ing at break of day.
grace a-bound-ed, Grace a-bound-ed and set us free.

197 Christ the Lord Is Risen Again

WORGAN 7 4 8L.

Michael Weisse, 1531
Tr. Catherine Winkworth, 1858

Lyra Davidica, 1708

1. Christ the Lord is ris'n a - gain; Hal - le - lu - jah!
2. He who bore all pain and loss, Hal - le - lu - jah!
3. He who slum-bered in the grave, Hal - le - lu - jah!
4. Now He bids us tell a - broad, Hal - le - lu - jah!

Christ hath brok- en ev - 'ry chain; Hal - le - lu - jah!
Com- fort - less up - on the cross, Hal - le - lu - jah!
Is ex - alt - ed now to save; Hal - le - lu - jah!
How the lost may be re - stored, Hal - le - lu - jah!

Hark, an - gel - ic voic - es cry, Hal - le - lu - jah!
Lives in glo - ry now on high, Hal - le - lu - jah!
Now thro' Chris-ten - dom it rings, Hal - le - lu - jah!
How the pen - i - tent for - giv'n, Hal - le - lu - jah!

Sing - ing ev - er - more on high, Hal - le - lu - jah!
Pleads for us and hears our cry; Hal - le - lu - jah!
That the Lamb is King of kings. Hal - le - lu - jah!
How we, too, may en - ter heav'n. Hal - le - lu - jah!

171

198 Ended His Strife, the Battle Done

VICTORY 8 8 8 and ALLELUIA

Latin, Anonymous, 1753
Tr. Francis Pott, 1861
Revised, V.E. Boe, 1932

Giovanni P. Palestrina, 1591
Arr. William H. Monk, 1861

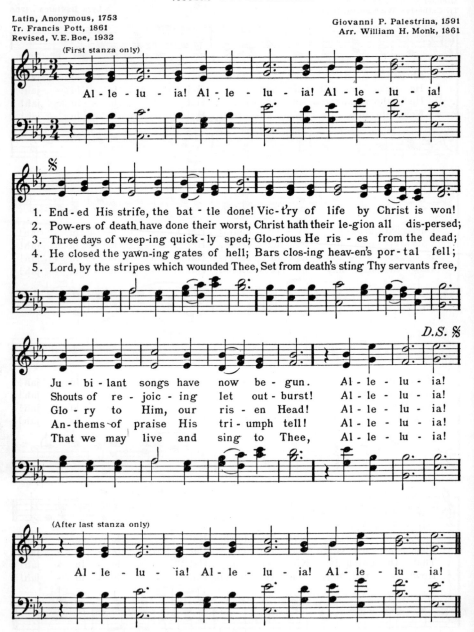

(First stanza only)

Al - le - lu - ia! Al - le - lu - ia! Al - le - lu - ia!

1. End - ed His strife, the bat - tle done! Vic-t'ry of life by Christ is won!
2. Pow-ers of death have done their worst, Christ hath their le-gion all dis-persed;
3. Three days of weep-ing quick - ly sped; Glo-rious He ris - es from the dead;
4. He closed the yawn-ing gates of hell; Bars clos-ing heav-en's por-tal fell;
5. Lord, by the stripes which wounded Thee, Set from death's sting Thy servants free,

D.S. %

Ju - bi - lant songs have now be - gun. Al - le - lu - ia!
Shouts of re - joic - ing let out - burst! Al - le - lu - ia!
Glo - ry to Him, our ris - en Head! Al - le - lu - ia!
An - thems of praise His tri - umph tell! Al - le - lu - ia!
That we may live and sing to Thee, Al - le - lu - ia!

(After last stanza only)

Al - le - lu - ia! Al - le - lu - ia! Al - le - lu - ia!

172

199 In Heavenly Love Abiding

HEAVENLY LOVE 7 6 8L.

Anna L. Waring, 1850

Felix Bartholdy Mendelssohn, 1809-1847

1. In heav'n-ly love a-bid-ing, No change my heart shall fear;
2. Wher-ev-er He may guide me, No want shall turn me back;
3. Green pas-tures are be-fore me, Which yet I have not seen;

And safe is such con-fid-ing, For noth-ing chang-es here.
My Shep-herd is be-side me, And noth-ing can I lack.
Bright skies will soon be o'er me, Where dark-est clouds have been.

The storm may roar with-out me, My heart may low be laid,
His wis-dom ev-er wak-eth, His sight is nev-er dim,
My hope I can-not meas-ure, My path to life is free,

But God is round a-bout me, And can I be dis-mayed?
He knows the way He tak-eth, And I will walk with Him.
My Sav-ior has my treas-ure, And He will walk with me.

200 Praise the Savior Now and Ever

PRAISE THE SAVIOR 8 7 6l.

Venantius H. C. Fortunatus, d. 609
Johan Olof Wallin, 1819
Tr. Augustus Nelson

German Melody from 1700

Not too slow tempo

1. Praise the Sav - ior now and ev - er! Praise Him all be - neath the skies! Pros - trate ly - ing, suf - f'ring, dy - ing, On the cross, a Sac - ri - fice; Vic - t'ry gain - ing, Life ob - tain - ing, Now in glo - ry He doth rise.

2. All is fin - ished, and ac - com-plish'd; Christ is now our Right-eous - ness: He, our Sav - ior, hath for - ev - er Set us free from dire dis - tress. Through His mer - it we in - her - it Light and peace and hap - pi - ness.

3. We're de - liv - ered, bonds are sev - ered, Christ hath bruised the ser - pent's head; Death no long - er is the strong - er, Hell it - self is cap - tive led. Christ hath ris - en from death's pris - on, O'er the tomb He light hath shed.

4. Praise for - ev - er for His fa - vor Un - to God the Fa - ther sing; Praise the Sav - ior, praise Him ev - er, Son of God, our Lord and King; Praise the Spir - it, through Christ's mer - it, He doth us sal - va - tion bring.

201 Stay with Us, Lord, the Day Is Dying

WHO KNOWS HOW NEAR 9 8, 9 8, 8 8

Casper J. Boye, 1791-1853
Tr. T. F. Gullixson, 1932

German, 1690

1. Stay with us, Lord, the day is dy-ing! Thy foot-steps turn'd to leave the Two, In lon-li-ness their hearts were cry-ing, Nor begged in vain a friend so true. O lov-ing Mas-ter, hear our cry, The self-same pray'r Thou'lt not de-ny!

2. Stay with us in Thy Spir-it's pow-er When-ev-er ev-'ning shad-ows fall; Thy pres-ence bless our ves-per hour, Hear Thou the sighs of souls that call And bear to Thee a plaint for sin, That heav'n's own peace may en-ter in.

3. Stay with us in Thy word of glad-ness When for-tune's fick-le gleam is dead. For sweat of an-guish, tears of sad-ness, With oil of joy a-noint the head. Show us how Thine own crown was won In sob-bing, "Lord, Thy will be done."

4. Stay with us, Lord, when day-light fad-eth, The light of life's last bit-ter day, When dark-ness from the tomb in-vad-eth And sor-row joins hand with dis-may. Help us to hold our faith's bright shield; To death's deep an-guish we'll not yield.

5. The hopes of earth prove un-a-vail-ing, But turn Thou in to sup with us! The cup of bless-ing, source un-fail-ing, The bread of strength im-part to us! In-to death's maw we fear-less gaze, Re-demp-tion gleams through dark'ning haze.

202 How Firm A Foundation

ADESTE FIDELES 11 11 4L

"K" in Rippon's
Selection, 1787

John F Wade's Cantus Diversi, 1751

1. How firm a foun - da-tion, ye saints of the Lord, Is laid for your
2. "Fear not, I am with thee, O be not dis - mayed, For I am thy
3. "When thro' the deep wa-ters I call thee to go, The riv-ers of
4. "When thro' fie-ry tri-als thy path-way shall lie, My grace, all suf -

faith in His ex - cel - lent word! What more can He say than to
God, and will still give thee aid; I'll strength-en thee, help thee, and
sor - row shall not o - ver-flow; For I will be with thee, thy
fi - cient, shall be thy sup - ply; The flame shall not hurt thee; I

you He hath said, Who un - to the Sav - ior for ref - uge have
cause thee to stand, Up - held by My right-eous, om - nip - o-tent
trou - bles to bless, And sanc - ti - fy to thee thy deep-est dis -
on - ly de - sign Thy dross to con - sume, and thy gold to re -

fled? Who un - to the Sav - ior for ref - uge have fled?
hand, Up - held by My right-eous, om - nip - o - tent hand."
tress, And sanc - ti - fy to thee thy deep-est dis - tress."
fine, Thy dross to con - sume, and thy gold to re - fine."

5. "E'en down to old age all my people shall prove
My sovereign, eternal, unchangeable love;
And when hoary hairs shall their temples adorn,
Like lambs they shall still in my bosom be borne."

6. "The soul that on Jesus hath leaned for repose,
I will not, I will not desert to his foes;
That soul, tho' all hell should endeavor to shake,
I'll never, no never, no never forsake!"

203 I Know That My Redeemer Lives

DUKE STREET L. M.

Samuel Medley, 1775, alt.

John Hatton, 1793

1. I know that my Re - deem - er lives! What com - fort
2. He lives to bless me with His love, He lives to
3. He lives to grant me rich sup - ply, He lives to
4. He lives to si - lence all my fears, He lives to
5. He lives, all glo - ry to His name! He lives, my

this sweet sen - tence gives! He lives, He lives, Who
plead for me a - bove, He lives my hun - gry
guide me with His eye, He lives to com - fort
wipe a - way my tears, He lives to calm my
Je - sus still the same; O the sweet joy this

once was dead, He lives, my ev - er - liv - ing Head.
soul to feed, He lives to help in time of need.
me when faint, He lives to hear my soul's com - plaint.
trou - bled heart, He lives all bless - ings to im - part.
sen - tence gives: I know that my Re - deem - er lives!

177

204 O Christ, Our Hope, Our Heart's Desire

O HAPPY DAY C. M.

Latin, 7th or 8th Century, Anonymous
Tr. John Chandler, 1837

Nicolaus Hermann, 1560

1. O Christ, our hope, our heart's de-sire, Re - demp-tion's on - ly
2. How vast the mer - cy and the love, Which laid our sins on
3. But now the bands of death are burst, The ran-som has been
4. O may Thy might-y love pre-vail Our sin - ful souls to

spring! Cre - a - tor of the world art Thou, Its
Thee, And led Thee to a cru - el death, To
paid; And Thou art on Thy Fa - ther's throne, In
spare! O may we come be - fore Thy throne, And

Sav - ior and its King, Its Sav - ior and its King.
set Thy peo - ple free! To set Thy peo - ple free!
glo - rious robes ar - rayed, In glo - rious robes ar - rayed.
find ac - cept-ance there! And find ac - cept-ance there!

5. O Christ, be Thou our present joy,
   Our future great reward;
   Our only glory may it be
   ‖: To glory in the Lord! :‖

178

205 There's A Kingdom Fair

IN HIS KINGDOM 10 10, 8 10 4

Oscar R. Overby, 1931

Norwegian Folk-Tune
Arr. Oscar R. Overby, 1931

1. There's a King-dom fair and gen-tly loom-ing, Where the spring-time of the soul is bloom-ing. In this King-dom the king is love, And his sov-'reign-ty is of God a-bove, In His King-dom.

2. Peace-ful-ly all mor-tal life a-dorn-ing, Spread-ing ra-diance like the rays of morn-ing, From the high-est where life be-gan, Comes this gift di-vine to the heart of man, In His King-dom.

3. Faith and hope and char-i-ty are dwell-ing, E-ven here ce-les-tial bliss fore-tell-ing, Where the tal-ents of fair-est youth Shall find grace to grow and to ren-der fruit, In His King-dom.

4. If you seek a-bid-ing joy and pleas-ure, Seek the King-dom and pre-serve your treas-ure: A-lien-a-ted you strive in vain; But pos-sess-ing Christ is e-ter-nal gain, In His King-dom.

5. Penitently and so gently looming,
Let the springtime of the soul be blooming,
Where the ruler of life is love,
And the king at last shall be Christ above,
In His Kingdom.

179

206 I Know Not How That Bethlehem's Babe

OUR CHRIST C. M.

Harry Webb Farrington

Oscar R. Overby, 1926

1. I know not how that Beth - le'ms babe
2. I know not how that Cal - v'ry's cross
3. I know not how that Jo - seph's tomb

Could in the God - head be; _____ I on - ly
A world from sin could free; _____ I on - ly
Could solve death's mys - ter - y; _____ I on - ly

know the man - ger child Has brought God's life to me.
know the match - less love Has brought God's love to me.
know a liv - ing Christ, Our im - mor - tal - i - ty.

Music Copyrighted by Oscar R. Overby. Text Copyrighted by The Hymn Society, N.Y. Used by permission.

207 The Lord's My Shepherd, I'll Not Want

DUNDEE C. M.

Scottish Psalter, alt.

Scottish Psalter, 1615

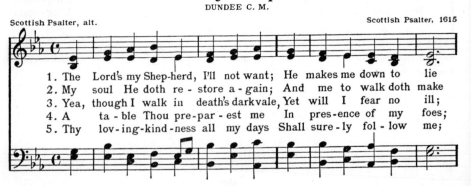

1. The Lord's my Shep - herd, I'll not want; He makes me down to lie
2. My soul He doth re - store a - gain; And me to walk doth make
3. Yea, though I walk in death's dark vale, Yet will I fear no ill;
4. A ta - ble Thou pre - par - est me In pres - ence of my foes;
5. Thy lov - ing - kind - ness all my days Shall sure - ly fol - low me;

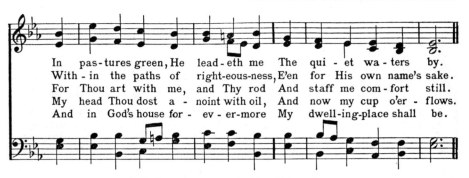

In pas-tures green, He lead-eth me The qui-et wa-ters by.
With-in the paths of right-eous-ness, E'en for His own name's sake.
For Thou art with me, and Thy rod And staff me com-fort still.
My head Thou dost a-noint with oil, And now my cup o'er-flows.
And in God's house for-ev-er-more My dwell-ing-place shall be.

208 Jesus All Glorious

JESUS ALL GLORIOUS 6 6 10, 5 5 10

V. E. Boe, 1926

V. E. Boe, 1931
Arr. Oscar R. Overby

1. Je-sus all glo-ri-ous, Christ all vic-to-ri-ous, Ris en in
2. Je-sus all glo-ri-ous, Sav-ior vic-to-ri-ous, Shed-ding for
3. Je-sus all glo-ri-ous, Mas-ter vic-to-ri-ous, Thee will we
4. Je-sus all glo-ri-ous, King all vic-to-ri-ous, Reign in Thy

tri-umph o'er death and the grave! Hom-age we bring Thee,
sin-ners Thy blood in the strife: Now there is stream-ing
fol-low, Thy man-dates o-bey: Bring ev'-ry na-tion
pow-er on earth and in heav'n! King-doms ter-res-trial,

Prais-es we sing Thee, Lord o-ver all, ev-er might-y to save.
Grace all re-deem-ing Forth from Thy cross with for-give-ness and life.
Words of sal-va-tion, Trust-ing Thy prom-ise, "I'm with you al-way."
Hon-ors ce-les-tial Un-to our Lord and His Christ shall be giv'n!

209 Jesus, Master, at Thy Word

JESUS CHRIST, MY SURE DEFENSE 7 8, 7 8, 7 7

F. M. Liebenberg, 1823
Tr. Carl Doving, 1910

German, 1656

1. Je - sus, Mas - ter! at Thy word   I will work what - e'er be - tide me,
2. Tho' my toil may seem un - blest,   And my lot ap - point - ed drear - y,
3. Tho' I be of joys be-reft,   And by sor - rows o - ver - tak - en,
4. At Thy word in faith I press   On - ward thro' this vale of sad - ness;

And I know Thou wilt, O Lord,   By Thy word and Spir - it guide me;
When at eve I go to rest,   From my la - bor faint and wea - ry,
Yet I know a sol - ace left: I am not by Thee for - sak - en;
By Thy grace I shall pos-sess   Vic - tor - palms in heav'n-ly glad-ness;

At Thy word my faith shall see   All things work for good to me.
At Thy word I will each morn   To my work with joy re - turn.
Je - sus, Thou canst aid af - ford,   Fraught with com-fort is Thy word.
To my lat - est hour, O Lord,   I will trust Thee at Thy word.

210 Peace, to Soothe Our Bitter Woes

PEACE, TO SOOTHE 7 7 6L.

Nicolai F. S. Grundtvig, 1845
Tr. George Taylor Rygh, 1908

J. P. E. Hartmann, 1852

1. Peace, to soothe our bit - ter woes,   God in Christ on us be-stows;
2. Peace, to us the Church doth tell,   'Tis her wel - come and fare-well:

Je - sus bought our peace with God With His ho - ly, pre - cious blood;
Peace was our bap - tis - mal dower, Peace shall bless our dy - ing hour;

Peace in Him for sin - ners found, Is the gos - pel's joy - ful sound.
Peace be with you, full and free, Now and thro' e - ter - ni - ty.

211 The Head That Once Was Crowned

REFUGE C. M.

Thomas Kelly, 1820

Unknown

1. The Head that once was crown'd with thorns Is crown'd with glo - ry
2. The high - est place that heav'n af - fords Is His by sov'r-eign
3. The joy of all who dwell a - bove, The joy of all be -
4. To them the cross, with all its shame, With all its grace is

now; A roy - al di - a - dem a - dorns The might-y Vic - tor's brow.
right, The King of kings and Lord of lords, And heav'n's e - ter - nal Light.
low, To whom He man - i - fests His love And grants His name to know.
giv'n; Their name an ev - er - last - ing name, Their joy the joy of heav'n.

5. They suffer with their Lord below,
They reign with Him above,
Their profit and their joy to know
The mystery of His love.

6. The cross He bore is life and health,
Though shame and death to Him;
His people's hope, His people's wealth,
Their everlasting theme.

212 Jesus, Thy Boundless Love to Me

ST CATHERINE L. M. 6L.

Paul Gerhardt, 1653
Tr. John Wesley, 1739

Henri F. Hemy, 1865
Alt. James G. Walton, 1871

1. Je - sus, Thy bound - less love to me No tho't can reach, no tongue de - clare; O knit my thank - ful heart to Thee, And reign with - out a ri - val there: Thine whol - ly, Thine a - lone, I am, Be Thou a - lone my con - stant flame.

2. O grant that noth - ing in my soul May dwell, but Thy pure love a - lone; O may Thy love pos - sess me whole, My joy, my treas - ure, and my crown: Strange fires far from my soul re - move; My ev - 'ry act, word, tho't, be love.

3. O love, how cheer - ing is Thy ray! All pain be - fore Thy pres - ence flies; Care, an - guish, sor - row, melt a - way, Wher - e'er Thy heal - ing beams a - rise. O Je - sus, noth - ing may I see, Or hear, or feel, or think, but Thee.

4. Still let Thy love point out my way: How won-drous things Thy love hath wrought! Still lead me, lest I go a - stray; Di - rect my work, in - spire my thought; And if I fall, soon may I hear Thy voice, and know that love is near.

5. In suf - f'ring, be Thy love my peace; In weak - ness, be Thy love my power; And when the storms of life shall cease, Je - sus, in that im - por - tant hour, In death, as life, be Thou my Guide, And save me, who for me hast died.

184

213 When Peace Like A River

IT IS WELL WITH MY SOUL 11 8, 11 9

H. G. Spafford, 1876

Philip P. Bliss, 1876

1. When peace like a riv - er at - tend - eth my way,
2. Though Sa - tan should buf - fet, though tri - als should come,
3. He lives, O the bliss of this glo - ri - ous thought;
4. And, Lord, haste the day when our faith shall be sight,

When sor - rows like sea bil - lows roll; What -
Let this blest as - sur - ance con - trol, That
My sin, not in part, but the whole, Is
The clouds be rolled back as a scroll, The

ev - er my lot, Thou hast taught me to say,
Christ hath re - gard - ed my help - less e - state,
nailed to His cross and I bear it no more,
trump - et shall sound and the Lord shall de - scend;

It is well, it is well with my soul.
And hath shed His own blood for my soul.
Praise the Lord, praise the Lord, O my soul.
E - ven so it is well with my soul.

214 Thou Art the Way, the Truth, the Life

INTEGER VITAE 11 11, 11 5

Friedrich A. Krummacher, 1767-1845

Friedrich F. Flemming, 1778-1813

1. Thou art the Way, the Truth, the Life from heav - en,
This blest as - sur - ance Thou to us hast giv - en;
O wilt Thou teach us, Lord, to win Thy pleas - ure In full - est meas - ure?

2. Thou art the Way: to reach our des - ti - na - tion
We sore - ly need Thee, fount of our sal - va - tion;
Lest we should stum - ble when our sins be - set us, Do not for - get us.

3. Thou art the Truth: though dark - ness o - ver - take us,
The heav'n - ly light will nev - er - more for - sake us;
O shine with - in us, all our gloom dis - pel - ling, Make us Thy dwell - ing.

4. Thou art the Life: to all Thine own Thou giv - est
E - ter - nal life where Thou for - ev - er liv - est;
There with - out ceas - ing, as we stand be - fore Thee, Let us a - dore Thee.

215 Draw Us to Thee in Mind and Heart

DRAW US TO THEE 8 7 4L.

Friedrich Funcke, 1686
Tr. Arthur T. Russell, 1851

Norwegian Folk-Tune

1. Draw us to Thee in mind and heart, On heav'n - ly things at - tend - ing;
2. Draw us to Thee, O Christ, and guide Our err - ing feet to heav - en;
3. Draw us to Thee, O Thou whose love The an - gels praise a - dor - ing;
4. Draw us to Thee, grant us to rise To yon a - bodes of glo - ry;

In spir-it hence let us de-part, To Thee, O Lord, as-cend-ing.
If Thou, O Lord, with us a-bide, Light to our path is giv-en.
Re-ceive our souls to Thee a-bove, Thy name in death im-plor-ing.
On Thee to rest our joy-ful eyes, And fall in praise be-fore Thee.

216 My Jesus, I Love Thee

MY JESUS, I LOVE THEE 11 11 4L

Anonymous   Adoniram J. Gordon, 1836-1895

1. My Je-sus, I love Thee, I know Thou art mine, For Thee all the
2. I love Thee be-cause Thou hast first lov-ed me, And pur-chased my
3. I'll love Thee in life, I will love Thee in death, And praise Thee as
4. In man-sions of glo-ry and end-less de-light, I'll ev-er a-

fol-lies of sin I re-sign; My gra-cious Re-deem-er, my
par-don on Cal-va-ry's tree; I love Thee for wear-ing the
long as Thou lend-est me breath; And say when the death-dew lies
dore Thee in heav-en so bright; I'll sing with the glit-ter-ing

Sav-ior art Thou, If ev-er I loved Thee, my Je-sus, 'tis now.
thorns on Thy brow; If ev-er I loved Thee, my Je-sus, 'tis now.
cold on my brow, If ev-er I loved Thee, my Je-sus, 'tis now.
crown on my brow, If ev-er I loved Thee, my Je-sus, 'tis now.

217 Jesus, Jesus, Only Jesus

JESUS ONLY 8 7, 8 7, 7 7

Ludämilia Elisabeth of
Schwartzburg-Rudolstadt, 1687
Tr. A. Crull, 1880

Ludvig M. Lindeman, 1812-1887

1. Je - sus, Je - sus, on - ly Je - sus, Can my heart - felt
2. One there is for whom I'm liv - ing, Whom I love most
3. Seems a thing to me a treas-ure, Which dis - pleas-ing
4. Grant that I may e'er en - deav - or Thy good pleas - ure
5. Lord, my praise shall be un - ceas - ing For Thou gav'st Thy-

long - ing still; See, I pledge my - self to Je - sus,
ten - der - ly; Je - sus, un - to whom I'm giv - ing,
is to Thee, Then re - move such dang - 'rous pleas - ure;
to ful - fill, In me, through me, with me ev - er,
self to me, And be - sides so ma - ny a bless - ing

What He wills, a - lone to will. For my heart, which
What in love He gave to me, Je - sus' blood hides
Give in - stead what prof - its me Let my heart by
Lord, ac - comp - lish Thou Thy will. Let me die, Lord,
That I now sing joy - ful - ly: Be it un - to

He hath filled, Ev - er cries: Lord, as Thou wilt
all my guilt; Lead me, Lord, then, as Thou wilt.
Thee be stilled, Make me Thine, Lord, as Thou wilt.
on Thee built, When, and where, and as Thou wilt.
me, my shield, As Thou wilt, Lord, as Thou wilt.

188

218 Lord Jesus Christ, My Savior Blest

LORD JESUS CHRIST, MY SAVIOR BLEST 4 4 7, 4 4 4 7

Hans Chr. Stehn, ca. 1578
Tr. J. C. Aaberg

Ludvig M. Lindeman, 1812-1887

1. Lord Je-sus Christ, My Sav-ior blest, My ref-uge and sal-va-tion, I trust in Thee; A-bide in me; Thy word shall be My hope and con-so-la-tion.

2. I will con-fide, What-e'er be-tide, In Thy com-pas-sion ten-der. When grief and stress My heart op-press, Thou wilt re-dress And con-so-la-tion ren-der.

3. When I must weep In sor-row deep, Thy lov-ing care en-folds me, I have no fear When Thou art near, My Sav-ior dear; Thy sav-ing hand up-holds me.

4. Lord, I would be Al-ways with Thee, Wher-ev-er Thou wilt have me. Do Thou con-trol My heart and soul And make me whole; Thy grace a-lone can save me.

5. Yea, help us, Lord,
   With one accord
   To love and serve Thee solely,
   That henceforth we
   May dwell with Thee
   In Jubilee
   And in Thy presence holy

219 Hark! Ten Thousand Harps and Voices

NEANDER 8 7, 8 7, 7 7

Thomas Kelly, 1804, alt.

Joachim Neander, 1679

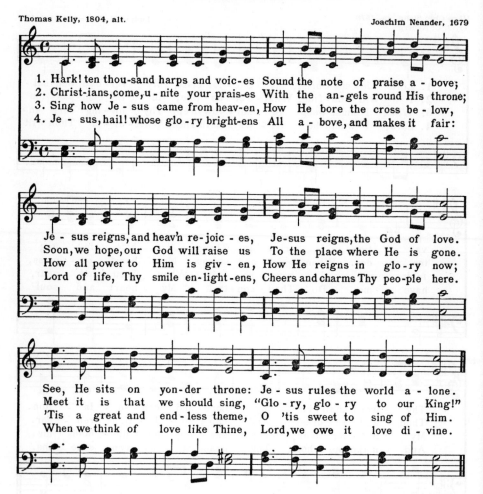

1. Hark! ten thou-sand harps and voic-es Sound the note of praise a - bove;
2. Christ-ians, come, u - nite your prais-es With the an-gels round His throne;
3. Sing how Je - sus came from heav-en, How He bore the cross be - low,
4. Je - sus, hail! whose glo - ry bright-ens All a - bove, and makes it fair:

Je - sus reigns, and heav'n re-joic - es, Je-sus reigns, the God of love.
Soon, we hope, our God will raise us To the place where He is gone.
How all power to Him is giv - en, How He reigns in glo-ry now;
Lord of life, Thy smile en-light-ens, Cheers and charms Thy peo-ple here.

See, He sits on yon-der throne: Je - sus rules the world a - lone.
Meet it is that we should sing, "Glo - ry, glo - ry to our King!"
'Tis a great and end - less theme, O 'tis sweet to sing of Him.
When we think of love like Thine, Lord, we owe it love di - vine.

5. King of glory, reign forever,
Thine an everlasting crown;
Nothing from Thy love shall sever.
Those whom Thou hast made Thine own,
Happy objects of Thy grace,
Destined to behold Thy face.

6. Savior, hasten Thine appearing;
Bring, O bring the glorious day
When, the awful summons hearing,
Heaven and earth shall pass away;
Then, with golden harps, we'll sing,
"Glory, glory to our King!"

220 I See Thee Standing, Lamb of God

I SEE THEE STANDING, LAMB OF GOD C. M. D.

Hans Adolf Brorson, 1694-1764
Tr. Olav Lee

Unknown

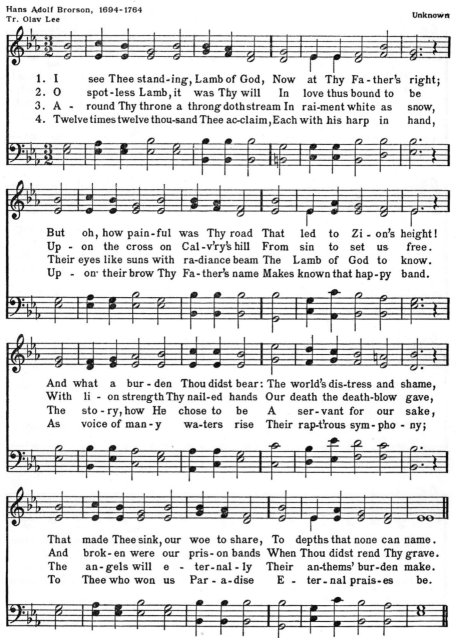

1. I   see Thee stand-ing, Lamb of God, Now   at Thy Fa-ther's right;
2. O   spot-less Lamb, it   was Thy will   In   love thus bound to   be
3. A - round Thy throne a throng doth stream In rai-ment white as   snow,
4. Twelve times twelve thou-sand Thee ac-claim, Each with his harp in   hand,

But   oh, how pain-ful was Thy road That   led   to   Zi - on's height!
Up - on the cross on Cal-v'ry's hill From sin   to set us   free.
Their eyes like suns with ra-diance beam The   Lamb of God to   know.
Up - on· their brow Thy Fa-ther's name Makes known that hap-py band.

And what   a bur - den Thou didst bear: The world's dis-tress and shame,
With li - on strength Thy nail-ed hands Our death the death-blow gave,
The   sto - ry, how He chose to   be   A   ser-vant for our sake,
As   voice of man - y   wa-ters rise Their rap-t'rous sym - pho - ny;

That made Thee sink, our woe to share, To depths that none can name.
And   brok-en were our pris-on bands When Thou didst rend Thy grave.
The   an-gels will e - ter-nal-ly Their   an-thems' bur-den make.
To   Thee who won us Par - a-dise E - ter-nal prais-es   be.

221 Hail, Thou Once Despised Jesus

LORD VICTORIOUS 8 7 8L.

John Bakewell, 1757, alt.

J. A. Freylinghausen's Gesangbuch, 1704

1. Hail, Thou once de - spis - ed Je - sus! Hail, Thou Ga - li - le - an King!
2. Pas - chal Lamb, by God ap - point - ed, All our sins on Thee were laid;
3. Je - sus, hail, en - throned in glo - ry, There for - ev - er to a - bide!
4. Wor-ship, hon - or, power, and bless-ing, Thou art wor-thy to re - ceive;

Thou didst suf - fer to re - lease us; Thou didst free sal - va - tion bring.
By al - might-y love a - noint - ed, Thou hast full a - tone-ment made.
All the heav'n-ly hosts a - dore Thee, Seat - ed at Thy Fa - ther's side:
Loud-est prais - es, with-out ceas - ing, Meet it is for us to give.

Hail, Thou ag - o - niz - ing Sav-ior, Bear - er of our sin and shame!
All Thy peo - ple are for-giv - en, Through the vir - tue of Thy blood:
There for sin - ners Thou art plead-ing, There Thou dost our place pre-pare,
Help, ye bright an - gel - ic spir - its, Bring your sweet-est, no - blest lays,

By Thy mer - its we find fa - vor; Life is giv - en through Thy name.
O - pened is the gate of heav - en; Peace is made'twixt man and God.
E - ven for us in - ter - ced-ing, Till in glo - ry we ap - pear.
Help to sing our Sav-ior's mer-its, Help to chant Im-man-uel's praise.

222 Golden Harps Are Sounding

HERMAS 6 5 8L. and Chorus

Frances R. Havergal, 1872   Frances R. Havergal, 1872

1. Gold - en harps are sound-ing, An-gel-voic-es ring, Pearl-y gates are o-pened,
2. He who came to save us, He who bled and died, Now is crown'd with glo-ry,
3. Plead-ing for His chil-dren In that bless-ed place, Call-ing them to glo-ry,

O - pened for the King. Christ, the King of Glo - ry, Je - sus, King of love,
At His Fa - ther's side. Nev-er more to suf-fer, Nev-er more to die;
Send-ing them His grace, His bright home pre-par-ing, Faith-ful ones, for you,

CHORUS

Is gone up in tri-umph To His throne a - bove.
Je - sus, King of glo - ry, Is gone up on high. All His work is end - ed;
Je - sus ev - er liv - eth, Ev - er lov - eth too.

Joy - ful - ly we sing, Je - sus hath as - cend - ed, Glo - ry to our King!

193

223 See the Conqueror Mounts in Triumph

REX GLORIAE 8 7 8L.

Christopher Wordsworth, 1862   Henry Smart, 1868

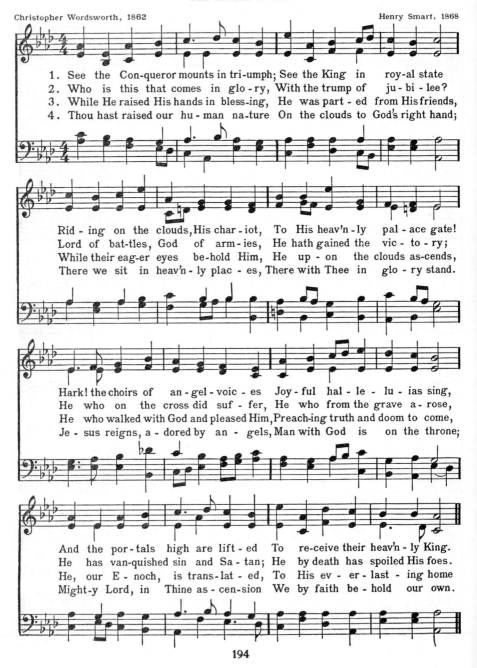

1. See the Con-queror mounts in tri-umph; See the King in roy-al state
2. Who is this that comes in glo-ry, With the trump of ju-bi-lee?
3. While He raised His hands in bless-ing, He was part-ed from His friends,
4. Thou hast raised our hu-man na-ture On the clouds to God's right hand;

Rid-ing on the clouds, His char-iot, To His heav'n-ly pal-ace gate!
Lord of bat-tles, God of arm-ies, He hath gained the vic-to-ry;
While their eag-er eyes be-hold Him, He up-on the clouds as-cends,
There we sit in heav'n-ly plac-es, There with Thee in glo-ry stand.

Hark! the choirs of an-gel-voic-es Joy-ful hal-le-lu-ias sing,
He who on the cross did suf-fer, He who from the grave a-rose,
He who walked with God and pleased Him, Preach-ing truth and doom to come,
Je-sus reigns, a-dored by an-gels, Man with God is on the throne;

And the por-tals high are lift-ed To re-ceive their heav'n-ly King.
He has van-quished sin and Sa-tan; He by death has spoiled His foes.
He, our E-noch, is trans-lat-ed, To His ev-er-last-ing home
Might-y Lord, in Thine as-cen-sion We by faith be-hold our own.

224 Most Wondrous Is of All on Earth

I KNOW A KINGDOM 8 7 4L.

Nicolai F. S Grundtvig, 1783-1872
Tr J C. Aaberg

German Folk-Tune, 16th Century

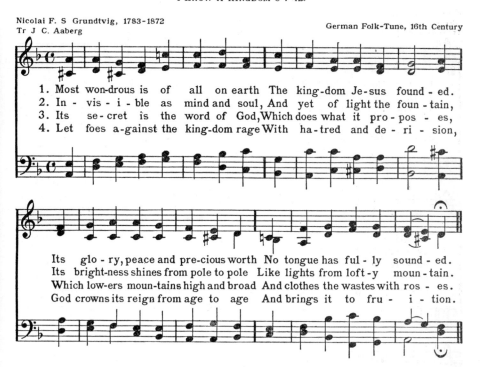

1. Most won-drous is of all on earth The king-dom Je-sus found - ed.
2. In - vis - i - ble as mind and soul, And yet of light the foun - tain,
3. Its se - cret is the word of God, Which does what it pro - pos - es,
4. Let foes a-gainst the king-dom rage With ha-tred and de - ri - sion,

Its glo - ry, peace and pre-cious worth No tongue has ful - ly sound - ed.
Its bright-ness shines from pole to pole Like lights from loft-y moun-tain.
Which low-ers moun-tains high and broad And clothes the wastes with ros - es.
God crowns its reign from age to age And brings it to fru - i - tion.

5, Its glory rises like the morn
When waves at sunrise glitter,
Or like in May the verdant corn
As birds above it twitter.

6. It is the glory of the King
Who bore afflictions solely
That He the crown of life might bring
To sinners poor and lowly.

7 And when His advent comes to pass
The Christian's strife is ended,
What here we see as in a glass
Shall then be comprehended.

8. Then shall the kingdom bright appear
With glory true and vernal
And bring His saved a golden year
Of peace and joy eternal.

See also:
Blessing and honor, 22
All hail the power of Jesus' name, 7
Majestic sweetness sits enthroned, 8
Crown Him with many crowns, 30
How blessed is the little flock, 268
Now hail we our Redeemer, 122

Also hymns under CHRISTIAN LIFE, 246-348

225 O Holy Ghost, Thou Gift Divine

O HOLY GHOST, THOU GIFT 8 7, 8 7, 8 8 7

Barttholomäus Ringwaldt, 1681
Sören Jonassön, 1693
Tr. O. H. Smeby, 1911

From Teutsch Kirchenampt, 1525

1. O   Ho - ly Ghost, Thou gift   di - vine,   And   giv - er   of   all
2. O   Spir - it blest, we   Thee   en - treat: O   grant us that   we
3. Our   hearts let new - cre - a - ted   be,   Our   walk make pure and
4. Thy   gra-cious heav'n-ly   dew   let   fall,   The   faint-ing Church to
5. Give strength and cour-age   to   con - tend   A - gainst the hosts of

bless-ing, Thou, with the Fa-ther   and the Son,   True God-head art pos -
ev - er,   With heart and soul, as   it   is meet, May serve our Lord and
quick-en; Thy   sooth-ing oint-ment pour on all   Whose souls are sad and
e - vil,   That   we may van-quish   in the end,   The world, the flesh, the

sess - ing,   And from them both art   shed a-broad,   E - ter - nal Spir-it
Sav - ior,   And Him con - fess till   our last breath, As Lord of life and
sole - ly,   So   that our faith in   Christ, our Lord, May prove it - self in
strick-en; Sus - tain us, Lord in   e - vil days, And   let our lives in
dev - il;   And when death's bil - low   o'er us rolls,   Bear Thou to heav'n our

Lord   and   God,   In   Thee all Chris - tians   glo - ry.
Lord   of   death,   And   give Him praise and   hon - or.
deed   and   word   Be - fore the world a - bout   us.
all   our   ways,   A - bound in   love and   mer - cy.
ran - somed souls,   While   dust to   dust   re - turn - eth.

226 O Day Full of Grace, Which We Behold

O DAY FULL OF GRACE 9 8 6L.

Danish, 14th Century, Anonymous
Nicolai F. S. Grundtvig, 1826
Tr. O. H. Smeby, G. T. Rygh, C. Doving, 1911

C. E. F. Weyse, 1826

1. O day full of grace, which we be - hold, Now gen - tly to view as - cend - ing; Thou o - ver the earth thy reign un - fold, Good cheer to all mor - tals lend - ing, That chil-dren of light in ev - 'ry clime May prove that the night is end - ing.

2. How blest was that gra - cious mid - night hour, When God in our flesh was giv - en; Then flush - ed the dawn with light and pow'r, That spread o'er the dark - ened heav - en; Then rose o'er the world that Sun di - vine Which gloom from our hearts hath driv - en.

3. Yea, were ev - 'ry tree en - dowed with speech, And ev - er - y leaf - let sing - ing, They nev - er with praise His worth could reach, Though earth with their praise be ring - ing. Who ful - ly could praise the Light of life Who light to our souls is bring - ing?

4. As birds in the morn - ing sing God's praise, His fa - ther - ly love we cher - ish, For giv - ing to us this day of grace, For life that shall nev - er per - ish. Church He hath kept these thousand years, And hun - ger - ing souls did nour - ish.

5. With joy we de - part for our fa - ther - land, Where God our Fa - ther is dwell - ing, Where read - y for us His man-sions stand, Where heav - en with praise is swell - ing; And there we shall walk in end-less light, With blest ones His praise forth tell - ing.

197

227 Come, Holy Ghost, Creator Blest

COME, HOLY GHOST L. M.

Rabanus Maurus, d. 856
Tr. Edward Caswall et al., 1849

German, 1524

1. Come, Holy Ghost, Creator blest, Vouchsafe within our souls to rest; Come with Thy grace and heav'n-ly aid, And fill the hearts which Thou hast made.

2. To Thee, the Comforter, we cry, To Thee, the gift of God most high, The fount of life, the fire of love, The souls' anointing from above.

3. The sev'n-fold gifts of grace are Thine, O finger of the hand divine; True promise of the Father Thou, Who dost the tongue with speech endow.

4. Thy light to ev-'ry thought impart, And shed Thy love in ev-'ry heart; The weakness of our mortal state With deathless might invigorate.

5. Drive far away our wil-y foe, And Thine abiding peace bestow; If Thou be our preventing guide, No evil can our steps betide.

6. Make Thou to us the Father known;
Teach us th'eternal Son to own,
And Thee, whose name we ever bless,
Of both the Spirit to confess.

7. Praise we the Father and the Son,
And Holy Spirit, Three in One:
And may the Son on us bestow
The gifts that from the Spirit flow.

228 The Glory of the Spring How Sweet

SERAPH C. M. D.

Thomas H. Gill, 1867

Old Melody

1. The glo-ry of the spring how sweet, The new-born life how glad;
2. But O these won-ders of Thy grace, These no-bler works of Thine,
3. This new-born glow of faith so strong, This bloom of love so fair;

What joy the hap-py earth to greet In new, bright rai-ment clad.
These mar-vels sweet-er far to trace, These new-births more di-vine.
This new-born ec-sta-sy of song And fra-gran-cy of pray'r!

Di-vine Re-new-er, Thee I bless; I greet Thy go-ing forth;
These sin-ful souls Thou hal-low-est, These hearts Thou mak-est new,
Cre-a-tor Spir-it, work in me These won-ders sweet of Thine,

I love Thee in the love-li-ness Of Thy re-new-ed earth.
These mourn-ful souls by Thee made blest, These faith-less hearts made true:
Di-vine Re-new-er, gra-cious-ly Re-new this heart of mine.

229 Heavenly Spirit, All Others Transcending

BLESSED COMMUNION 11 10 8L.

Johan Nordahl Brun, 1786
Tr George Taylor Rygh, 1909

Schörring's Koralbog, 1781

1. Heav - en - ly Spir - it, all oth - ers tran - scend - ing, Thou who with
2. Mer - ci - ful Je - sus, with love nev - er fail - ing, Send-ing Thy
3. Heav'n-ly Con - sol - er, with unc - tion ce - les - tial, Heal Thou the

Fa - ther and Son dost a - bide! Come Thou, our spir - its in
Spir - it, the pledge ev - er new, That Thy a - tone-ment for
wounds of each sin - bur-dened heart! Strength-en our faith, and with

u - ni - ty blend - ing, Come and make read-y the heav - en - ly bride!
all is a - vail - ing, Faith ev - er sees that Thy prom-ise is true.
zeal Pen - te - cos - tal Fill our faint souls, and Thy bless-ings im - part!

Call - ing and gath'ring, and Je - sus de - clar - ing, Build - ing God's
Crown'd are Thy ser - vants with heav - en - ly fire, Speak-ing with
Cre - ate with - in us new hearts and new spir - its; Lead us in

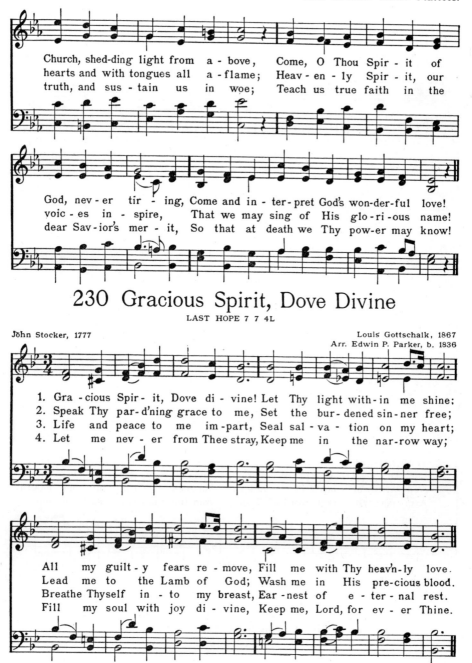

Church, shed-ding light from a - bove, Come, O Thou Spir - it of
hearts and with tongues all a - flame; Heav - en - ly Spir - it, our
truth, and sus - tain us in woe; Teach us true faith in the

God, nev - er tir - ing, Come and in - ter - pret God's won-der-ful love!
voic - es in - spire, That we may sing of His glo - ri -ous name!
dear Sav-ior's mer - it, So that at death we Thy pow-er may know!

230 Gracious Spirit, Dove Divine
LAST HOPE 7 7 4L

John Stocker, 1777

Louis Gottschalk, 1867
Arr. Edwin P. Parker, b. 1836

1. Gra - cious Spir - it, Dove di - vine! Let Thy light with-in me shine;
2. Speak Thy par - d'ning grace to me, Set the bur - dened sin - ner free;
3. Life and peace to me im-part, Seal sal - va - tion on my heart;
4. Let me nev - er from Thee stray, Keep me in the nar-row way;

All my guilt - y fears re - move, Fill me with Thy heav'n-ly love.
Lead me to the Lamb of God; Wash me in His pre-cious blood.
Breathe Thyself in - to my breast, Ear - nest of e - ter - nal rest.
Fill my soul with joy di - vine, Keep me, Lord, for ev - er Thine.

201

231 Come, O Come, Thou Quickening Spirit

COME, THOU QUICKENING SPIRIT 8 7, 8 7, 7 7

Heinrich Held, ca. 1664
Tr. Charles W. Schaffer, 1866

Johann Christopher Bach, 1693

1. Come, O come, Thou quick'ning Spir-it, Thou for-ev-er art di-vine;
2. Grant my mind and my af-fec-tions Wis-dom, coun-sel, pur-i-ty,
3. Lead me to green pas-tures, lead me By the true and liv-ing way;
4. Ho-ly Spir-it, strong and might-y, Thou who mak-est all things new,

Let Thy pow-er nev-er fail me, Al-ways this heart of mine;
That I may be ev-er seek-ing Naught but that which pleas-es Thee,
Shield me from each strong temp-ta-tion, That might lead my heart a-stray;
Make Thy work with-in me per-fect, Help me by Thy word so true,

Thus shall grace, and truth, and light, Dis-si-pate the gloom of night.
Let Thy knowl-edge spread and grow, And all er-ror o-ver-throw.
And if e'er my feet should turn, For each er-ror let me mourn.
Arm me with that sword of Thine, And the vic-t'ry shall be mine.

See also.

Glorious things of Thee are spoken, 78
Built on the Rock, 81
O Holy Spirit, enter in, 53

Also hymns under CHRISTIAN LIFE, 246-348

232 Holy, Holy, Holy

NICAEA Irregular

Reginald Heber, 1829   John B. Dykes, 1860

1. Ho - ly, ho - ly, ho - ly! Lord God Al - might - y!
2. Ho - ly, ho - ly, ho - ly! all the saints a - dore Thee!
3. Ho - ly, ho - ly, ho - ly! though the dark - ness hide Thee!

Ear - ly in the morn - ing our song shall rise to Thee;
Cast - ing down their gold - en crowns a - round the glass - y sea;
Tho' the eye of sin - ful man Thy glo - ry may not see;

Ho - ly, ho - ly, ho - ly! mer - ci - ful and might - y!
Cher - u - bim and ser - a - phim fall - ing down be - fore Thee,
On - ly Thou art ho - ly; there is none be - side Thee,

God in Three Per - sons, bless - ed Trin - i - ty!
Which wert, and art, and ev - er - more shalt be.
Per - fect in power, in love, and pur - i - ty.

203

233 Praise to the Father, the Glorious King

PRAISE TO THE LORD 14 14,4 7 8

John H. Hopkins, 1866

German, 1668
Arr. F. Melius Christiansen, 1907

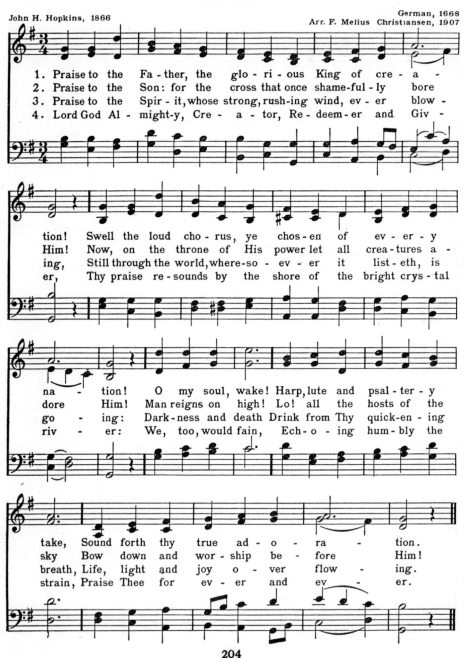

1. Praise to the Fa - ther, the glo - ri - ous King of cre - a - tion! Swell the loud cho - rus, ye chos - en of ev - er - y na - tion! O my soul, wake! Harp, lute and psal - ter - y take, Sound forth thy true ad - o - ra - tion.

2. Praise to the Son: for the cross that once shame - ful - ly bore Him! Now, on the throne of His power let all crea - tures a - dore Him! Man reigns on high! Lo! all the hosts of the sky Bow down and wor - ship be - fore Him!

3. Praise to the Spir - it, whose strong, rush - ing wind, ev - er blow - ing, Still through the world, where - so - ev - er it list - eth, is go - ing: Dark - ness and death Drink from Thy quick - en - ing breath, Life, light and joy o - ver flow - ing.

4. Lord God Al - might - y, Cre - a - tor, Re - deem - er and Giv - er, Thy praise re - sounds by the shore of the bright crys - tal riv - er: We, too, would fain, Ech - o - ing hum - bly the strain, Praise Thee for ev - er and ev - er.

204

234 Let Me Be Thine Forever

PASSION CHORALE 7 6 8L.

Nikolaus Selnecker, 1572, et. al.
Tr. Matthias Loy, 1880

Hans Leo Hassler, 1601
Arr. F. Melius Christiansen, 1907

1. Let me be Thine for - ev - er, My gra-cious God and Lord,
2. Lord Je - sus! boun-teous giv - er Of light and life di - vine,
3. O Ho - ly Ghost, who pour - est Sweet peace in - to my heart,

May I for-sake Thee nev - er, Nor wan - der from Thy word:
Thou didst my soul de - liv - er, To Thee I all re - sign:
And all my soul re - stor - est, Let not Thy grace de - part.

Pre - serve me from the maz - es Of er - ror and dis - trust,
Thou hast in mer - cy bought me With blood and bit - ter pain;
And while His name con - fess - ing Whom I by faith have known,

And I shall sing Thy prais - es For - ev - er with the just.
Let me, since Thou hast sought me, E - ter - nal life ob - tain.
Grant me Thy con-stant, bless - ing; Make me for aye Thine own.

235 To Thee All Praise Ascendeth

MY SOUL, NOW BLESS THY MAKER 78, 78, 76, 76, 76, 76

Johann Rist, 1651
Tr Unknown, 1866

Ludvig M. Lindeman, 1812-1887

1. To Thee all praise as-cend-eth, Al-might-y ev-er bless-ed God; The
2. Our hearts o'er-flow with glad-ness, For we have learn'd Thy pow'r and grace We
3. Thy name, O Lord, a-bid-eth, Thou shalt be hon-ored on the earth, Thy

an-them nev-er end-eth A-round Thy throne, O ho-ly Lord. E'en
may not sink in sad-ness, We stand, in Christ, be-fore Thy face. Thy
hand our all pro-vid-eth, Thou car-edst for us ere our birth. O

here in trib-u-la-tion When we are sore-ly tried, Thou art our con-so-
name be ev-er prais-ed, Thou do-est won-ders great; Our voice may well be
Lord! what shall we ren-der For all the debt we owe, For all Thy care so

la-tion, Thy ref-uge where we hide. Day un-to day Thy glo-ry, Thy
rais-ed, Thy mer-cies to re-late. Oh! be it all our pleas-ure Whilst
ten-der, Thy love too vast to know? The theme of Thy sal-va-tion Shall

good-ness doth con-fess, And we take up the sto - ry Of all Thy faith-ful-ness.
pil-grim-days en-dure, To find in Thee our treas-ure To rest in Thee se-cure.
be our one em-ploy, We bless Thee for cre-a-tion, And for e ter-nal joy!

236 Glory Be to God the Father

WORCESTER 8 7, 8 7, 4 7

Horatius Bonar, 1866

W. G. Whinfield

1. Glo - ry be to God the Fa - ther, Glo - ry be to
2. Glo - ry be to Him who loved us, Washed us from each
3. Glo - ry to the King of an - gels, Glo - ry to the
4. Glo - ry, bless - ing, praise e - ter - nal! Thus the choir of

God the Son, Glo - ry be to God the Spir - it, Great Je - ho - vah,
spot and stain; Glo - ry be to Him who bought us, Made us kings with
Church-'s King, Glo - ry to the King of na - tions, Heav'n and earth, your
an - gels sings; Hon - or, rich - es, pow'r, do - min - ion! Thus its praise cre-

Three in One! Glo - ry, glo - ry, While e - ter - nal a - ges run!
Him to reign! Glo - ry, glo - ry, To the Lamb that once was slain!
prais - es bring! Glo - ry, glo - ry, To the King of glo - ry bring!
a - tion brings; Glo - ry, glo - ry, Glo - ry to the King of kings!

237 Come, Thou Almighty King

ITALIAN HYMN 6 6 4, 6 6 6 4

Anonymous, 1757   Felice Giardini, 1769

1. Come, Thou al - might - y King, Help us Thy name to sing,
   Help us to praise! Fa - ther all glo - ri - ous, O'er all vic -
   to - ri - ous, Come and reign o - ver us, An - cient of Days!

2. Je - sus, our Lord, de - scend; From all our foes de - fend,
   Nor let us fall; Let Thine al - might - y aid Our sure de -
   fense be made: Our souls on Thee be stay'd; Lord, hear our call!

3. Come, Thou in - car - nate Word, Gird on Thy might - y sword,
   Our pray'r at - tend. Come and Thy peo - ple bless, And give Thy
   word suc - cess; Spir - it of ho - li - ness, On us de - scend.

4. Come, holy Comforter,
   Thy sacred witness bear
   In this glad hour;
   Thou who almighty art,
   Now rule in every heart,
   And ne'er from us depart,
   Spirit of power!

5. To the great One in Three
   Eternal praises be,
   Hence evermore;
   His sovereign majesty
   May we in glory see,
   And to eternity
   Love and adore.

238 Father Most Holy, Merciful and Tender

FATHER MOST HOLY 11 11, 11 5

Latin, Anonymous, 11th Century
Tr. Percy Dearmer, 1867

Johann Crüger, 1640

1. Fa-ther most ho-ly, mer-ci-ful and ten-der; Je-sus our
2. Trin-i-ty sa-cred, U-ni-ty un-shak-en: De-i-ty
3. Mak-er of all things, all Thy crea-tures praise Thee; Lo, all things
4. To the al-might-y tri-une God be glo-ry: High-est and

Sav-ior, with the Fa-ther reign-ing; Spir-it of
per-fect, giv-ing and for-giv-ing, Light of the
serve Thee through Thy whole cre-a-tion: Hear us, Al-
great-est, help Thou our en-deav-or; We, too, would

mer-cy, Ad-vo-cate, de-fend-er, Light nev-er wan-ing;
an-gels, Life of the for-sak-en, Hope of all liv-ing;
might-y, hear us as we raise Thee Heart's ad-o-ra-tion.
praise Thee, giv-ing hon-or wor-thy, Now and for-ev-er.

See also:
Father, source of life and light, 49
Praise ye the Father, 17
Jesus, Master, at Thy word, 209
Give praise to God, our King, 5

For Trinity Season see
Hymns under CHRISTIAN LIFE, 246-348

239 A Mighty Fortress Is Our God

EIN FESTE BURG 8 7, 8 7, 6 6, 6 6 7

Martin Luther, 1529
Tr. from Book of Praise, Canada, alt

Martin Luther, 1529

1. A might-y for-tress is our God, A trust-y shield and weap - on;
2. Stood we a-lone in our own might, Our striv-ing would be los - ing;
3. And were the world with dev-ils filled, All watch-ing to de-vour us,
4. Still they must leave God's word its might, For which no thanks they mer - it;

Our help is He in all our need, Our stay, what-e'er doth hap - pen;
For us the one true Man doth fight, The Man of God's own choos - ing.
Our souls to fear we need not yield, They can-not o - ver - power us;
Still He is with us in the fight, With His good gifts and Spir - it.

For still our an-cient foe Doth seek to work us woe: Strong mail of craft and
Who is this chos-en One? 'Tis Je-sus Christ, the Son, The Lord of hosts, 'tis
Their dread-ed prince no more Can harm us as of yore; His rage we can en-
And should they, in the strife, Take kin-dred, goods and life, We free-ly let them

power He wear-eth in this hour; On earth is not his e - qual.
He Who wins the vic-to - ry In ev - 'ry field of bat - tle.
dure; For lo! his doom is sure, A word shall o - ver - throw him.
go, They pro-fit not the foe; With us re-mains the king - dom.

240 From All Thy Saints in Warfare

AURELIA 7 6 8L.

Earl Nelson, 1864   Samuel S. Wesley, 1864

1. From all Thy saints in war - fare, For all Thy saints at rest,
2. A - pos - tles, pro - phets, mar - tyrs, And all the sa - cred throng,
3. Then praise we God the Fa - ther, And praise we God the Son,

To Thee, O bless - ed Je - sus, All prais - es be ad - dressed
Who wear the spot - less rai - ment, Who raise the cease - less song;
And God the Ho - ly Spir - it, E - ter - nal Three in One;

Thou, Lord, didst win the bat - tle, That they might con - querors be;
For these, passed on be - fore us, O Lord, we Thee a - dore,
Till all the ran - somed num - ber Fall down be - fore the throne,

Their crowns of liv - ing glo - ry Are lit with rays from Thee.
And, walk - ing in their foot - steps, Would serve Thee more and more.
And hon - or, power, and glo - ry A - scribe to God a - lone.

211

241 Christ Is Made the Sure Foundation

REGENT SQUARE 8 7 6L.

Latin, 6th or 7th Century, Anonymous
Tr. John Mason Neale, 1851

Henry Smart, 1867

1. Christ is made the sure foun-da-tion, Christ the head and cor-ner-stone,
2. All that ded-i-cat-ed cit-y, Dear-ly loved of God on high,
3. To this tem-ple, where we call Thee, Come, O Lord of hosts, to-day:
4. Here vouch-safe to all Thy ser-vants What they ask of Thee to gain,

Chos-en of the Lord, and pre-cious, Bind-ing all the Church in one;
In ex-ult-ant ju-bi-la-tion Pours per-pet-ual mel-o-dy;
With Thy wont-ed lov-ing-kind-ness, Hear Thy peo-ple as they pray;
What they gain from Thee for-ev-er With the bless-ed to re-tain,

Ho-ly Zi-on's help for-ev-er, And her con-fi-dence a-lone.
God the One in Three a-dor-ing In glad hymns e-ter-nal-ly.
And Thy full-est ben-e-dic-tion Shed with-in its walls al-way.
And here-aft-er in Thy glo-ry Ev-er-more with Thee to reign.

See also:

Lord, keep us steadfast, 86
The church's one foundation, 80
Glorious things of Thee are spoken, 78
Built on the Rock, 81
God's Word is our great heritage, 91
Lord of our life, 14
O Word of God incarnate, 89

242 Now Thank We All Our God

NOW THANK WE ALL OUR GOD 6 4, 6 4, 6 6, 6 4

Martin Rinkart, 1648
Tr Catherine Winkworth, 1858

Johann Cruger, 1647

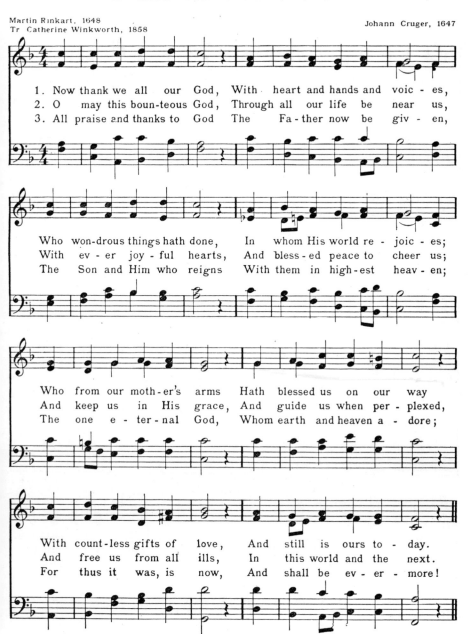

1. Now thank we all our God, With heart and hands and voic - es,
2. O may this boun-teous God, Through all our life be near us,
3. All praise and thanks to God The Fa - ther now be giv - en,

Who won-drous things hath done, In whom His world re - joic - es;
With ev - er joy - ful hearts, And bless - ed peace to cheer us;
The Son and Him who reigns With them in high - est heav - en;

Who from our moth - er's arms Hath blessed us on our way
And keep us in His grace, And guide us when per - plexed,
The one e - ter - nal God, Whom earth and heaven a - dore;

With count - less gifts of love, And still is ours to - day.
And free us from all ills, In this world and the next.
For thus it was, is now, And shall be ev - er - more!

213

243 Come, Ye Thankful People, Come

MENDELSSOHN 7 7 8L.

Henry Alford, 1845
Charles Wesley, 1739

Felix Bartholdy Mendelssohn, 1840
Arr. William H. Cummings, 1855

1. Come, ye thank-ful peo-ple, come, Raise the song of har-vest home: All is safe-ly
2. All the world is God's own field, Fruit un-to His praise to yield; Wheat and tares to-
3. For the Lord our God shall come, And shall take His har-vest home; From His field shall
4. E - ven so, Lord Je-sus, come, To Thy fi-nal har-vest home; Gath-er Thou Thy

gath-ered in, Ere the win-ter storms be-gin; God, our Mak-er, doth pro-vide
geth-er sown, Un-to joy or sor-row grown: First the blade, and then the ear,
in that day All of-fenc-es purge a-way; Give His an-gels charge at last
peo-ple in, Free from sor-row, free from sin; There for ev-er pur-i-fied,

For our wants to be sup-plied; Come to God's own tem-ple, come, Raise the song of
Then the full corn shall ap-pear: Lord of har-vest, grant that we Whole-some grain and
In the fire the tares to cast, But the fruit-ful ears to store In His Gar-ner
In Thy Pres-ence to a-bide: Come, with all Thine an-gels, come, Raise the glorious

har-vest home, Come to God's own tem-ple, come, Raise the song of har-vest home.
pure may be, Lord of har-vest, grant that we Whole-some grain and pure may be.
ev - er-more, But the fruit-ful ears to store In His Gar-ner ev-er-more.
har-vest home, Come, with all Thine an-gels, come, Raise the glorious har-vest home.

244 We Plow the Fields and Scatter

WE PLOW THE FIELDS 7 6 8L.

Matthias Claudius, 1782
Tr. Jane M. Campbell, 1861

R. Bay

1. We plow the fields, and scat - ter The good seed on the land, But it is fed and wa - tered By God's al - might- y hand; He sends the snow in win - ter, The warmth to swell the grain, The breez - es and the sun - shine, And soft re - fresh - ing rain.

2. He on - ly is the Mak - er Of all things near and far; He paints the way-side flow - er, He lights the eve-ning star; The winds and waves o - bey Him, By Him the birds are fed; Much more to us, His chil - dren, He gives our dai - ly bread.

3. We thank Thee, then, O Fa - ther, For all things bright and good, The seed-time and the har - vest, Our life, our health, our food; Ac - cept the gifts we of - fer, For all Thy love im - parts, And what Thou most de - sir - est, Our hum - ble, thank-ful hearts.

245 For the Beauty of the Earth

JESUS, SON OF RIGHTEOUSNESS 7 7 6L.

Folliot S. Pierpont, 1864

Ludvig M. Lindeman, 1812-1887

1. For the beau-ty of the earth, For the glo-ry of the skies,
2. For the won-der of each hour Of the day and of the night:
3. For the joy of hu-man love, Broth-er, sis - ter, par-ent, child;
4. For Thy Church that ev - er -more Lifts her ho - ly hands a - bove,

For the love which from our birth O - ver and a - round us lies;
Hill and vale, and tree and flower, Sun and moon and stars of light;
Friends on earth, and friends a-bove, Pleas-ures pure and un - de - filed;
Of-f'ring up - on ev - 'ry shore Her pure sac- ri - fice of love;

Lord of all, to Thee we raise This our grate-ful psalm of praise,
Lord of all, to Thee we raise This our grate-ful psalm of praise.
Lord of all, to Thee we raise This our grate-ful psalm of praise.
Lord of all, to Thee we raise This our grate-ful psalm of praise.

See also:

As wide as the skies, 292
Praise ye the Father, 17
My soul, now bless, 9
Ye lands, to the Lord, 27

IV. Christian Life

246 O Seek the Lord Today

O GOD, THOU FAITHFUL GOD 6 7, 6 7, 6 6, 6 6

Hans Adolf Brorson, 1694 - 1764
Tr. P. C. Paulsen

Meiningisches Gesangbuch, 1693

1. O seek the Lord to - day! To - day He hath sal - va - tion.
2. Be - hold, the sun of grace So bright-ly on thee shin - eth;
3. There is sal - va - tion still For hearts con - trite - ly cry - ing
4. As in its moth - er's arm The child sweet com - fort gain - eth,

Ap - proach Him while He may Still hear thy sup - pli - ca - tion.
O take with Christ thy place While He to thee in - clin - eth.
To Him whose gra - cious will Is now to save the dy - ing.
So, shield - ing thee from harm, The Lord thy heart sus - tain - eth,

Re - pent and seek His grace, His call to thee doth sound;
Per - chance His sum - mons may Ere long be sent to thee;
His grace doth beck - on thee To seek thy Sav - ior blest;
O seek that sweet re - pose, Come un - to Him to stay;

O turn to Him thy face While yet He may be found.
O turn to Him to - day, Let Him thy sol - ace be.
O has - ten, swift - ly flee Un - to His bless - ed rest.
Thy Sav - ior now is close, O come to Him to - day.

247 One Resolve, One Resolve

ONE RESOLVE 12 9, 12 9, 12 12 8.

H. A. Urseth, 1891
Tr. Oscar R. Overby, 1932

F. Melius Christiansen, 1891

1. One re-solve, one re-solve, you who fal-ter and fear On a way you re-luc-tant-ly roam: It will gain you ap-proach; it will o-pen a year Full of peace and a prom-ise of home. One re-solve to re-turn to the fold from a-broad! Will you come, will you

2. One ap-peal, one ap-peal, from the far land of fate, Car-ried home to the Fa-ther in pray'r: It will light-en your heart, and pro-mote your es-tate. It will ban-ish the bur-dens you bear. One ap-peal in your an-guish and pain where you plod! Have you faith, have you

3. One re-sponse, one re-sponse, from a Calv-'ry of pain, Where the Sav-ior once died in His love: It will ren-der you peace and a-tone for your bane. It will lift you to kin-ship a-bove. One re-sponse to your soul in dis-tress and de-cline! Have you seen, have you

Will you come,
Have you faith,
Have you seen,

220

come, have you cour-age to take One step o'er the bor-der to God?
faith it will o - pen the way, One word from your heart un - to God?
seen that com-pas-sion, that love, That look from the Sav-ior di - vine?

248 Just As I Am, without One Plea

WOODWORTH L. M.

Charlotte Elliott, 1836   William B. Bradbury, 1849

1. Just as I am, with - out one plea, But that Thy
2. Just as I am, and wait - ing not To rid my
3. Just as I am, tho' tossed a - bout With ma-ny a
4. Just as I am, poor, wretch-ed, blind; Sight, rich - es,
5. Just as I am! Thou wilt re - ceive, Wilt wel - come,
6. Just as I am! Thy love un - known Hast brok - en

blood was shed for me, And that Thou bid'st me come to
soul of one dark blot, To Thee whose blood can cleanse each
con - flict, ma - ny a doubt, Dread fears with - in and strife with-
heal - ing of the mind, Yea, all I need, in Thee to
par - don, cleanse, re - lieve; Be - cause Thy prom - ise I be -
ev - 'ry bar - rier down; Now to be Thine, yea, Thine a -

Thee, O Lamb of God, I come, I come.
spot, O Lamb of God, I come, I come.
out, O Lamb of God, I come, I come.
find, O Lamb of God, I come, I come.
lieve, O Lamb of God, I come, I come.
lone, O Lamb of God, I come, I come.

249 Come Unto Me, Ye Weary

MUNICH 7 6 8L.

William Chatterton Dix, 1867   Meiningisches Gesangbuch, 1693

1. "Come un-to Me, ye wear-y, And I will give you rest."
2. "Come un-to Me, dear chil-dren, And I will give you light."
3. "Come un-to Me, ye wear-y, And I will give you life."
4. "And who-so-ev-er com-eth I will not cast him out."

O bless-ed voice of Je-sus, Which comes to hearts op-pressed!
O lov-ing voice of Je-sus, Which comes to cheer the night.
O cheer-ing voice of Je-sus, Which comes to aid our strife,
O wel-come voice of Je-sus, Which drives a-way our doubt,

It tells of ben-e-dic-tion, Of par-don, grace and peace,
Our hearts were filled with sad-ness, And we had lost our way;
The foe is stern and ea-ger, The fight is fierce and long;
Which calls us, ver-y sin-ners, Un-wor-thy though we be

Of joy that hath no end-ing, Of love that can-not cease.
But He hath brought us glad-ness And songs at break of day.
But Thou hast made us might-y, And strong-er than the strong.
Of love so free and bound-less, To come, O Lord, to Thee.

250 As after the Waterbrooks Panteth

AS AFTER THE WATERBROOKS 9 8,9 8,9 9 8

Nicolai F. S. Grundtvig, 1812
Tr. Carl Doving, 1904

Ludvig M. Lindeman, 1812-1887

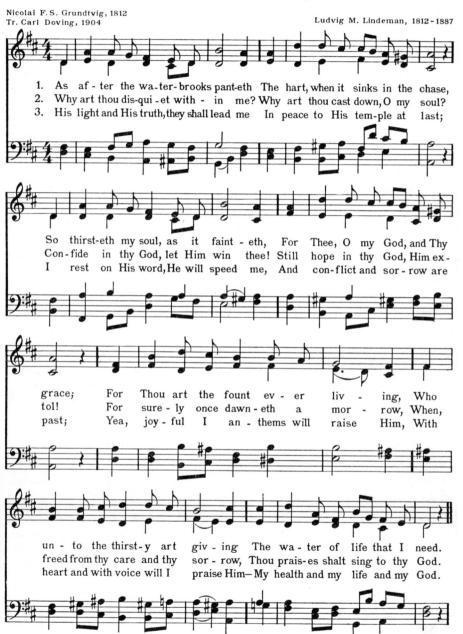

1. As af - ter the wa-ter-brooks pant-eth The hart, when it sinks in the chase,
2. Why art thou dis-qui - et with - in me? Why art thou cast down, O my soul?
3. His light and His truth, they shall lead me In peace to His tem-ple at last;

So thirst-eth my soul, as it faint - eth, For Thee, O my God, and Thy
Con - fide in thy God, let Him win thee! Still hope in thy God, Him ex -
I rest on His word, He will speed me, And con-flict and sor - row are

grace; For Thou art the fount ev - er liv - ing, Who
tol! For sure - ly once dawn - eth a mor - row, When,
past; Yea, joy - ful I an - thems will raise Him, With

un - to the thirst-y art giv - ing The wa - ter of life that I need.
freed from thy care and thy sor - row, Thou prais-es shalt sing to thy God.
heart and with voice will I praise Him—My health and my life and my God.

223

251 Almost Persuaded Now to Believe

ST. EDMUND 6 4, 6 4, 6 6, 6 4
(See No. 256)

Philip P. Bliss

Arthur S. Sullivan, 1842-1900

1. "Al-most per-suad-ed" Now to be-lieve; "Al-most per-
2. "Al-most per-suad-ed" Come, come to-day; "Al-most per-
3. "Al-most per-suad-ed," Har-vest is past! "Al-most per-

suad-ed" Christ to re-ceive; Seems now some soul to say, "Go Spir-it,
suad-ed," Turn not a-way; Je-sus in-vites you here, An-gels are
suad-ed," Doom comes at last. "Al-most" can-not a-vail; "Al-most" is

go Thy way, Some more con-ven-ient day On Thee I'll call."
lin-g'ring near, Pray'rs rise from hearts so dear: O wan-d'rer, come.
but to fail! Sad, sad, that bit-ter wail— "Al-most—but lost!"

252 How Helpless Guilty Nature Lies

AZMON C. M.

Anna Steele, 1780

Carl G. Gläser, 1828
Arr. Lowell Mason, 1839

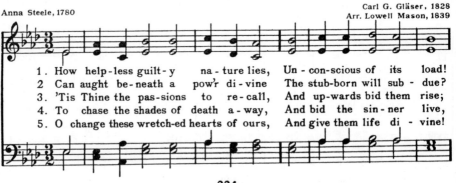

1. How help-less guilt-y na-ture lies, Un-con-scious of its load!
2. Can aught be-neath a pow'r di-vine The stub-born will sub-due?
3. 'Tis Thine the pas-sions to re-call, And up-wards bid them rise;
4. To chase the shades of death a-way, And bid the sin-ner live,
5. O change these wretch-ed hearts of ours, And give them life di-vine!

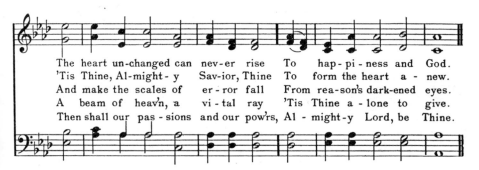

The heart un-changed can nev-er rise To hap - pi - ness and God.
'Tis Thine, Al-might - y Sav-ior, Thine To form the heart a - new.
And make the scales of er - ror fall From rea-son's dark-ened eyes.
A beam of heav'n, a vi - tal ray 'Tis Thine a - lone to give.
Then shall our pas - sions and our pow'rs, Al - might-y Lord, be Thine.

253 Come to Calvary's Holy Mountain

JESUS ONLY 8 7, 8 7, 7 7

James Montgomery, 1819   Ludvig M. Lindeman, 1812-1887

1. Come to Cal-v'ry's ho - ly moun-tain, Sin-ners, ru - ined by the fall;
2. Come in pov - er - ty and mean-ness, Come de-filed with-out, with - in;
3. Come in sor - row and con-tri - tion, Wounded, im - po - tent, and blind;
4. He that drinks shall live for ev - er; 'Tis a soul re - new-ing flood:

Here a pure and heal-ing foun-tain Flows to you, to me, to all;
From in - fec-tion and un-clean-ness, From the lep-ro - sy of sin,
Here the guilt - y free re - mis-sion, Here the troub-led peace may find:
God is faith-ful; God will nev - er Break His cov - e - nant of blood,

In a full per - pet - ual tide, O - pened when our Sav - ior died
Wash your robes and make them white; Ye shall walk with God in light.
Health this foun-tain will re - store; He that drinks shall thirst no more
Signed when our Re - deem - er died, Seal'd when He was glo - ri - fied.

254 O Jesus, Lord, to Thee I Cry

TAKE ME AS I AM 8 8, 8 6 and Chorus

Eliza H. Hamilton

Ira D. Sankey, 1840-1908

In slow tempo

1. O Je - sus, Lord, to Thee I cry; Un - less Thou help me I must die:
2. I help-less am, and full of guilt; But yet for me Thy blood was spilt,
3. No prep - a - ra - tion can I make, My best re-solves I on - ly break,
4. Be - hold me, Sav-ior, at Thy feet, Deal with me as Thou se - est meet;

Oh, bring Thy free sal - va - tion nigh, And take me as I am.
And Thou canst make me what Thou wilt, And take me as I am.
Yet save me for Thine own name's sake, And take me as I am.
Thy work be - gin, Thy work com-plete, And take me as I am.

CHORUS

And take me as I am, And take me as I am;

My on - ly plea—Christ died for me! Oh, take me as I am.

226

255 There Is a Sea of Mercy

WEBB 7 6 8L.

C.K. Solberg, 1910

George J. Webb, 1837

1. There is a sea of mer - cy, Wide as e - ter - ni - ty;
2. There is a sea of prom -ise, Its wa - ters, deep and wide,
3. There is a sea of ser - vice That you must dai - ly brave;
4. Tho' doubts shall make you fal - ter, And foes shall make you fear,

It gives the vile and guilt - y Sal - va - tion full and free;
Most safe - ly on its bos - om You reach the oth - er side.
In spite of rag - ing tem -pest, Sail out the lost to save!
Tho' dis - ap-point-ments gath - er And sure de - feat seems near.

It is the blood of Je - sus, Come, sin - ner, do not weep,
It is the word of Scrip-ture With pow'r to save and keep,
O Chris-tian, do not lin - ger, Shake off the sense of sleep,
Tho' storms are dai - ly rag-ing With fierce and aw - ful sweep,

From sin and guilt it cleans - es, "Launch out in - to the deep!"
So full of sweet as - sur - ance, "Launch out in - to the deep!"
A - way, a - way to res - cue, "Launch out in - to the deep!"
If Je - sus is your pi - lot, "Launch out in - to the deep!"

256 Almost Persuaded Now to Believe

ALMOST PERSUADED 5 4, 5 4, 6 6, 6 4
(See No. 251)

Philip P. Bliss

Philip P. Bliss, 1838-1876

1. "Al-most per-suad-ed" Now to be-lieve; "Al-most per-suad-ed"
2. "Al-most per-suad-ed," Come, come to-day; "Al-most per-suad-ed,"
3. "Al-most per-suad-ed," Har-vest is past! "Al-most per-suad-ed"

Christ to re-ceive; Seems now some soul to say, "Go, Spir-it
Turn not a-way; Je-sus in-vites you here, An-gels are
Doom comes at last! "Al-most" can-not a-vail; "Al-most" is

go Thy way, Some more con'-ven-ient day On Thee I'll call?"
lin-g'ring near, Pray'rs rise from hearts so dear: O wan-d'rer, come.
but to fail! Sad, sad, that bit-ter wail— "Al-most—but lost!"

257 My God, Accept My Heart This Day

EVAN C.M.

Matthew Bridges, 1848

William H. Havergal, 1846

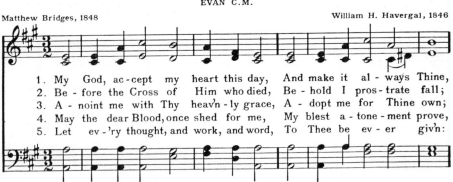

1. My God, ac-cept my heart this day, And make it al-ways Thine,
2. Be-fore the Cross of Him who died, Be-hold I pros-trate fall;
3. A-noint me with Thy heav'n-ly grace, A-dopt me for Thine own;
4. May the dear Blood, once shed for me, My blest a-tone-ment prove,
5. Let ev-'ry thought, and work, and word, To Thee be ev-er giv'n:

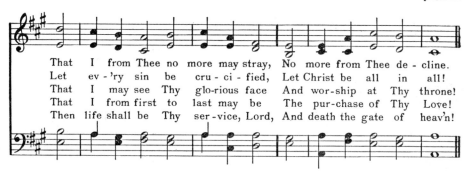

That   I   from Thee no more may stray, No more from Thee de - cline.
Let   ev - 'ry sin   be   cru - ci - fied, Let Christ be   all   in   all!
That   I   may see Thy glo-rious face   And wor-ship at Thy throne!
That   I   from first to last may be   The pur-chase of Thy Love!
Then life shall be Thy ser -vice, Lord, And death the gate of heav'n!

258 O Wonderful Words of the Gospel

O WONDERFUL WORDS 9 8 4L

Fanny J. Crosby, 1820 - 1915, alt.   Swedish Folk-Tune

1. O   won - der - ful words of the gos - pel: A
2. He   came from the throne of His glo - ry,   And
3. O   come to this won - der - ful Sav - ior, Come
4. There's no oth - er ref - uge but Je - sus,   No

mes-sage of bless-ing they bring, Pro-claim-ing a fin-ished re -
left the bright man-sions a - bove, The world to re-deem from its
wea - ry and sor - row - op-press'd; Be - hold on the cross how He
shel-ter where lost ones may fly;   And now, while He's ten-der-ly

demp - tion Through Je - sus, our Sav - ior and King.
bond - age; So great His com - pas - sion and love.
suf - fered, That you in His king - dom might rest.
call - ing: O "turn ye," "for why will ye die?"

229

259 There's a Wideness in God's Mercy

RIPLEY 8 7 8L.

Frederick W. Faber, 1854

From a Gregorian Chant by Lowell Mason, 1839

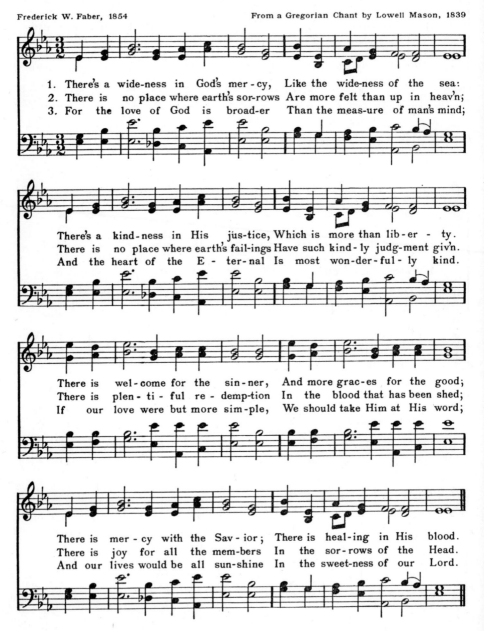

1. There's a wide-ness in God's mer-cy, Like the wide-ness of the sea:
2. There is no place where earth's sor-rows Are more felt than up in heav'n;
3. For the love of God is broad-er Than the meas-ure of man's mind;

There's a kind-ness in His jus-tice, Which is more than lib-er - ty.
There is no place where earth's fail-ings Have such kind - ly judg-ment giv'n.
And the heart of the E - ter-nal Is most won-der-ful - ly kind.

There is wel-come for the sin-ner, And more grac-es for the good;
There is plen - ti - ful re - demp-tion In the blood that has been shed;
If our love were but more sim-ple, We should take Him at His word;

There is mer - cy with the Sav - ior; There is heal-ing in His blood.
There is joy for all the mem-bers In the sor-rows of the Head.
And our lives would be all sun-shine In the sweet-ness of our Lord.

260 O Come to the Merciful Savior

MERCIFUL SAVIOR 12 11 4L.

Frederick W. Faber, ca. 1850

Folk-Tune

1. O come to the mer - ci - ful Sav - ior who
2. O come then to Je - sus, whose arms are ex -
3. Yes, come to the Sav - ior whose mer - cy grows
4. Come, come to His feet, and lay o - pen your

calls you, O come to the Lord who for - gives and for -
tend - ed To fold His dear chil - dren in clos - est em -
bright - er The long - er you look at the depths of His
sto - ry Of suff - 'ring and sor - row, of guilt and of

gets; Though dark be the for - tune on earth that be -
brace; O come, for your ex - ile will short - ly be
love; And fear not! 'tis Je - sus, and life's cares grow
shame; For the par - don of sin is the crown of His

falls you, There's a bright home a - bove where the sun nev - er sets.
end - ed, And Je - sus will show you His beau - ti - ful face.
light - er As you think of the home and the glo - ry a - bove.
glo - ry, And the joy of our Lord to be true to His name.

261 Blest Is He That Never Walketh

SCHOP 8 7, 8 7, 7 7, 8 8

Paul Gerhardt, 1607-1676
Tr. H. Brueckner, 1924

Johann Schop, 1642

1. Blest is he that nev-er walk-eth Where the wick-ed coun-sel take,
2. Blest is he whose soul de-light-eth In the stat-utes of the Lord,
3. E-ven so in ver-dure gain-eth He who makes God's word his guide.
4. But the wick-ed, God for-sak-ing, Shall not with the right-eous stay;

Nor with wan-ton sin-ners talk-eth Who the path of truth for-sake,
Day and night His law re-cit-eth, With the saints in sweet ac-cord.
From the Lord he strength ob-tain-eth, And his zeal shall not sub-side.
They, with all their un-der-tak-ing, Like the chaff are blown a-way.

Be-ing loathe to take his seat Where un-god-ly scoff-ers meet,
God his treas-ure will in-crease, Nor shall he to pros-per cease;
Like a tree whose leaves grow old, Yet whose fruits are man-i-fold,
Where the Lord His own doth claim, There His foes are put to shame.

Who dis-dain what God from heav-en In His word to us hath giv-en.
Like a palm tree he shall flour-ish Whose fair leaves the wa-ters nour-ish
Such a man in vir-tue grow-eth By the grace that God be-stow-eth.
God loves all who good-ness cher-ish, But the wick-ed all shall per-ish.

262 I Hear Thy Welcome Voice

I HEAR THY WELCOME VOICE 6 6, 8 6 and Chorus

Lewis Hartsough, 1872   Lewis Hartsough, 1872

1. I hear Thy wel-come voice That calls me, Lord, to Thee For
2. Tho' com-ing weak and vile, Thou dost my strength as-sure; Thou
3. 'Tis Je-sus calls me on To per-fect faith and love, To
4. 'Tis Je-sus who con-firms The bless-ed work with-in, By
5. And He the wit-ness gives To loy-al hearts and free, That
6. All hail, a-ton-ing blood! All hail, re-deem-ing grace! All

cleans-ing in Thy pre-cious blood That flow'd on Cal-va-ry.
dost my vile-ness ful-ly cleanse, Till spot-less all and pure.
per-fect hope, and peace, and trust, For earth and heav'n a-bove.
add-ing grace to wel-comed grace, Where reign'd the pow'r of sin.
ev-'ry prom-ise is ful-filled, If faith but brings the plea.
hail, the Gift of Christ, our Lord, Our Strength and Right-eous-ness.

CHORUS

I am com-ing, Lord! Com-ing now to Thee!

Wash me, cleanse me in the blood That flow'd on Cal-va-ry

263 There Is a Gate That Stands Ajar

I KNOW A KINGDOM 8 7 4L

Lydia Baxter, 1874   German, 16th Century

1. There is a gate that stands a - jar, And
   through its por - tals gleam - ing, A ra - diance from the
   cross a - far, The Sav - ior's love re - veal - ing

2. That gate a - jar stands free for all Who
   seek through it sal - va - tion; The rich and poor, the
   great and small, Of ev - 'ry tribe and na - tion.

3. Press on - ward, then, though foes may frown, While
   mer - cy's gate is o - pen; Ac - cept the cross and
   win the crown, Love's ev - er - last - ing tok - en

4. Be - yond the riv - er's brink we'll lay The
   cross that here is giv - en, And bear the crown of
   life a - way, And love Him more in heav - en.

234

264 Smite Us Not in Anger, Lord

CONFIRMATION 76, 7 6, 3 3, 6 6

Johann Georg Albinus, 1655
Tr. John Caspar Mattes, 1914

Johann Rosenmüller, 1655
Arr. F. Melius Christiansen, 1907

1. Smite us not in an - ger, Lord, But in mer - cy spare us, Save us from our just re - ward, In Thy pit - y hear us. Though our sin Great hath been, Let Christ's in - ter - ces - sion Cov - er our trans - gres - sion.

2. Strength-en us in love, O Lord, Gen - tly as a Fa - ther; When Thou dost Thy help af - ford, All our fears are o - ver. Weak in - deed, We have need That Thy love cor - rect us, And Thy grace pro - tect us.

3. Glo - rious God, Thy name we praise; Fa - ther, Son, and Spir - it; Now and through e - ter - nal days, As Thy mer - cies mer - it. Glo - ry be Un - to Thee Who hast pit - y on us, And with love hast won us.

265 God Calling Yet! Shall I Not Hear

FEDERAL STREET 8 8 4L.

Gerhard Tersteegen, 1735
Tr. Sarah Findlater, 1855

Henry K. Oliver, 1832

1. God call-ing yet! — shall I not hear? Earth's pleas-ures shall I still hold dear? Shall life's swift pass - ing years all fly, And still my soul in slum-bers lie?
2. God call-ing yet! — shall I not rise? Can I His lov - ing voice de - spise, And base - ly His kind care re - pay? He calls me still: can I de - lay?
3. God call-ing yet! — and shall He knock And I my heart the clos - er lock? He still is wait - ing to re - ceive, And shall I dare His Spir - it grieve?
4. God call-ing yet! — and shall I give No heed, but still in bond - age live? I wait, but He does not for - sake; He calls me still: My heart, a - wake!

5. Ah, yield Him all; in Him confide:
Where but with Him doth peace abide?
Break loose, let earthly bonds be riven,
And let the spirit rise to heav'n!

6. God calling yet!—I cannot stay;
My heart I yield without delay:
Vain world, farewell! from thee I part;
The voice of God hath reached my heart!

266 Come, Ye Disconsolate

CONSOLATOR 11 10 4L.

Thomas Moore, 1816
Stanza 3, Thomas Hastings, 1832

Samuel Webbe, 1816

1. Come, ye dis - con - so - late, wher - e'er ye lan - guish,
2. Joy of the des - o - late, light of the stray - ing,
3. Here see the bread of life, see wa - ters flow - ing

Come to the mer - cy - seat, fer - vent - ly kneel;
Hope of the pen - i - tent, fade - less and pure,
Forth from the throne of God, pure from a - bove;

Here bring your wound - ed hearts, here tell your an - guish;
Here speaks the Com - fort - er, ten - der - ly say - ing,
Come to the feast of love, come, ev - er know - ing

Earth has no sor - row that Heav'n can - not heal.
Earth has no sor - row that Heav'n can - not cure.
Earth has no sor - row but Heav'n can re - move.

267 Lord Jesus, I Long to Be Perfectly Whole

WHITER THAN SNOW 11 11 4L. and Chorus

James Nicholson, 1871

William G. Fischer, 1872

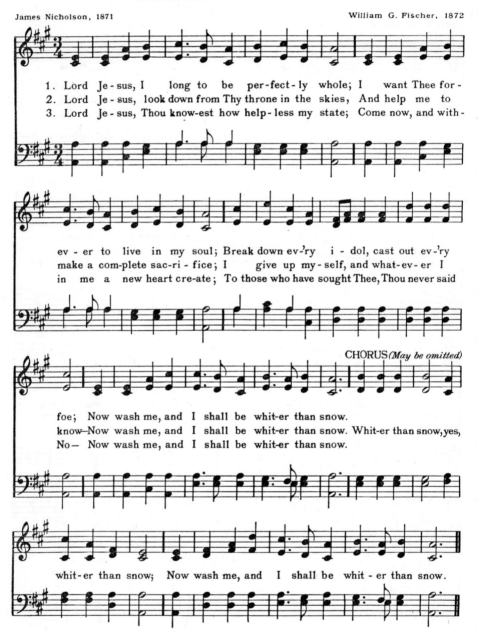

1. Lord Je-sus, I long to be per-fect-ly whole; I want Thee for-
2. Lord Je-sus, look down from Thy throne in the skies, And help me to
3. Lord Je-sus, Thou know-est how help-less my state; Come now, and with-

ev-er to live in my soul; Break down ev-'ry i-dol, cast out ev-'ry
make a com-plete sac-ri-fice; I give up my-self, and what-ev-er I
in me a new heart cre-ate; To those who have sought Thee, Thou never said

CHORUS (May be omitted)

foe; Now wash me, and I shall be whit-er than snow.
know—Now wash me, and I shall be whit-er than snow. Whit-er than snow, yes,
No— Now wash me, and I shall be whit-er than snow.

whit-er than snow; Now wash me, and I shall be whit-er than snow.

238

268 How Blessed Is the Little Flock

HOW BLESSED IS THE LITTLE FLOCK 8 7, 8 7, 8 8, 8 7

Nils J. Holm, 1829
Tr. Carl Doving, 1906

Ludvig M. Lindeman, 1812-1887

1 How bless-ed is the lit-tle flock, Whom Je-sus calls His own!
2 My Je-sus, am I in that band, And wilt Thou call me Thine?
3 And e-ven if with tears it be, That this to Thee I say,

He is their Sav-ior and their rock, They trust in Him a-lone; They
Do I a-mong the cho-sen stand Whose lamps so bright-ly shine? O
Yet Thou in grace wilt look on me And wipe my tears a-way; Yea,

walk by faith and hope and love, But they shall dwell with Him a-bove,
let me not lie down to rest Till this I know, my Sav-ior blest,
when but Thou who all dost know In me canst find Thy love be-low

When hope and faith shall pass a-way, And love shall last for aye.
Till I can say, by grace re-stored: "Thou know'st I love Thee, Lord!"
And own me Thine, then well is me,— My all I have in Thee.

See also:

Upon the cross the robber prayed, 166
Jesus, Jesus, come to me, 341
Lord Jesus, by Thy passion, 171
O Father, may Thy word prevail, 159
Repent, the kingdom draweth nigh, 116

269 My Faith Looks Up to Thee

OLIVET 6 6 4, 6 6 6 4

Ray Palmer, 1830   Lowell Mason, 1832

1. My faith looks up to Thee, Thou Lamb of Cal - va - ry,
2. May Thy rich grace im - part Strength to my faint - ing heart,
3. While life's dark maze I tread, And griefs a - round me spread,
4. When ends life's tran-sient dream, When death's cold, sul - len stream

Sav - ior di - vine! Now hear me while I pray, Take all my
My zeal in - spire; As Thou hast died for me, O may my
Be Thou my Guide; Bid dark-ness turn to day, Wipe sor-row's
Shall o'er me roll; Blest Sav - ior, then, in love, Fear and dis -

guilt a - way, O let me from this day Be whol - ly Thine.
love to Thee Pure, warm, and change-less be, A liv - ing fire.
tears a - way, Nor let me ev - er stray From Thee a - side.
trust re-move; O bear me safe a - bove, A ran-somed soul!

270 When Sinners See Their Lost Condition

WHO KNOWS HOW NEAR 9 8, 9 8, 8 8

Magnus Brostrup Landstad, 1863
Tr. Smeby, Solberg, Doving, 1909   German. 1690

1. When sin-ners see their lost con - di - tion, And feel the press-ing
2. When Je - sus en - ters meek and low - ly, To fill the home with
3. When Je - sus en - ters land and na - tion, And moves the peo - ple
4. When Je - sus comes, O bless-ed sto - ry! He works a change in

load of sin, And Je - sus com - eth on His mis - sion
sweet-est peace; When hearts have felt His bless-ing ho - ly,
with His love, When yield-ing to His kind per - sua - sion,
heart and life; God's king-dom comes with pow'r and glo - ry

To heal the sin - sick heart with - in, All grief must
And found from sin com - plete re - lease, Then light and
Our hearts His truth and bless - ings prove, Then shall our
To young and old, to man and wife; Through sa - cra -

flee be - fore His grace, And joy di - vine will take its place.
calm with - in shall reign, And hearts di - vid - ed love a - gain.
life on earth be blest, The peace of God on us shall rest.
ment and liv - ing word, Faith, love, and hope are now con-ferred.

5. O may He soon to every nation
   Find entrance where He is unknown,
   With life and light and full salvation
   That heathendom may be o'erthrown,
   And healing to the hearts may come
   In heathen land and Christian home!

271 The Great Physician Now Is Near

GREAT PHYSICIAN 8 7 4L. and Chorus

William Hunter

Arr. J. H. Stockton

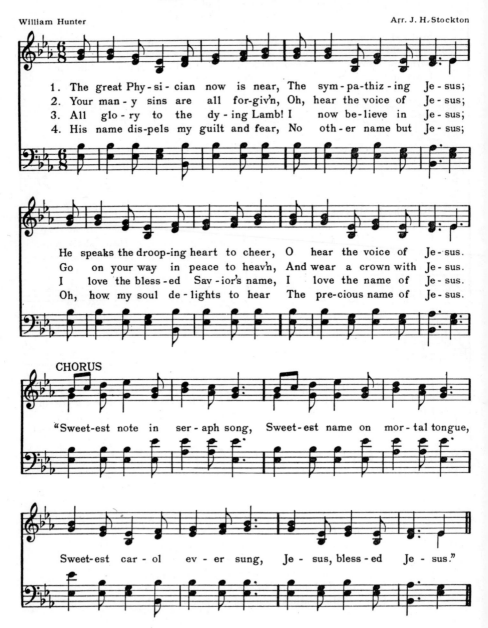

1. The great Phy-si-cian now is near, The sym-pa-thiz-ing Je-sus;
2. Your man-y sins are all for-giv'n, Oh, hear the voice of Je-sus;
3. All glo-ry to the dy-ing Lamb! I now be-lieve in Je-sus;
4. His name dis-pels my guilt and fear, No oth-er name but Je-sus;

He speaks the droop-ing heart to cheer, O hear the voice of Je-sus.
Go on your way in peace to heav'n, And wear a crown with Je-sus.
I love the bless-ed Sav-ior's name, I love the name of Je-sus.
Oh, how my soul de-lights to hear The pre-cious name of Je-sus.

CHORUS

"Sweet-est note in ser-aph song, Sweet-est name on mor-tal tongue,

Sweet-est car-ol ev-er sung, Je-sus, bless-ed Je-sus."

272 Who Will Now Indict Me

JESUS, PRICELESS TREASURE 6 6 5, 6 6 5, 7 8 6

Johann Franck, 1618-1677
Tr. T.F. Gullixson, 1932

Ludvig M. Lindeman, 1812-1887

1. Who will now in - dict me And in judg-ment cite me Up high Si - na - i? O - pen-ly con - fess - ing, Peace in Christ pos - sess - ing, Guilt has dropp'd a - way. Meet me here; with Cal-v'ry near Je - sus will be my de - fend - er, Shall I then sur - ren - der?

2. Who brings ac - cu - sa - tion? Bit - ter mem-'ries wak - en, Old scars bleed a - new— Sins of weak-ness, hat - ed, Whis-per-ing of doom. Christ was here. The is - sues clear: Grace, thro' grace is my sal - va - tion! Who brings ac-cu - sa - tion?

3. Who brings con-dem - na - tion? I in con - ster - na - tion Find the Sav - ior's wounds. God, the Judge of na - tions, ma - tion: "Guilt-y he"—"Now free!" Je - sus saves though all hell raves. Death holds not my con - sum-ma - tion! Who brings con-dem-na - tion?

243

273 I Lay My Sins on Jesus

CRUCIFIX 7 6 8L.
(Or use AURELIA, No. 44)

Horatius Bonar, ca. 1845

Greek Melody

1. I lay my sins on Je - sus, The spot - less Lamb of God;
2. I lay my wants on Je - sus; All full - ness dwells in Him:
3. I long to be like Je - sus, Meek, lov - ing, low - ly, mild:

He bears them all and frees us From the ac - curs - ed load.
He heals all my dis - eas - es, He doth my soul re - deem.
I long to be like Je - sus, The Fa - ther's ho - ly Child.

I bring my guilt to Je - sus, To wash my crim - son stains
I lay my griefs on Je - sus, My bur - dens and my cares:
I long to be with Je - sus, A - mid the heav'n - ly throng,

White in His blood most pre - cious, Till not a spot re - mains.
He from them all re - leas - es, He all my sor - rows shares.
To sing with saints His prais - es, To learn the an - gels' song.

274 By Grace I Am an Heir of Heaven

IF THOU BUT SUFFER GOD 9 8,9 8,8 8

Chr. Ludwig Scheit, 1742
Tr. H. Brueckner, 1925

Georg Neumark, 1622-1681

1. By grace I am an heir of heav - en: Why
2. By grace a - lone shall I in - her - it That
3. By grace! These pre - cious words re - mem - ber When
4. By grace! This fount of our sal - va - tion As
5. By grace! Be this in death my com - fort; De -

doubt this, O my trem - bling heart? If what the Scrip-tures prom-ise
bliss - ful home be - yond the skies. Works count for naught, the Lord in -
sore - ly by thy sins op-pressed, When Sa - tan comes to vex thy
long as God is truth shall flow. What all the men of God have
spite my fears 'tis well with me. I know my sin in all its

clear - ly Is true and firm in ev - 'ry part, This al - so
car - nate Hath won for me the heav'n-ly prize. Sal - va - tion
spir - it, When troub-led con-science sighs for rest; What rea-son
writ - ten, What God's own words so plain - ly show, What faith a -
great-ness, But al - so Him who sets me free. My heart to

must be truth di - vine: By grace a crown of life is thine.
by His death He wrought, His grace a - lone my par - don bought.
can - not com-pre - hend, God doth to thee by grace ex - tend.
lone can rest up - on Is grace, in Christ, God's on - ly Son.
naught but joy gives place Since I am saved by grace, by grace.

245

275 If God Himself Be for Me

O LIVING BREAD 7 6 8L.

Paul Gerhardt, 1664
Tr. Richard Massie, 1857

Zinck's Koralbog, 1801

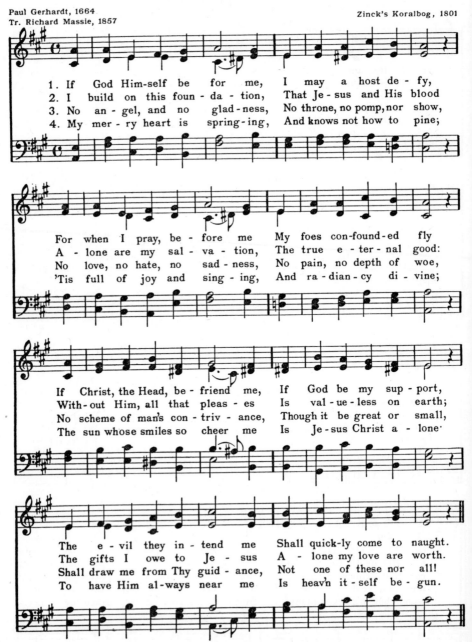

1. If God Him-self be for me, I may a host de - fy,
2. I build on this foun - da - tion, That Je - sus and His blood
3. No an - gel, and no glad - ness, No throne, no pomp, nor show,
4. My mer - ry heart is spring - ing, And knows not how to pine;

For when I pray, be - fore me My foes con-found-ed fly
A - lone are my sal - va - tion, The true e - ter - nal good:
No love, no hate, no sad - ness, No pain, no depth of woe,
'Tis full of joy and sing - ing, And ra - dian-cy di - vine;

If Christ, the Head, be-friend me, If God be my sup - port,
With-out Him, all that pleas - es Is val - ue - less on earth;
No scheme of man's con - triv - ance, Though it be great or small,
The sun whose smiles so cheer me Is Je - sus Christ a - lone·

The e - vil they in - tend me Shall quick-ly come to naught.
The gifts I owe to Je - sus A - lone my love are worth.
Shall draw me from Thy guid - ance, Not one of these nor all!
To have Him al-ways near me Is heav'n it - self be - gun.

276 I Could Not Do without Thee

PASSION CHORALE 7 6 8L.

Frances P Havergal, 1873

Hans Leo Hassler, 1601

1. I could not do with - out Thee, O Sav - ior of the lost,
2. I could not do with - out Thee, I can - not stand a - lone,
3. I could not do with - out Thee, For O the way is long,
4. I could not do with - out Thee, O Je - sus, Sav - ior dear;
5. I could not do with - out Thee, For years are fleet - ing fast,

Whose won-drous love re - deemed me At such tre - men - dous cost;
I have no strength or good - ness, No wis - dom of my own,
And I am of - ten wear y, And sigh re - plac - es song:
E'en when my eyes are hold - en, I know that Thou art near,
And soon in sol - emn lon - li-ness The riv - er must be passed;

Thy right-eous-ness, Thy par - don, Thy pre - cious blood must be
But Thou, be - lov - ed Sav - ior, Art all in all to me;
How could I do with - out Thee? I do not know the way;
How drear - y and how lone - ly This change-ful life would be,
But Thou wilt nev - er leave me, And though the waves roll high,

My on - ly hope and com - fort, My glo - ry and my plea.
And weak-ness will be pow - er, If lean - ing hard on Thee
Thou know-est, and Thou lead - est, And wilt not let me stray.
With-out the sweet com - mun - ion, The se - cret rest with Thee.
I know Thou wilt be near me, And whis-per, "It is I"

277 There Is a Fountain Filled with Blood

EVAN C. M.

William Cowper, 1771, alt

William H. Havergal, 1846

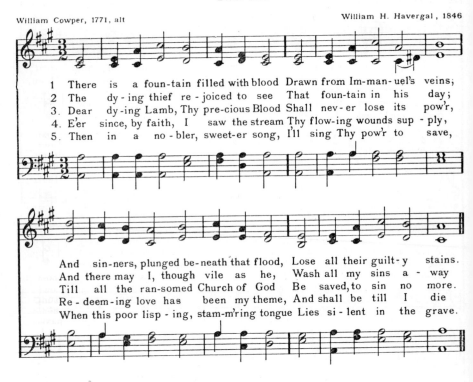

1 There is a foun-tain filled with blood Drawn from Im-man-uel's veins;
2 The dy-ing thief re-joiced to see That foun-tain in his day;
3. Dear dy-ing Lamb, Thy pre-cious Blood Shall nev-er lose its pow'r,
4. E'er since, by faith, I saw the stream Thy flow-ing wounds sup-ply,
5. Then in a no-bler, sweet-er song, I'll sing Thy pow'r to save,

And sin-ners, plunged be-neath that flood, Lose all their guilt-y stains.
And there may I, though vile as he, Wash all my sins a-way
Till all the ran-somed Church of God Be saved, to sin no more.
Re-deem-ing love has been my theme, And shall be till I die
When this poor lisp-ing, stam-m'ring tongue Lies si-lent in the grave.

278 How Sweet the Name of Jesus Sounds

ARLINGTON C. M.

John Newton, 1779

Thomas A Arne, 1762

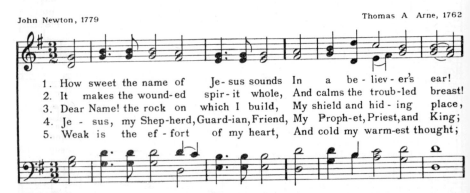

1. How sweet the name of Je-sus sounds In a be-liev-er's ear!
2. It makes the wound-ed spir-it whole, And calms the troub-led breast!
3. Dear Name! the rock on which I build, My shield and hid-ing place,
4. Je-sus, my Shep-herd, Guard-ian, Friend, My Proph-et, Priest, and King;
5. Weak is the ef-fort of my heart, And cold my warm-est thought;

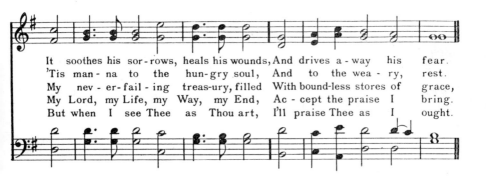

It   soothes his sor-rows, heals his wounds, And drives a - way   his   fear.
'Tis man - na to   the   hun-gry soul, And   to   the wea - ry,   rest.
My   nev - er- fail - ing treas-ury, filled With bound-less stores of grace,
My Lord, my Life, my Way, my End, Ac - cept the praise I   bring.
But when   I see Thee   as   Thou art, I'll praise Thee as   I   ought.

279 Lord Jesus Christ, I Flee to Thee

REFUGE C.M.

Author Unknown
Tr. S.O. Sigmond, 1931

English (?)

1. Lord Je - sus Christ, I   flee   to   Thee, Let   me   Thy   grace ob -
2. In   all the world of   hu - man strife No   man can ev - er
3. To   Thee, my Lord, I   hum - bly pray, My   sins Thou me for -
4. Give strength of heart and peace of mind, My   God so   full of
5. Then shall I   al - ways praise Thy name And fol - low af - ter

tain! But if Thou should-est turn from me, My quest would all be   vain.
save; Thou on - ly   hast the word of   life That fall- en sin - ners crave.
give! Wash all my guilt - y stains a - way, That I   may ev - er live.
grace! That I may have a   faith sub-lime And thus Thy love em - brace.
Thee, The glo - ry   of Thy cross pro-claim Un - til   I crown'd shall be.

280 How Gladly I My Place Have Taken

P.S. Vig
Tr. P.C. Paulsen

HOW GLADLY 9 8, 9 8, 8 8
(Or use WHO KNOWS HOW NEAR, No. 98)

Folk-Tune

1. How glad-ly I my place have tak-en A-mong the flock of God's e-lect! With them I have the world for-sak-en And Je-sus' com-ing now ex-pect. Re-deemed by His un-bound-ed love, My home will be with Christ a-bove.

2. How sweet the words, how re-as-sur-ing, That I to God am rec-on-ciled! His par-don for my sins se-cur-ing, My soul no long-er is de-filed. The peace of God I now pos-sess, Which ev-'ry e-vil can re-dress.

3. I bid the wick-ed world de-fi-ance, Tho' fierce-ly it God's word de-ride; In Him I place my firm re-li-ance, Whose prom-ise ev-er shall a-bide; Tho' earth and heav-en pass a-way, His word shall ev-er be my stay.

4. How glad-ly I His prom-ise pon-der! Tho' sin-ful, yet in grace I stand; A her-i-tage a-waits me yon-der, And heav-en is my fa-ther-land. My Lord, as Vic-tor in the strife, A-wards to me the crown of life.

5. How good to hear my Sav-ior call-ing, To see Him e-ven face to face! What bliss, be-fore Him pros-trate fall-ing, To find with Him a rest-ing place, And with the saints in sweet ac-cord, To sing the praise of Christ, my Lord!

281 Now I Have Found the Ground Wherein

HOW FAIR THE CHURCH L.M. 6L.

Johann Andreas Rothe, 1727
Tr. John Wesley, 1740, alt.

Schumann's Gesangbuoh, 1539

1. Now I have found the ground where-in My soul's sure an-chor
2. O Fa-ther, Thine e-ter-nal grace Our scant-y thought sur-
3. O love, so great, so bot-tom-less! My sins are swal-lowed
4. Fixed on this ground I will re-main, Though heart may fail and

may re-main: The wounds of Je-sus, for my sin Be-
pass-es far; Thy heart still melts with ten-der-ness, Thine
up in Thee: And cov-ered my un-right-eous-ness; No
flesh de-cay; This an-chor shall my soul sus-tain, When

fore the world's foun-da-tion slain; Whose mer-cy shall un-
arms of love still o-pen are Re-turn-ing sin-ners
spot of guilt re-mains in me: While Je-sus' blood, thro'
earth's foun-da-tions melt a-way: Then sing I in e-

shak-en stay, When heav'n and earth are fled a-way.
to re-ceive, That mer-cy they may taste, and live.
earth and skies, For mer-cy, bound-less mer-cy, cries!
ter-ni-ty, Un-bound-ed mer-cy, still of Thee

251

282 Redeemed, Restored, Forgiven

MUNICH 7 6 8L.

Henry William Baker, 1876   Meiningisches Gesangbuch, 1693

1. Re - deemed, re-stored, for - giv - en Through Je - sus' pre-cious blood,
2. Once on the drear - y moun - tain We wan - der'd far and wide,
3. Dear Mas - ter, Thine the glo - ry Of each re - cov - er'd soul;
4. Now keep us, Ho - ly Sav - ior, In Thy true love and fear;

Heirs of His home in heav - en, O praise our pard-'ning God!
Far from the cleans-ing foun - tain, Far from the pierc-ed side;
Ah, who can tell the sto - ry Of love that made us whole?
And grant us of Thy fav - or The grace to per - se - vere;

Praise Him in tune - ful meas-ures, Who gave His Son to die;
But Je - sus sought and found us, And wash'd our guilt a - way;
Not ours, not ours the mer - it; Be Thine a - lone the praise,
Till, in Thy new cre - a - tion, Earth's time-long tra - vail o'er,

Praise Him whose sev'n-fold treas-ures, En - rich and sanc - ti - fy!
With cords of love He bound us To be His own for aye.
And ours a thank-ful spir - it To serve Thee all our days.
We find our full sal - va - tion, And praise Thee ev - er - more.

252

283 My Hope Is Built on Nothing Less

HOW FAIR THE CHURCH 8 8 6L.

Edward Mote, 1836

Schumann's Gesangbuch, 1539

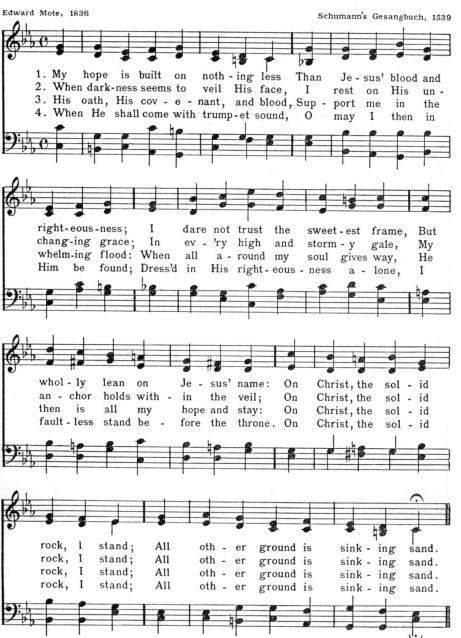

1. My hope is built on noth-ing less Than Je-sus' blood and
2. When dark-ness seems to veil His face, I rest on His un-
3. His oath, His cov-e-nant, and blood, Sup-port me in the
4. When He shall come with trump-et sound, O may I then in

right-eous-ness; I dare not trust the sweet-est frame, But
chang-ing grace; In ev-'ry high and storm-y gale, My
whelm-ing flood: When all a-round my soul gives way, He
Him be found; Dress'd in His right-eous-ness a-lone, I

whol-ly lean on Je-sus' name: On Christ, the sol-id
an-chor holds with-in the veil; On Christ, the sol-id
then is all my hope and stay: On Christ, the sol-id
fault-less stand be-fore the throne. On Christ, the sol-id

rock, I stand; All oth-er ground is sink-ing sand.
rock, I stand; All oth-er ground is sink-ing sand.
rock, I stand; All oth-er ground is sink-ing sand.
rock, I stand; All oth-er ground is sink-ing sand.

284 Rock of Ages, Cleft for Me

TOPLADY 7 7 6L.

August M. Toplady, 1776

Thomas Hastings, 1830

1. Rock of A - ges, cleft for me, Let me hide my-self in Thee;
2. Not the la - bor of my hands Can ful - fil Thy law's de - mands;
3. Noth-ing in my hands I bring, Sim - ply to Thy cross I cling;
4. While I draw this fleet-ing breath, When my eyes shall close in death,

Let the wa - ter and the blood, From Thy riv - en side which flowed,
Could my zeal no res - pite know, Could my tears for - ev - er flow,
Nak - ed, come to Thee for dress, Help - less look to Thee for grace;
When I soar to worlds un - known, See Thee on Thy judg-ment-throne,

Be of sin the doub - le cure, Save me from its guilt and pow'r
All for sin could not a - tone; Thou must save, and Thou a - lone.
Foul, I to the foun-tain fly, Wash me, Sav - ior, or I die.
Rock of A - ges, cleft for me, Let me hide my-self in Thee.

See also:

254

285 Commit Thou All That Grieves Thee

PASSION CHORALE 7 6 8L.

Paul Gerhardt, 1656
Tr. Composite

Hans Leo Hassler, 1601
Arr. F. Melius Christiansen, 1907

1. Com-mit thou all that grieves thee And fills thy heart with care
2. The Lord must be thy ref - uge, If thou would feel se - cure;
3. Thy lov - ing heart so faith - ful, O Fa - ther, know-eth well
4. Hope on, then, weak be - liev - er, In troub-le un - dis - may'd;

To Him whose might and glo - ry The star - ry skies de - clare.
His work must thou con - sid - er, If thine is to en - dure
The needs of all Thy chil - dren Who in Thy shad-ow dwell.
The gloom-y night is wan - ing, Thy fears shall be al - lay'd

He shows the winds their cours - es And points the clouds their way;
No prof - it will it yield thee To pine in grief and care;
And what Thy wis - dom choos - eth Thy might will sure - ly do;
Pos - sess thy soul in pa - tience, Be firm in God's em - ploy,

Will He not guide thy foot-steps And be thy staff and stay?
But God will lend His bless - ing In an - swer to thy pray'r
Ac - cord-ing to Thy coun - sel Wilt Thou Thy work pur - sue.
And thou in ra - diant beau - ty Shalt see the Sun of joy.

286 To the Hills I Lift Mine Eyes

CARE FOR ME, O GOD OF GRACE 7 6 8L.

Andreas Bersagel, 1931

Ludvig M. Lindeman, 1812 - 1887

1. To the hills I lift mine eyes, To the God e - ter - nal,
2. In His pres-ence I am safe, Naught can me en - cum - ber.
3. Though I can-not al - ways see Where my path is lead-ing,

He who dwell - eth in the light On His throne su - per - nal.
He is watch-ing night and day, He will nev - er slum - ber.
Yet I know I need not fear, If His voice I'm heed - ing.

In His prom-ise I can trust, Doubt-ing not the meas-ure;
He's my ref - uge and my strength And my Fa - ther ten - der,
He will care for all my wants, Bring me peace in sad - ness,

He's my help - er and my stay, All my hope and treas-ure.
In temp - ta - tions and in strife He is my de - fend - er.
From the storms and stress of life Call me home to glad - ness.

287 In God, My Savior

IN GOD, MY SAVIOR 5 6 10L

Danish, ca. 1600, Anonymous
Tr. Carl Doving, 1908

Zinck's Koralbog, 1801
Arr. F. Melius Christiansen, 1907

1. In God, my Sav - ior, I put my trust a - lone; His word and fa - vor My help in need I own; My life I ten - der, And all I have as well, In full sur - ren - der To Thee, whose grace I tell, My soul's be - friend - er, My God, Im - man - u - el.

2. The loss sin wrought me, Through Sa-tan's wiles, O Lord, Thou, who hast bought me, Hast all by grace re-stored: My thanks I ren - der, My - self to Thee I yield, My Sav-ior ten - der, My rock, my sun and shield, My soul's de - fend - er, On Thee my hopes I build.

3. Keep me Thy ser - vant, Let me o - bey Thee, Lord, In spir - it fer - vent, Ac - cord - ing to Thy word; When doth for - sake me The frown-ing world for aye, And suff'rings shake me, Grant pa - tience, be my stay, Un - til Thou take me From this ill world a - way.

4. O faith - ful Sav - ior, My sweet-est rest and stay! O let me nev - er From Thee in dark-ness stray! My soul de - liv - er, And guide Thy wea - ry dove, By grace and fa - vor, Home to the place I love — My home for - ev - er — Je - ru - sa - lem a - bove.

5. There, past life's sad - ness, 'Tis good to be at rest, In joy and glad - ness, With saints for - ev - er blest; Lord, let me ev - er Walk in Thy faith and fear, That, past death's riv - er, I may Thy wel-come hear: "Come blest for - ev - er, Come in, my ser - vant dear!"

257

288 O Love That Wilt Not Let Me Go

ST MARGARET 8 8, 8 8 5

George Matheson, 1882

Albert L. Peace, 1885

1. O Love that wilt not let me go, I rest my wea-ry soul in
2. O Light that fol-l'west all my way, I yield my flick'ring torch to
3. O Joy that seek-est me thro' pain, I can-not close my heart to
4. O Cross that lift-est up my head, I dare not ask to fly from

Thee; I give Thee back the life I owe, That in Thine
Thee; My heart re-stores its bor-rowed ray, That in Thy
Thee; I trace the rain-bow thro' the rain, And feel the
Thee; I lay in dust life's glo-ry dead, And from the

o - cean depths its flow May rich - er, full - er be.
sun - shine's blaze its day May bright-er, fair - er be.
prom - ise is not vain That morn shall tear - less be.
ground there blos-soms red Life that shall end - less be.

289 God Is Faithful, He Will Never

STRICKEN, SMITTEN 8 7 4L.

T O. Burntvedt, 1931

Ludvig M. Lindeman, 1812 - 1887

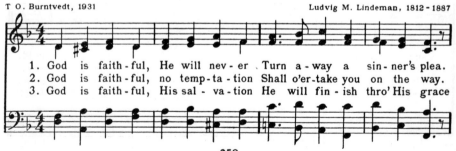

1. God is faith - ful, He will nev - er Turn a - way a sin - ner's plea.
2. God is faith - ful, no temp-ta - tion Shall o'er-take you on the way.
3. God is faith - ful, His sal - va - tion He will fin - ish thro' His grace

God is just and He will ev - er Set the bur-den'd sin - ner free.
God is love, His con - so - la - tion Turns the dark-ness in - to day.
Till in glo - rious con - sum - ma - tion We shall see Him face to face.

290 God Is the Refuge of His Saints

WHEN IN THE HOUR OF UTMOST NEED L M

Isaac Watts, 1719   Louis Bourgeois, 154?

1. God is the ref - uge of His saints, When
2. Let moun - tains from their seats be hurl'd Down
3. Loud may the troub - led o - cean roar; In
4. There is a stream whose gen - tle flow Sup -
5. That sa - cred stream, Thy ho - ly word, Our

storms of sharp dis - tress in - vade, Ere we can of - fer
to the deep, and bur - ied there, Con - vul - sions shake the
sa - cred peace our souls a - bide; While ev - 'ry na - tion,
plies the cit - y of our God, Life, love, and joy, still
grief al - lays, our fear con - trols; Sweet peace Thy prom - is -

our com - plaints, Be - hold Him pres - ent with His aid.
sol - id world— Our faith shall nev - er yield to fear.
ev - 'ry shore, May trem - ble at the swell - ing tide.
glid - ing through, And wa - t'ring our di - vine a - bode.
es af - ford, And gives new strength to faint - ing souls.

291 Evening and Morning

EVENING AND MORNING 5 5, 5 5 10, 5 6, 5 6 10

Paul Gerhardt, 1607-1676
Tr Richard Massie, 1800-1887

Johann Georg Ebeling, 1620-1676

1. Eve-ning and morn - ing, Sun-set and dawn-ing, Wealth, peace, and glad-ness, Com-fort in sad-ness, These are Thy works; all the glo-ry be Thine! Times with-out num-ber, A-wake or in slum-ber, Thine eye ob-serves us, From dan-ger pre-serves us, Caus-ing Thy mer-cy up-on us to shine.

2. Fa-ther, O hear me; Par-don and spare me; Calm all my ter-rors, Blot out my er-rors, That by Thine eyes they may no more be scanned. Or-der my go-ings; Di-rect all my do-ings; As it may please Thee, Re-tain or re-lease me; All I com-mit to Thy Fa-ther-ly hand.

3. Griefs of God's send-ing Soon have an end-ing; Clouds may be pour-ing, Wind and wave roar-ing; Sun-shine will come when the tem-pest has past. Joys still in-creas-ing, And peace nev-er ceas-ing, Foun-tains that dry not, And ros-es that die not, Bloom-ing in E-den, a-wait me at last.

292 As Wide As the Skies Is Thy Mercy, O God!

AS WIDE AS THE SKIES 11 9 4L.

Bernhard S. Ingeman, 1789-1862
Tr. P.C. Paulsen

Unknown Composer, abr.

1. As wide as the skies is Thy mer - cy, O God!
Thy faith - ful - ness shield - eth cre - a - tion. Thy
boun - te - ous hand from the moun - tains a - broad
Is stretched o - ver coun - try and na - tion.

2. Like heav - en's em - brace is Thy love, O my Lord!
In judg - ment pro - found Thou ap - pear - est. Thou
sav - est our souls through Thy life giv - ing word.
The cries of Thy chil - dren Thou hear - est.

3. How pre - cious Thy good - ness, O Fa - ther a - bove,
Where chil - dren of men are a - bid - ing. Thou
spread - est through dark - ness the wings of Thy love;
We un - der their pin - ions are hid - ing.

4. For lan - guish - ing souls Thou pre - par - est a rest,
The quiv - er - ing dove Thou pro - tect - est; Thou
giv - est us be - ing, e - ter - nal and blest,
In mer - cy our life Thou per - fect - est.

293 Love, the Fount of Light from Heaven

LOVE, THE FOUNT OF LIGHT 8 7, 8 7, 8 8, 7 7

Nicolai F. S. Grundtvig, 1853
Tr. Carl Doving, 1909

Ludvig M. Lindeman, 1812-1887

1. Love, the fount of light from heav-en, Is the root and source of life;
2. Love doth crown the life e - ter - nal, Love the bright-ness is of light,
3. Love, a - lone the law ful - fill - ing, Is the bond of per - fect-ness,

There-fore God's de-crees are giv - en With His lov - ing - kind - ness rife,
There-fore on His throne su - per - nal Je - sus sits in glo - ry bright;
Love, who came a vic - tim will-ing, Paid our debt and brought us peace;

As our Sav - ior God de-clar-eth, And the Spir - it wit - ness bear-eth,
He, the light and life of heav-en, Who Him-self for us hath giv-en,
There-fore love and peace in un - ion Ev - er grow in sweet com-mun-ion,

As we in God's peace do prove, God is light and God is love.
Still a - bides and reigns a - bove In His Fa - ther's bound-less love.
And thro' love we may a - bide One with Him who for us died.

294 Why Art Thou Cast Down, My Soul

WHY ART THOU CAST DOWN 7 8,7 8,7 7

Benjamin Schmolck, 1704
Hans Adolf Brorson, 1734
Tr. Carl Doving

German, 1656

1. Why art thou cast down, my soul? O what mean thy sighs and sad-ness?
2. On this ground thy an-chor cast; Safe thou art, in Christ con-fid-ing;
3. Christ's own way is al-ways good, Chris-tians find this con-so-la-tion:
4. Je-sus gives us joy and tears, Bless-ed be His name for-ev-er!

Trust in Him who makes thee whole, And thy griefs can turn to glad-ness,
All the griefs which here thou hast Are but shad-ows un-a-bid-ing.
He who bought thee with His blood, Now stands pledged for thy sal-va-tion.
When thy way most dark ap-pears, Trust in Him, des-pond thou nev-er;

Oft-en in the dark-est hour He re-veals His love and pow'r.
Soon thy cross shall pass a-way, Joy shall come that lasts for aye.
Rest up-on His sa-cred word That as-sur-ance doth af-ford!
Wear-y soul, when sore dis-tressed, Call on Him and be at rest.

5. Surely, narrow is the way
   To the land of gladness yonder;
   While on this sad earth we stay,
   We must here as pilgrims wander.
   Through the desert we must roam,
   Till we Canaan reach, our home.

6. Upward, then, my weary soul,
   Where the crown of life is given!
   Pressing onward to the goal,
   I shall win the bliss of heaven;
   For, O Jesus, I am Thine,
   Blest am I, for Thou art mine!

295 I Have a Friend So Patient, Kind, Forbearing

ONE RADIANT MORN 11 10 4L.

Carl Oluf Rosenius, 1816-1868
Tr. John Jesperson

1. I have a Friend so pa-tient, kind, for-bear-ing,
2. He is my Lord, my Friend, my lov-ing Broth-er,
3. My poor and wretch-ed soul He lib-er-at-ed
4. I am re-deemed: no more the law pre-vail-eth,
5. With hal-le-lu-jahs here I'll tell the sto-ry,

Of all my friends this Friend doth love me best;
And Je-sus Christ is His most bless-ed name.
From sin and con-dem-na-tion, death and hell;
And Christ, the Lord, is my Re-deem-er's name;
My Lord to praise, to laud and mag-ni-fy,

Though I am weak and sin-ful, yet, when shar-ing
He loves more ten-der-ly than an-y moth-er;
The ser-pent's head is bruised, his might de-feat-ed,
His pre-cious blood more than my sin a-vail-eth;
And praise His name for ev-er-more in glo-ry,

His love and mer-cy, I am ev-er blest.
To rest in Him is more than wealth and fame.
Re-joice, my ran-somed soul, for all is well!
His mer-it cov-ers all my guilt and shame.
Be-fore His throne, with all the saints on high.

296 Through the Love of God Our Father

WELSH HYMN 84, 84, 88, 84

Mary Peters, 1847

Welsh Traditional
Jones' Relics of the Welsh Bards, 1784

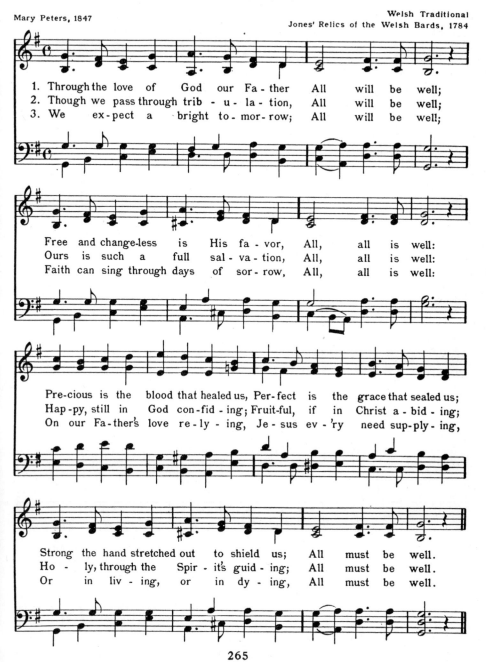

1. Through the love of God our Fa - ther   All   will   be   well;
2. Though we pass through trib - u - la - tion,   All   will   be   well;
3. We   ex - pect a   bright to - mor - row;   All   will   be   well;

Free and change-less   is   His fa - vor,   All,   all   is   well:
Ours   is such a   full   sal - va - tion,   All,   all   is   well:
Faith can sing through days   of   sor - row,   All,   all   is   well:

Pre - cious is the   blood that healed us,   Per - fect   is   the   grace that sealed us;
Hap - py, still in   God con - fid - ing;   Fruit - ful,   if   in   Christ a - bid - ing;
On   our Fa - ther's   love re - ly - ing,   Je - sus ev - 'ry   need sup - ply - ing,

Strong   the hand stretched out   to shield   us;   All   must   be   well.
Ho -   ly, through the   Spir - it's guid - ing;   All   must   be   well.
Or   in   liv - ing,   or   in   dy - ing,   All   must   be   well.

265

297 When Winds Are Raging o'er the Upper Ocean

REVELATION 11 10 4L.

Harriet Beecher Stowe, 1811-1896   Andreas Peter Berggren, 1801-1880

1. When winds are rag - ing o'er the up - per o - cean
2. Far, far be - neath, the noise of tem - pests di - eth,
3. So to the heart that knows Thy love, O Pur - est!
4. Far, far a - way the roar of pas - sion di - eth,

And bil - lows wild con - tend with an - gry roar,
And sil - ver waves chime ev - er peace - ful - ly,
There is a tem - ple sa - cred ev - er - more;
And lov - ing thoughts rise calm and peace - ful - ly,

'Tis said— far down be - neath the wild com - mo - tion
And no rude storm, how fierce so - e'er it fli - eth,
And all the Ba - bel of life's an - gry voic - es
And no rude storm, how fierce so - e'er it fli - eth,

That peace-ful still - ness reign-eth ev - er - more.
Dis - turbs the sab - bath of that deep - er sea.
Dies in hushed still - ness at its peace - ful door.
Dis - turbs the soul that rests, O Lord, in Thee.

298 O Safe to the Rock That Is Higher Than I

HIDING IN THEE 11 11 4L. and Chorus

William O. Cushing, b. 1823

Ira D. Sankey, 1840-1910

1. O safe to the Rock that is high - er than I,
2. In the calm of the noon - tide, in sor - row's lone hour,
3. How oft in the con - flict, when press'd by the foe,

My soul in its con - flicts and sor - rows would fly;
In times when temp - ta - tion casts o'er me its pow'r;
I have fled to my Ref - uge and breathed out my woe;

So sin - ful, so wea - ry, Thine, Thine would I be,
In the tem - pests of life, on its wide, heav - ing sea,
How oft - en, when tri - als like sea bil - lows roll,

CHORUS

Thou blest "Rock of A - ges," I'm hid - ing in Thee.
Thou blest "Rock of A - ges," I'm hid - ing in Thee. Hid - ing in Thee,
Have I hid - den in Thee, O Thou Rock of my soul.

Hid - ing in Thee, Thou blest "Rock of A - ges," I'm hid - ing in Thee.

299 If Thou But Suffer God to Guide Thee

IF THOU BUT SUFFER GOD 9 8, 9 8, 8 8

Georg Neumark, 1657
Tr. Catherine Winkworth, 1863

Georg Neumark, 1657

1. If thou but suf - fer God to guide thee, And
2. What can these anx - ious cares a - vail thee, These
3. Be thou but still and wait His lei - sure In
4. He knows the time for joy, and tru - ly Will

hope in Him thro' all thy ways, He'll give thee strength, what-e'er be -
nev - er - ceas - ing moans and sighs? What can it help if thou be -
cheer-ful hope, with heart con-tent To take what - e'er thy Fa - ther's
send it when He sees it meet: When He has tried and purged thee

tide thee, And bear thee through the e - vil days; Who trusts in
wail thee O'er each dark mo - ment as it flies? Our cross and
pleas-ure And all - dis - cern - ing love have sent; Nor doubt our
du - ly, And finds thee free from all de - ceit, He comes to

God's un-chang-ing love Builds on the rock that naught can move.
tri - als do but press The heav-ier for our bit - ter - ness.
in - most wants are known To Him who chose us for His own.
thee all un - a - ware And makes thee own His lov - ing care.

300 Though Troubles Assail Us and Dangers Affright

ADESTE FIDELES 11 11 4L.

John Newton, 1779, alt.

John F. Wade's Cantus Diversi, 1751

1. Though troub-les as-sail us, and dan-gers af-fright, Tho' friends should all fail us, and foes all u-nite, Yet one thing se-cures us, what-ev-er be-tide, The prom-ise as-sures us, "The Lord will pro-vide." The prom-ise as-sures us, "The Lord will pro-vide."

2. The birds, with-out gar-ner or store-house, are fed; From them let us learn to trust God for our bread: His saints what is fit-ting shall ne'er be de-nied, So long as 'tis writ-ten, "The Lord will pro-vide." So long as 'tis writ-ten, "The Lord will pro-vide."

3. When Sa-tan as-sails us to stop up our path, And cour-age all fails us, we tri-umph by faith. He can-not take from us, tho' oft he has tried, This heart-cheer-ing prom-ise, "The Lord will pro-vide." This heart-cheer-ing prom-ise, "The Lord will pro-vide."

4. No strength of our own, and no good-ness we claim; Yet, since we have known of the Sav-ior's great name, In this our strong tow-er for safe-ty we hide: The Lord is our pow-er, "The Lord will pro-vide." The Lord is our pow-er, "The Lord will pro-vide."

301 What Our Father Does Is Well

PEACE TO SOOTHE 7 7 6L.

Benjamin Schmolck, 1720
Tr. Henry W. Baker, 1861

J. P. E. Hartmann, 1852

1. What our Fa - ther does is well: Bless - ed truth His chil - dren tell! Though He send us try - ing want, Though the har - vest store be scant, Yet we rest up - on His love, Seek - ing bet - ter things a - bove.

2. What our Fa - ther does is well: Shall the will - ful heart re - bel If a bless - ing He with - hold In the field or in the fold? Is He not Him - self to be All our store e - ter - nal - ly? Can we mur - mur at His rod?

3. What our Fa - ther does is well: Though He sad - den hill and dell, Up - ward yet our prais - es rise For the strength His Word sup - plies. He has called us sons of God:— Can we mur - mur at His rod?

4. What our Fa - ther does is well: May the thought with - in us dwell; Though nor milk nor hon - ey flow In this bar - ren land be - low, God will save us in our need, God will bless us, God will feed.

5. There - fore un - to Him we raise Hymns of glo - ry, songs of praise; To the Fa - ther and the Son And the Spir - it, Three in One, Hon - or, might and glo - ry be, Now and through e - ter - ni - ty.

302 Care for Me, O God of Grace

CARE FOR ME 7 6 8L.

Laudamilie Elisabeth, 1640-1672
Tr. C.K. Solberg, alt.

Ludvig M. Lindeman, 1812-1887

1. Care for me, O God of grace, Help me that I nev-er,
   Anx-ious, look to fu-ture days, But may trust Thee ev-er.
   Care for me and care for mine Ev-er-y day and hour,
   Care for ev-'ry one of Thine, God of grace and pow-er!

2. Care for bo-dy and for soul, Be Thou my de-fend-er!
   Come what may, have full con-trol, All I now sur-ren-der.
   Care Thou for my soul and mind, Lest my thoughts should grieve Thee;
   And, what-ev-er lot I find, May I nev-er leave Thee!

3. Thro' the means of grace, I pray, Grant me grace to know Thee;
   Care for me that I o-bey What Thy word doth show me.
   Care for those who now con-trol Church and schools and na-tions,
   Care for ev-'ry faith-ful soul La-bor-ing in pa-tience!

4. Care for me at ev-en-tide, In my sleep pro-tect me;
   Thro' the day be at my side, In my work di-rect me!
   All I think and do and say, And my task and sta-tion
   Sanc-ti-fy, Lord, lest I stray, Bless my oc-cu-pa-tion!

5. Care for goods and house and home, Guard my rep-u-ta-tion;
   Care for me when tri-als come, Be my con-so-la-tion!
   Care for me while on my way, Fa-ther, go be-fore me!
   Lead me home in peace, I pray, To Thy home in glo-ry!

271

303 Under His Wings I'm Safely Abiding

WILLINGHAM 11 10 4L.

William O. Cushing, b. 1823   Frantz Abt, 1819-1885

1. Un - der His wings, I'm safe - ly a - bid - ing;
2. Un - der His wings, what ref - uge in sor - row!
3. Un - der His wings, what pre - cious en - joy - ment!

Tho' the night deep - ens and tem - pests are wild,
How the heart yearn - ing - ly turns to His rest!
There will I hide till life's tri - als are o'er;

Still I can trust Him; I know He will keep me;
Of - ten when earth has no balm for my heal - ing,
Shel - tered, pro - tect - ed, no e - vil can harm me;

He has re - deemed me, and I am His child.
There I find com - fort, and there I am blest.
Rest - ing in Je - sus I'm safe ev - er - more.

304 God Moves in a Mysterious Way

ST. ANNE C.M.

William Cowper, 1774
William Croft, 1708

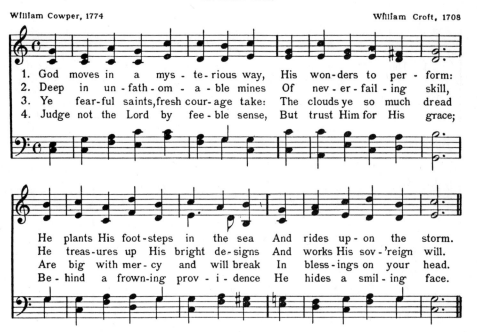

1. God moves in a mys-te-rious way, His won-ders to per-form:
2. Deep in un-fath-om-a-ble mines Of nev-er-fail-ing skill,
3. Ye fear-ful saints, fresh cour-age take: The clouds ye so much dread
4. Judge not the Lord by fee-ble sense, But trust Him for His grace;

He plants His foot-steps in the sea And rides up-on the storm.
He treas-ures up His bright de-signs And works His sov-'reign will.
Are big with mer-cy and will break In bless-ings on your head.
Be-hind a frown-ing prov-i-dence He hides a smil-ing face.

5. His purposes will ripen fast,
   Unfolding every hour;
   The bud may have a bitter taste,
   But sweet will be the flower

6. Blind unbelief is sure to err
   And scan His work in vain;
   God is His own interpreter,
   And He will make it plain.

See also:

Lord Jesus Christ, I flee to Thee, 279

Jesus, lover of my soul, 154

How firm a foundation, 202

Alone with Thee, O Lord, 332

As after the waterbrooks panteth, 250

A mighty fortress is our God, 239

Lord Jesus Christ, my Savior blest, 218

Jesus, Savior, pilot me, 161

O God, our help in ages past, 142

We saw Thee not, 162

Immortal love, forever full, 152

305 Thine, O Jesus, Now and Ever

CRUCIFIXION 8 8 7 6L.

Theodor W. Oldenburg, 1805 - 1842
Tr. T. F. Gullixson, 1932

'Zinck's Koralbog, 1801
Arr. Ludvig M. Lindeman, 1812-1887

1. Thine, O Je - sus, now and ev - er, My de - sire and my en - deav - or, Thine to be in life, in death. I will wage by grace my war - fare; Knight to Thee 'gainst hell a cor - sair! Give me joy on bat - tle heath!

2. Yea, I know that crowns of glo - ry, Palms of peace with vic - t'ry's sto - ry, Thou to them a - lone dost grant Who through all their trib - u - la - tions, Trea - sons, tri - als, and temp - ta - tions In Thy steps their foot - steps plant.

3. I will bear my cross with glad - ness, Though it brings re - proach and sad - ness, As Thou, Sav - ior, car - ried Thine. Goes my path through vales of sha - dows, On it leads to pleas - ant mead - ows Where e - ter - nal glo - ries shine.

4. Lead me out through trials un - end - ing, Lead me in past deaths im - pend - ing, Through wild storms and rag - ing sea; I will meet them, bold - er, brav - er, As Thou wilt, O Je - sus, Sav - ior, But,— Thou rod and staff must be!

5. All the way by grace sur - round - ed, Sove - reign un - seen, Pow'r un - bound - ed, Lead me, Mas - ter, day by day. And when cross - days here are end - ed Take me, Lord, where Thou as - cend - ed, With Thy glo - rious Self to be.

306 I Know a Way Besieged and Thronging

I KNOW A WAY 9 8, 8 9, 8 8 7

M. Falk Gjertsen, 1847 - 1913
Tr. Oscar R. Overby, 1932

Israel Sandtröm

1. I know a way be - sieged and throng-ing With pain and sor-row, steep and long; But on that way re-sounds a song Of test-ed faith and heav'n-ly long - ing. It is the way the Chris-tians trod To gain the crown of life with God, 'Mid trib - u - la - tions throng - ing.

2. I know a Friend who nev - er fails me, When sore op-press'd I ply the way. In life, in death He is my stay, A Friend so might - y and so fair, No mor - tal can with Him com - pare; A Friend who nev - er fails me.

3. I know a robe of match-less splen-dor In which all earth-ly glo - ries fade; A rai-ment rich and heav-en-made For sin - ners who to Christ sur-ren - der; A wed-ding robe to cov-er shame And shield from God the sin - ner's blame; A robe of match-less splen - dor.

4. I know a call that breaks my pris - on When rest-ful rays at eve - ning burn; When win-ter scenes no more re - turn, But glad ce - les - tial spring is ris - en; When pend-ing pet - als press the sod, And ros - es, blos - som-ing with God, A - wake to break their pris - on.

5. I know a home of joy e - ter - nal, Where all the pil-grim hosts shall meet In ra-dian-cy and bliss com-plete A - round the Christ in realms su - per - nal From east and west, from ev - 'ry zone, They gath-er there be - fore the throne, At home in joy e - ter - nal.

307 Guide Me, O Thou Great Jehovah

EASTER MORROW 8 7 6L.

William Williams, 1745, alt.　　　　　　　　　Ludvig M. Lindeman, 1812 - 1887

1. Guide me, O Thou great Je - ho - vah, Pil - grim through this
2. O - pen now the crys - tal foun - tain, Whence the heal - ing
3. When I tread the verge of Jor - dan, Bid my anx - ious

bar - ren land; I am weak, but Thou art might - y;
streams do flow; Let the fir - y, cloud - y pil - lar
fears sub - side; Bear me through the swell - ing cur - rent,

Hold me with Thy pow'r - ful hand. Bread of heav - en,
Lead me all my jour - ney through; Strong De - liv - 'rer,
Land me safe on Ca - naan's side: Songs of prais - es,

Bread of heav - en, Feed me till I want no more!
strong De - liv - 'rer, Be Thou still my Strength and Shield!
songs of prais - es, I will ev - er give to Thee.

308 I Saw Him in Childhood

VISIONS OF CHRIST 12 12 4L.

Wilhelm Birkedal, 1809-1892
Tr. Oscar R. Overby, 1932

Norwegian Folk-Tune
Arr. Oscar R. Overby, 1932

1. I saw Him in child - hood with eyes bright - ly beam - ing,
2. I saw Him in youth when all life was a - dorn - ing
3. I saw Him in man - hood in ho - ly de - cor - um;
4. 'Twas then I be - held Him as mer - ci - ful Sav - ior
5. A - gain I shall see Him when e - ven comes o'er me,

In rays of the rain - bow on moun - tain - tops gleam - ing;
The flights of my spir - it in glo - ri - ous morn - ing.
The sin - ner sur - ren - dered in judg - ment be - fore Him;
Whose cross lost of - fence and re - stored me to fa - vor
When day - light shall si - lent - ly ca - dence be - fore me,

He fond - ly em - braced me, my fan - cy be - friend - ing,
He beck - oned my soul as the glow of His por - tal
And, trem - bling, my heart in con - tri - tion was burn - ing,
Em - brac - ing my bur - den I found a re - un - ion:
And death o'er my vis - ion dim sha - dows is cast - ing,

But veiled by the ver - dure the cross was im - pend - ing.
Shed ra - diance and rap - ture on all that is mor - tal.
As death - ter - rors closed o'er my spir - it in yearn - ing.
The Sav - ior and sin - ner once more in com - mun - ion.
O then I shall greet Him in joy ev - er - last - ing.

309 Thee Will I Love, My Strength, My Tower

ST. CATHERINE L.M.6L.

Johann Scheffler, 1657

Henri F. Hemy, 1865
Alt. James G. Walton, 1871

1 Thee will I love, my strength, my tow'r, Thee will I love, my
2. I thank Thee, un - cre - a - ted Sun, That Thy bright beams on
3 Up - hold me in the doubt - ful race, Nor suf - fer me a -
4 Thee will I love, my joy, my crown; Thee will I love, my

joy, my crown; Thee will I love with all my pow'r,
me have shined; I thank Thee, who hast o - ver - thrown
gain to stray; Strength-en my feet, with stead - y pace
Lord, my God! Thee will I love, be - neath Thy frown

In all my works, and Thee a - lone: Thee will I
My foes, and healed my wound - ed mind; I thank Thee,
Still to press for - ward in Thy way; That all my
Or smile, Thy scep - ter or Thy rod. What though my

love, till the pure fire Fill my whole soul with chaste de - sire
whose en - liv'n - ing voice Bids my freed heart in Thee re - joice.
pow'rs,with all their might, In Thy sole glo - ry may u - nite
flesh and heart de - cay? Thee shall I love in end - less day.

278

310 More Love to Thee, O Christ

MORE LOVE TO THEE 6 4, 6 4, 6 6, 6 4

Elizabeth Prentiss, 1869   Theodore E. Perkins, 1875

1. More love to Thee, O Christ, More love to Thee!
2. Once earth-ly joy I craved, Sought peace and rest;
3. Let sor-row do its work, Send grief and pain;
4. Then shall my lat-est breath Whis-per Thy praise;

Hear Thou the pray'r I make On bend-ed knee;
Now Thee a-lone I seek; Give what is best:
Sweet are Thy mes-sen-gers, Sweet their re-frain,
This is the part-ing cry My heart shall raise;

This is my ear-nest plea, More love, O Christ, to Thee,
This all my pray'r shall be, More love, O Christ, to Thee,
When they can sing with me, More love, O Christ, to Thee,
This still its pray'r shall be, More love, O Christ, to Thee,

More love, O Christ, to Thee, More love to Thee!
More love, O Christ, to Thee, More love to Thee!
More love, O Christ, to Thee, More love to Thee!
More love, O Christ, to Thee, More love to Thee!

311 Merciful Savior, Come and Be My Comfort

COME O LORD JESUS 11 11 4L.

Katharina Elisabet Posse, 1818 - 1880
Tr. S.M. Hill, E.W. Olson, Adapted

Polish Folk - Tune

1. Mer - ci - ful Sav - ior, come and be my com - fort;
2. Come as the Bride - groom to the bride be - lov - ed,
3. Come in my plea - sures, come to me in sor - row,

Van - ish all i - dols in Thy ho - ly pres - ence;
Come Thou to strength - en faith and love and pa - tience;
Come in the an - guished hour of dire temp - ta - tion,

Come and es - tab - lish in my heart Thy king - dom;
Be Thou a ver - y pres - ent help in dan - ger;
Come and de - liv - er me from sin and e - vil;

Come, O Lord Je - sus, come with grace a - bid - ing.'
Come, O Lord Je - sus, be my strong de - fend - er.
Come, O Lord Je - sus, hear my sup - pli - ca - tion

312 O Take My Hand, Dear Father

O TAKE MY HAND 7 4 6L.

Julia von Hautzmann, d. 1901
Tr. H. Brueckner, 1925

Friedrich Silcher, 1789-1860

1 Oh, take my hand, dear Fa - ther, And lead Thou me,
2. Oh, cov - er with Thy mer - cy My fail - ing heart,
3 Tho' oft Thy pow'r but faint - ly May stir my soul,

Till at my jour - ney's end - ing I dwell with Thee.
Lest I in joy, or sor - row, From Thee de - part.
With Thee, my Light in dark - ness, I reach the goal.

A - lone I dare not jour - ney One sin - gle day,
Per - mit Thy child to lin - ger Here at Thy feet,
Take then my hands, dear Fa - ther, And lead Thou me,

So do Thou guide my foot - steps On life's rough way.
Thy good - ness firm - ly trust - ing With faith com - plete.
Till at my jour - ney's end - ing I dwell with Thee.

313 I Walk in Danger All the Way

PILGRIMAGE 8 7, 8 7, 6 6, 8 8

Hans Adolf Brorson, 1734
Tr. D. G. Ristad, 1909

Freylinghausen's Gesangbuch, 1704

1 I walk in dan-ger all the way; The thought shall nev-er
2. I pass thro' tri-als all the way, With sin and ills con-
3. I walk with Je-sus all the way, His guid-ance nev-er
4. My walk is heav'n-ward all the way, A-wait, my soul, the

leave me, That Sa-tan, who has marked his prey, Is
tend-ing; In pa-tience I must bear each day The
fails me, With-in His wounds I find a stay, When
mor-row, When thou shalt find re-lease for aye From

plot-ting to de-ceive me. This foe with hid-den snares
cross of God's own send-ing; Oft in ad-ver-si-ty
Sa-tan's pow'r as-sails me; And by His foot-steps led,
all thy sin and sor-row; All world-ly pomp, be-gone!

May seize me un-a-wares If e'er I fail to
I know not where to flee; When storms of woe my
My path I safe-ly tread, In spite of ills that
To heav'n I now press on; For all the world I

watch	and	pray:	I	walk	in	dan - ger	all the way.
soul	dis - may,	I	pass	through	tri - als	all the way.
threat - en	may,	I	walk	with	Je - sus	all the way.
would	not	stay,	My	walk	is	heav'n - ward	all the way.

314 Must Jesus Bear the Cross Alone

MY CROSS C. M.

(Or use DUNDEE, No. 19)

Thomas Shepherd, 1692, alt.   Norwegian Folk-Tune

1. Must Je - sus bear the cross a - lone, And
2. How hap - py are the saints a - bove, Who
3. The con - se - crat - ed cross I'll bear Till
4. Up - on the crys - tal pave - ment, down At
5. O pre - cious cross! O glo - rious crown! O

all the world go free?___ No, there's a cross for
once went sor - row - ing here;___ But now they taste un -
death shall set me free;___ And then go home my
Je - sus' pierc - ed feet,___ I'll joy - ful, cast my
res - ur - rec - tion day!___ Ye an - gels, from the

ev - 'ry one, And there's a cross for me.
min - gled love, And joy with - out a tear.
crown to wear, For there's a crown for me.
gol - den crown, And His dear Name re - peat.
stars come down, And bear my soul a - way.

315 Jesus, for Thee and Thy Blessed Communion

BLESSED COMMUNION 11 10 8L.

German, Anonymous, 1712, Peter J. Hygom, ca. 1740
Tr. Carl Doving, 1911

Schörring's Koralbog, 1781

1. Je - sus, for Thee and Thy bless-ed com - mun-ion Long-ing pos-sess-es my
2. Quicken my soul thro' Thy blood and Thy mer - it, That I the work of Thy
3. Oh, who could ful - ly make this his en - deav-or: Self to sur-ren-der with

heart and my mind; Break down all bar-riers that hin-der our u - nion,
Spir - it may prove! Cap - tive to Thee take my soul and my spir - it,
heart and with soul! Oh, that my all were my Je - sus for ev - er,

Draw me to Thee, O Re-deem-er most kind! Show me right plain-ly my
Lead me and draw me, lo, faint-ing I rove! Fain I from self and all
I am, a - las, far a - way from my goal! Je - sus, who gav'st me an

need that is cry - ing, Show Thou the depth of my. sins un - to me! That un-to
i - dols would sev - er, When but Thy-self in my soul might-est dwell. Grant me Thy
ear that is heed-ing, Reach me Thy hand and Thy suc-cor me give, That I here-

sin I may dai-ly be dy-ing And in the Spir-it live on-ly to Thee.
peace which en-dur-eth for - ev - er, Peace that all sor-rows and con-flicts doth quell.
af - ter that life may be lead-ing Which Thy true Christians in ho - li - ness live.

316 Jesus, Lord and Precious Savior

JESUS, LORD AND PRECIOUS SAVIOR 8 7, 8 7, 7 7

Johan Olof Wallin, 1819
Tr. Augustus Nelson, 1819

Swedish, 1689

1. Je - sus, Lord and pre-cious Sav - ior, All my com-fort and my joy!
2. All I do, O let me ev - er, Je - sus, in Thy Name be - gin;
3. Let my words and thoughts, O Sav - ior, To Thy praise and glo - ry tend;
4. When my days on earth are o - ver, Let me en - ter in - to rest.

Gra-cious - ly ex - tend Thy fav - or, Let Thy Word my soul em - ploy.
Give suc - cess to my en - deav-or, Fi - nal vic - to - ry there - in.
Help me, Lord, that I may gath-er Trea-sures that shall nev - er end.
Bear me home, O bless-ed Sav - ior, When to Thee it seem-eth best.

CHORUS

Je - sus, come, a - bide with me, Let me ev - er be with Thee.

285

317 O For a Closer Walk with God

CAITHNESS C. M.

William Cowper, 1772

Scottish Psalter, 1615

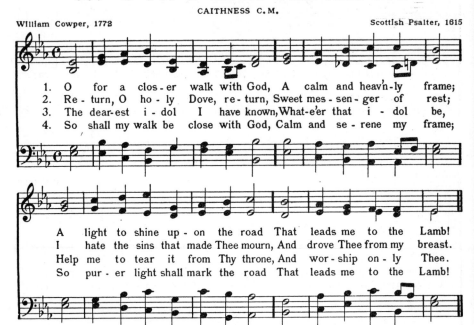

1. O for a clos - er walk with God, A calm and heav'n - ly frame;
2. Re - turn, O ho - ly Dove, re - turn, Sweet mes - sen - ger of rest;
3. The dear-est i - dol I have known, What-e'er that i - dol be,
4. So shall my walk be close with God, Calm and se - rene my frame;

A light to shine up - on the road That leads me to the Lamb!
I hate the sins that made Thee mourn, And drove Thee from my breast.
Help me to tear it from Thy throne, And wor - ship on - ly Thee.
So pur - er light shall mark the road That leads me to the Lamb!

318 Jesus, Thou Art Mine Forever

STRIVE ARIGHT 8 7 4L.

Matthias Loy, 1863

Gnadauer Choralbuch, 1735

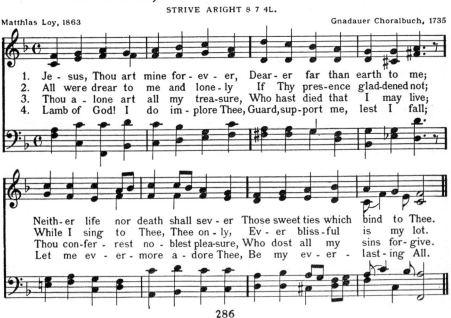

1. Je - sus, Thou art mine for - ev - er, Dear - er far than earth to me;
2. All were drear to me and lone - ly If Thy pres-ence glad-dened not;
3. Thou a - lone art all my trea-sure, Who hast died that I may live;
4. Lamb of God! I do im - plore Thee, Guard, sup-port me, lest I fall;

Neith - er life nor death shall sev - er Those sweet ties which bind to Thee.
While I sing to Thee, Thee on - ly, Ev - er bliss - ful is my lot.
Thou con - fer - rest no - blest plea-sure, Who dost all my sins for - give.
Let me ev - er - more a - dore Thee, Be my ev - er - last - ing All.

319 I Need Thee Ev'ry Hour

NEED 6. 4 4L. and Chorus

Mrs. Annie S. Hawks, 1872

Robert Lowry, 1872

1. I need Thee ev - 'ry hour, Most gra - cious Lord;
2. I need Thee ev - 'ry hour, Stay Thou near by;
3. I need Thee ev - 'ry hour, In joy or pain;
4. I need Thee ev - 'ry hour; Teach me Thy will;
5. I need Thee ev - 'ry hour, Most Ho - ly One;

No ten - der voice like Thine Can peace af - ford.
Temp - ta - tions lose their pow'r When Thou art nigh.
Come quick - ly and a - bide, Or life is vain.
And Thy rich prom - is - es In me ful - fill.
Oh, make me Thine in - deed, Thou bless - ed Son.

CHORUS

I need Thee, oh! I need Thee; Ev - 'ry hour I

need Thee; O bless me now, my Sav - ior! I come to Thee.

320 O That the Lord Would Guide My Ways

EVAN C.M.

Isaac Watts, 1719

William H. Havergal, 1846

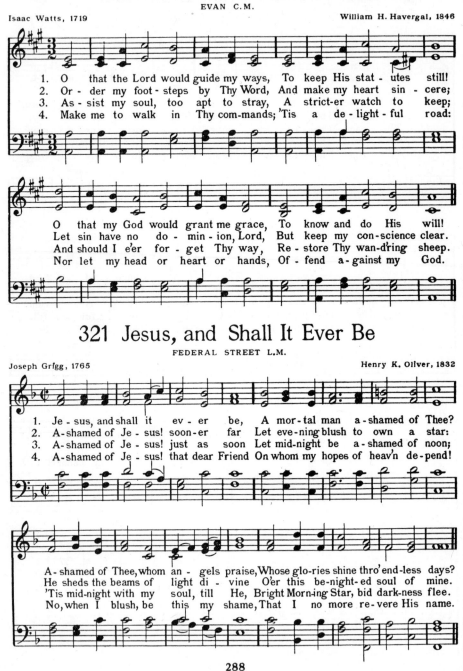

1. O that the Lord would guide my ways, To keep His stat - utes still!
2. Or - der my foot - steps by Thy Word, And make my heart sin - cere;
3. As - sist my soul, too apt to stray, A strict-er watch to keep;
4. Make me to walk in Thy com-mands; 'Tis a de - light - ful road:

O that my God would grant me grace, To know and do His will!
Let sin have no do - min - ion, Lord, But keep my con-science clear.
And should I e'er for - get Thy way, Re - store Thy wan-d'ring sheep.
Nor let my head or heart or hands, Of - fend a - gainst my God.

321 Jesus, and Shall It Ever Be

FEDERAL STREET L.M.

Joseph Grigg, 1765

Henry K. Oliver, 1832

1. Je - sus, and shall it ev - er be, A mor-tal man a - shamed of Thee?
2. A - shamed of Je - sus! soon-er far Let eve-ning blush to own a star:
3. A - shamed of Je - sus! just as soon Let mid-night be a - shamed of noon;
4. A - shamed of Je - sus! that dear Friend On whom my hopes of heav'n de-pend!

A - shamed of Thee, whom an - gels praise, Whose glo-ries shine thro' end-less days?
He sheds the beams of light di - vine O'er this be-night- ed soul of mine.
'Tis mid-night with my soul, till He, Bright Morn-ing Star, bid dark-ness flee.
No, when I blush, be this my shame, That I no more re - vere His name.

322 I Have Heard Thy Voice, Lord Jesus

WENNERBERG 8 7 8L.

Edith G. Cherry, alt.   Gunnar Wennerberg, 1817-1901

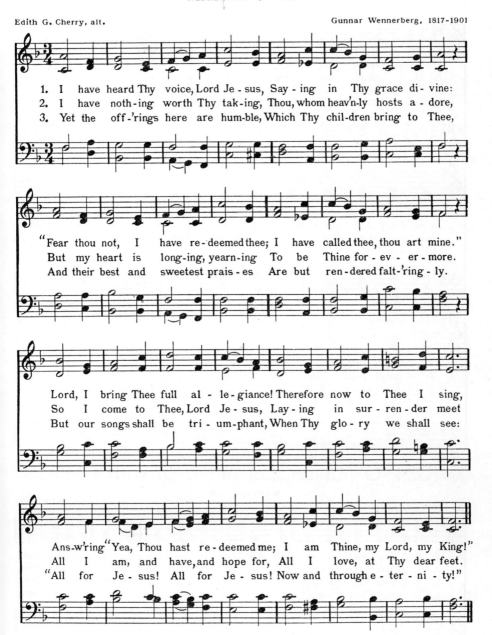

1. I have heard Thy voice, Lord Je - sus, Say - ing in Thy grace di - vine:
2. I have noth-ing worth Thy tak-ing, Thou, whom heav'n-ly hosts a - dore,
3. Yet the off-'rings here are hum-ble, Which Thy chil-dren bring to Thee,

"Fear thou not, I have re-deemed thee; I have called thee, thou art mine."
But my heart is long-ing, yearn-ing To be Thine for - ev - er - more.
And their best and sweetest prais - es Are but ren - dered falt-'ring - ly.

Lord, I bring Thee full al - le - giance! Therefore now to Thee I sing,
So I come to Thee, Lord Je - sus, Lay - ing in sur - ren - der meet
But our songs shall be tri - um-phant, When Thy glo - ry we shall see:

Ans-w'ring "Yea, Thou hast re - deemed me; I am Thine, my Lord, my King!"
All I am, and have, and hope for, All I love, at Thy dear feet.
"All for Je - sus! All for Je - sus! Now and through e - ter - ni - ty!"

289

323 Lord, Speak to Me That I May Speak

CANONBURY L.M.

Frances R. Havergal, 1836-1879

Robert Schumann, 1839

1. Lord, speak to me, that I may speak In liv-ing ech-oes of Thy tone; As Thou hast sought, so let me seek Thy err-ing chil-dren lost and lone.
2. O lead me, Lord, that I may lead The wan-d'ring and the wav-'ring feet; O feed me, Lord, that I may feed Thy hun-g'ring ones with man-na sweet.
3. O teach me, Lord, that I may teach The prec-ious things Thou dost im-part; And wing my words, that they may reach The hid-den depths of ma-ny a heart.
4. O fill me with Thy ful-ness, Lord, Un-til my ver-y heart o'er-flow In kind-ling thought and glow-ing word, Thy love to tell, Thy praise to show.

324 O Master, Let Me Walk with Thee

MARYTON L.M.

Washington Gladden, 1879

Henry Percy Smith, 1874

1. O Mas-ter, let me walk with Thee In low-ly paths of serv-ice free;
2. Help me the slow of heart to move By some clear, win-ning word of love;
3. Teach me Thy pa-tience! still with Thee In clos-er, dear-er com-pa-ny,
4. In hope that sends a shin-ing ray, Far down the fu-ture's broad'ning way,

Tell me Thy se-cret; help me bear The strain of toil, the fret of care.
Teach me the way-ward feet to stay, And guide them in the home-ward way.
In work that keeps faith sweet and strong, In trust that tri-umphs o - ver wrong.
In peace that on - ly Thou canst give, With Thee, O Mas-ter, let me live.

325 Savior, Thy Dying Love

SOMETHING FOR JESUS 6 4, 6 4, 6 6 6 4

Sylvanus D. Phelps, 1867   Robert Lowry, 1826-1899

1. Sav - ior, Thy dy - ing love Thou gav-est me, Nor should I
2. At the blest mer - cy - seat, Plead-ing for me, My fee - ble
3. Give me a faith - ful heart, Like - ness to Thee, That each de-
4. All that I am and have, Thy gifts so free, In joy, in

aught with - hold, Dear Lord, from Thee: In love my soul would bow,
faith looks up, Je - sus, to Thee: Help me the cross to bear,
part - ing day Hence-forth may see Some work of love be - gun,
grief, thro' life, Dear Lord, for Thee! And when Thy face I see,

My heart ful - fill its vow, Some of - fring bring Thee now, Some-thing for Thee.
Thy won-drous love de-clare, Some song to raise, or pray'r, Some-thing for Thee.
Some deed of kind-ness done, Some wand'rer sought and won, Some-thing for Thee.
My ran-somed soul shall be, Thro' all e - ter - ni - ty, Some-thing for Thee.

326 With God in Grace I'm Dwelling

PASSION CHORALE 7 6 8L.

Hans Nielsen Hauge, 1799
Tr. P. A. Sveeggen, 1931

Hans Leo Hassler, 1601
Arr. F. Melius Christiansen, 1907

1. With God in grace I'm dwell - ing, What harm can come to me
2. The e - vil crowds per - ceive not The Spir - it's pow'r and grace;
3. Our God has prom - ised sure - ly To free each seek - ing soul,
4. Be - lov - ed friends, as ev - er, We who in Christ are one
5. God grant us now His pow - er, And help us by His might

From world - ly pow'rs com - pel - ling My way thus closed to be?
Be - liev - ers they re - ceive not, Ex - cept with scorn - ful face.
Who walks in spir - it pure - ly With truth as way and goal.
Must fight with brave en - deav - or The bat - tle that's be - gun.
To fol - low truth this hour, All guid - ed by His light;

Though they in chains may bind me In - side this pris - on cell,
They see not, nor as - pi - re To seek en - dur - ing peace;
Whose heart the world's de - ceiv - ing Can nev - er lead a - stray,
Our ranks must nev - er wav - er, De - ceived by world - ly wiles,
And may we work to - geth - er As one in mu - tual love,

Yet Christ-mas here can find me; With - in my heart 'tis well.
But race in vain de - si - re To pain with - out sur - cease.
Who, con - stant - ly be - liev - ing, Will walk the King-dom's way.
But on - ward with the Sav - ior Through all these bit - ter trials.
For - sak - ing self and gath - er At last in heav'n a - bove.

292

327 O Blessed Sun Whose Splendor

IN HEAVEN IS JOY 7 6 8L.

Carl J.P. Spitta, 1833
Tr. Richard Massie, 1860

Norwegian Folk-Tune

1. O bless - ed Sun, whose splen-dor Dis - pells the shades of night;
2. I know no life di - vid - ed, O Lord of life, from Thee;
3. I fear no trib - u - la - tion, Since, what-so - e'er it be,
4. If while on earth I wan - der, My heart is light and blest,

O Je - sus, my De - fend - er, My soul's su - preme de - light,
In Thee is life pro - vid - ed, For all man - kind and me;
It makes no sep - ar - a - tion Be - tween my Lord and me.
Ah, what shall I be yon - der, In per - fect peace and rest?

Though for-tune should be - reave me Of all I love the best,
I know no death, O Je - sus, Be - cause I live in Thee;
If Thou, my God, my Teach-er, Vouch-safe to be my own,
O bless-ed thought in dy - ing, We go to meet the Lord,

If Thou Thy love still leave me, I free - ly give the rest.
Thy death it is which frees us From death e - ter - nal - ly.
Though poor, I shall be rich - er Than mon-arch on his throne.
Where there shall be no sigh - ing, A king - dom our re - ward.

293

328 He Leadeth Me! O Blessed Thought

HE LEADETH ME L. M. and Chorus

Joseph H. Gilmore, 1861

William B. Bradbury, 1864

1. He lead-eth me! O bless-ed thought! O words with heav'n-ly com-fort fraught!
2. Sometimes 'mid scenes of deep-est gloom, Sometimes where E-den's bow-ers bloom,
3. Lord, I would clasp Thy hand in mine, Nor ev-er mur-mur nor re-pine,
4. And when my task on earth is done, When, by Thy grace, the vic-t'ry's won,

What-e'er I do, wher-e'er I be, Still 'tis God's hand that lead-eth me.
By wa ters still, or trou-bled sea, Still 'tis His hand that lead-eth me.
Con-tent, what-ev-er lot I see, Since 'tis my God that lead-eth me.
E'en death's cold wave I will not flee, Since God thro' Jor-dan lead-eth me.

CHORUS

He lead-eth me, He lead-eth me, By His own hand He lead-eth me:

His faith-ful fol-low'r I would be, For by His hand He lead-eth me.

329 Thy Life Was Given for Me

PRO ME PERFORATUS 6 6 6L.

Frances R. Havergal, 1858

Joseph Barnby, 1838-1896

1. Thy life was giv'n for me, Thy pre-cious blood was shed,
2. Long years were spent for me In wea-ri-ness and woe,
3. Thy Fa-ther's home of light, Thy rain-bow-cir-cled throne,
4. And Thou hast brought to me, Down from Thy home a-bove,
5. O let my life be giv'n, My years for Thee be spent,

That I might ran-somed be, And quick-ened from the dead.
That through e-ter-ni-ty Thy glo-ry I might know.
Were left for earth-ly night, For wan-d'rings sad and lone.
Sal-va-tion full and free, Thy par-don and Thy love.
World-fet-ters all be riv'n, And joy and suf-f'ring blent!

Thy life was giv'n for me: What have I giv'n for Thee?
Long years were spent for me: Have I spent one for Thee?
Yea, all was left for me: Have I left aught for Thee?
Great gifts Thou brought-est me: What have I brought to Thee?
Thou gav'st Thy-self for me; I give my-self for Thee.

See also:

330 What Joy to Reach the Harbor

WHAT JOY TO REACH 76, 76, 88, 76

Hans Adolf Brorson, 1694 - 1764
Tr. Olav Lee

Norwegian Folk-Tune
Arr. Oscar R. Overby

1. What joy to reach the har - bor Of heav'n-ly peace and rest,
2. How sweet to taste the man - na, The good-ness of the Lord,
3. What bliss to wear for - ev - er The brid - al crown of life,

To sing, re-leased from sor - row, The an-thems of the blest;
While rings the glad ho - san - na A - round the fes - tal board;
The to - ken of God's fa - vor To con - quer-ors in strife;

As chil - dren there in man-sions fair, The Fa - ther's love with
Nay, e'en to see, e - ter - nal - ly En - rapt, the glo - rious
While all re - joice to hear the voice Of an - gels shar - ing

Christ to share. What joy to reach the har - bor Of heav'n-ly peace and rest.
Trin - i - ty. How sweet to taste the man - na, The good-ness of the Lord.
in our joys. What bliss to wear for - ev - er The brid - al crown of life.

331 I Know of a Sleep in Jesus' Name

O DAY FULL OF GRACE 9 8 6L.

Magnus Brostrup Landstad, 1861
Tr. K.A. Kasberg, O.H. Smeby, C. Doving

Christopher E. F. Weyse, 1826

1. I know of a sleep in Je - sus' name, A rest from all toil and sor - row; Earth folds in her arms my wea - ry frame, And shel - ters it till the mor - row; My soul is at home with God in heav'n, Her sor - rows are past and o - ver.

2. I know of a peace-ful ev - en - tide; And when I am faint and wea - ry, At times with the jour - ney sore - ly tried, Through hours that are long and drear - y; Then oft - en I yearn to lay me down, And sink in - to bliss - ful slum - ber.

3. I know of a morn-ing bright and fair, When tid - ings of joy shall wake us, When songs from on high shall fill the air, And God to His glo - ry take us, When Je - sus shall bid us rise from sleep— How joyous that hour of a - wak - ing!

4. Now o - pens the Fa - ther's house a - bove, The names of the blest are giv - en: Lord, gath - er us there; let none we love Be missed in the joys of heav - en. Vouch-safe Thou us all a place with Thee; We ask through our dear Re - deem - er.

5. O Je - sus, draw near my dy - ing bed, And take me in - to Thy keep - ing, And say when my spir - it hence is fled: "This child is not dead, but sleep - ing." And leave me not, Sav - ior, till I rise, To praise Thee in life e - ter - nal.

297

332 Alone with Thee, O Lord, When Day Is Dead

ALONE WITH THEE 10 10 4L.
(Or use EVENTIDE, No. 340)

H. A. Urseth, 1892

J. G. Conradi, b. 1831

1. A - lone with Thee, O Lord, when day is dead And all its fad - ed
2. A - lone with Thee, dear Lamb of Cal - va - ry, Who shed Thy blood, and
3. A - lone with Thee I on - ly pray to be When light and way I

splen-dors on have fled, I fond - ly dwell, and
died, and lives for me, I long to stay to
can no long-er see, That I may safe - ly

lis - ten at Thy knee The Words, the wond'rous Words that come from Thee.
see Thy wound-ed side, And know that all my sor-rows it can hide.
reach a-cross the line, And hold in mine no oth - er hand but Thine.

333 Children of the Heavenly King

PLEYEL'S HYMN 7 7 4L.

John Cennick, 1742

Ignaz Joseph Pleyel, 1790

1. Chil - dren of the heav'n - ly King, As ye jour - ney, sweet - ly sing;
2. We are trav - 'ling home to God, In the way the fa - thers trod:
3. Lift your eyes, ye sons of light, Zi - on's ci - ty is in sight:
4. Fear not, breth - ren, joy - ful stand On the bor - ders of your land;
5. Lord, o - be - dient - ly we go, Glad - ly leav - ing all be - low;

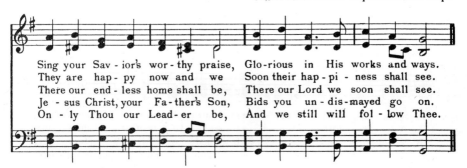

Sing your Sav - ior's wor - thy praise, Glo - rious in His works and ways.
They are hap - py now and we Soon their hap - pi - ness shall see.
There our end - less home shall be, There our Lord we soon shall see.
Je - sus Christ, your Fa - ther's Son, Bids you un - dis - mayed go on.
On - ly Thou our Lead - er be, And we still will fol - low Thee.

334 The Radiant Morn Hath Passed Away

HOUR OF PRAYER 8 8, 8 4

Godfrey Thring, 1864   H. Matthias Hansen

1. The ra - diant morn hath passed a - way, And
2. Our life is but an au - tumn day, Its
3. O by Thy soul — in - spir - ing grace Up -
4. Where light and life and joy and peace In
5. Where saints are clothed in spot - less white, And

spent too soon her gold - en store: The shad - ows
glo - rious noon — how quick - ly past! Lead us, O
lift our hearts to realms on high; Help us to
un - di - vid - ed em - pire reign, And throng - ing
eve - ning shad - ows nev - er fall, Where Thou, e -

of de - part - ing day Creep on once more.
Christ, Thou liv - ing way, Safe home at last.
look to that bright place Be - yond the sky,
an - gels nev - er cease Their death - less strain;
ter - nal Light of light, Art Lord of all.

299

335 Still, Still with Thee

WILLINGHAM 11 10 4L.

Harriet Beecher Stowe, 1855   Erantz Abt, 1819-1885

1. Still, still with Thee, when pur-ple morn-ing break-eth,
2. A-lone with Thee, a-mid the mys-tic shad-ows,
3. When sinks the soul, sub-dued by toil, to slum-ber,
4. So shall it be at last, in that bright morn-ing,

When the bird wak-eth, and the shad-ows flee;
The sol-emn hush of na-ture new-ly born;
Its clos-ing eye looks up to Thee in pray'r;
When the soul wak-eth, and life's shad-ows flee;

Fair-er than morn-ing, love-lier than the day-light,
A-lone with Thee, in breath-less ad-o-ra-tion,
Sweet the re-pose be-neath Thy wings o'er-shad-ing,
O for that hour when fair-er than the dawn-ing

Dawns the sweet con-scious-ness, I am with Thee!
In the calm dew and fresh-ness of the morn.
But sweet-er still to wake and find Thee there.
Shall rise the glo-rious thought, I am with Thee!

336 Nearer, My God, to Thee

BETHANY 6 4, 6 4, 6 6, 64

Sarah F. Adams, 1841   Lowell Mason, 1856

1. Near - er, my God, to Thee, Near - er to Thee!
2. Though, like the wan - der - er, The sun gone down,
3. There let the way ap - pear Steps un - to heav'n;
4. Then, with my wak - ing thoughts Bright with Thy praise,
5. Or if on joy - ful wing, Cleav - ing the sky,

E'en tho' it be a cross That rais - eth me;
Dark - ness be o - ver me, My rest a stone;
All that Thou send - est me In mer - cy giv'n;
Out of my ston - y griefs, Beth - el I'll raise;
Sun, moon, and stars for - got, Up - wards I fly.

Still all my song shall be, Near - er, my God, to Thee,
Yet in my dreams I'd be Near - er, my God, to Thee,
An - gels to beck - on me Near - er, my God, to Thee,
So by my woes to be Near - er, my God, to Thee,
Still all my song shall be, Near - er, my God, to Thee,

Near - er, my God, to Thee, Near - er to Thee.

337 One Radiant Morn the Mists Will All Surrender

ONE RADIANT MORN 11 10 4L.

Wilhelm Andreas Wexels, 1797-1866
Tr. Oscar R. Overby, 1931

1. One ra - diant morn the mists will all sur - ren - der,
2. One ra - diant morn the mys - ter - ies I pon - der,
3. One ra - diant morn when hearts bowed down in sor - row
4. One ra - diant morn with eyes un - veiled be - fore Him,
5. One ra - diant morn when sin - less souls as - sem - ble,

And life's un - cer - tain shad - ows pass a - way;
But leave un - solved on all my quests a - broad,
Are com - fort - ed and re - con - ciled a - bove,
I'll see the One my faith and hope em - brace;
Where each de - sire is born in pur - i - ty,

When light ce - les - tial breaks in dazz - ling splen - dor
Shall be con - strued for me in full - ness yon - der
All pain and tears I here in an - guish bor - row
With - in the ho - ly realms I'll praise, a - dore Him,
No more the thought of wrong shall make me trem - ble,

To lead my step in - to e - ter - nal day.
When I a - wake to sense the ways of God.
Shall be dis - solved in foun - tain - rays of love.
And kneel to thank my Sav - ior face to face.
But, ran - somed, I shall live for - ev - er free.

6. One radiant morn in halls of home supernal,
   I'll meet again the friend I here esteem,
   In glory speak with him of life eternal,
   And of the life that vanished like a dream.

7. O Jesus, stir within my heart of sadness
   This vision fair whene'er I grieve forlorn,
   That it may turn all bitter tears to gladness,
   And lead my spirit to that radiant morn.

338 One Sweetly Solemn Thought

DULCE DOMUM S.M.
(See No. 339)

Phoebe Cary, 1852   R.S. Ambrose, 1876

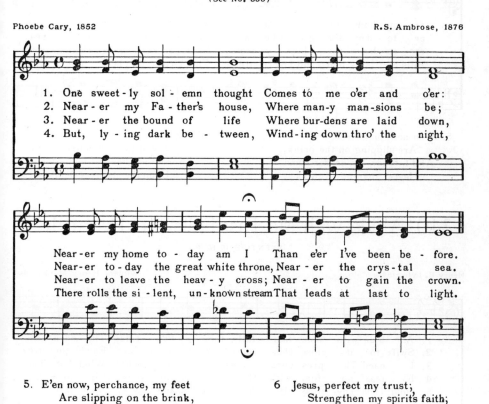

1. One sweet-ly sol - emn thought Comes to me o'er and o'er:
2. Near - er my Fa - ther's house, Where man-y man-sions be;
3. Near - er the bound of life Where bur-dens are laid down,
4. But, ly - ing dark be - tween, Wind-ing down thro' the night,

Near-er my home to - day am I Than e'er I've been be - fore.
Near-er to - day the great white throne, Near - er the crys-tal sea.
Near-er to leave the heav - y cross; Near - er to gain the crown.
There rolls the si - lent, un-known stream That leads at last to light.

5. E'en now, perchance, my feet
   Are slipping on the brink,
   And I, today, am nearer home
   Nearer than now I think.

6 Jesus, perfect my trust;
   Strengthen my spirit's faith;
   Nor let me stand, at last, alone
   Upon the shore of death.

339 One Sweetly Solemn Thought

STILLINGFLEET S.M.
(See No. 338)

Phoebe Cary, 1852

Swiss Tune

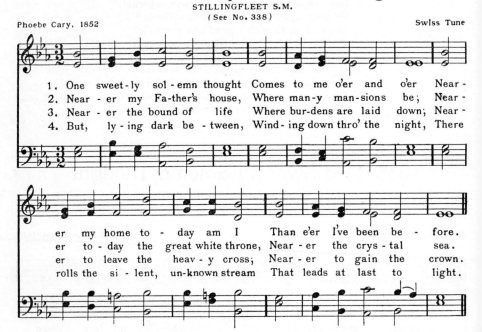

1. One sweet-ly sol-emn thought Comes to me o'er and o'er Near-
2. Near-er my Fa-ther's house, Where man-y man-sions be; Near-
3. Near-er the bound of life Where bur-dens are laid down; Near-
4. But, ly-ing dark be-tween, Wind-ing down thro' the night, There

er my home to-day am I Than e'er I've been be-fore.
er to-day the great white throne, Near-er the crys-tal sea.
er to leave the heav-y cross; Near-er to gain the crown.
rolls the si-lent, un-known stream That leads at last to light.

5. E'en now, perchance, my feet
   Are slipping on the brink,
   And I, today, am nearer home —
   Nearer than now I think

6. Jesus, perfect my trust;
   Strengthen my spirit's faith;
   Nor let me stand, at last, alone
   Upon the shore of death.

340 Abide with Me, Fast Falls the Eventide

EVENTIDE 10 10 4L.

Henry B. Lyte, 1847

William Henry Monk, 1861

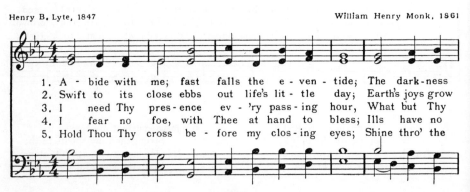

1. A - bide with me; fast falls the e - ven - tide; The dark-ness
2. Swift to its close ebbs out life's lit - tle day; Earth's joys grow
3. I need Thy pres - ence ev - 'ry pass - ing hour, What but Thy
4. I fear no foe, with Thee at hand to bless; Ills have no
5. Hold Thou Thy cross be - fore my clos - ing eyes; Shine thro' the

deep - ens; Lord, with me a - bide· When oth - er help - ers
dim, its glo - ries pass a - way; Change and de - cay in
grace can foil the temp-ter's pow'r? Who like Thy - self my
weight, and tears no bit - ter - ness; Where is death's sting? where,
gloom, and point me to the skies; Heav'n's morn - ing breaks, and

fail, and com-forts flee, Help of the help-less, O a-bide with me.
all a-round I see; O Thou who chang-est not, a-bide with me.
guide and stay can be? Through cloud and sun-shine, O a-bide with me
grave, thy vic - to - ry? I tri-umph still, if Thou a-bide with me.
earth's vain shad-ows flee; In life, in death, O Lord, a-bide with me

341 Jesus, Jesus, Come to Me

JESUS, COME TO ME 7 7 4L.

Johann Scheffler, 1657
Tr. R.P. Dunn, 1859, alt.

Jakob Hveding Sletten, 1923

1. Je - sus, Je - sus, come to me; How my soul longs af - ter Thee!
2. Lord, my long-ings nev - er cease; With-out Thee I find no peace;
3. Thou a - lone, my gra-cious Lord, Art my shield and great re - ward;
4. Come, and dwell with - in my heart; Purge its sin, and heal its smart;

When, my best, my dear-est friend, Shall our sep - a - ra-tion end?
Naught but Thy be - lov - ed voice Can my wretch-ed heart re-joice.
All my hope, my Sav - ior Thou, To Thy sov -'reign will I bow.
See, I ev - er cry to Thee, Je - sus, Je - sus, come to me!

342 We Would See Jesus, for the Shadows Lengthen

CONSOLATION 11 10 4L.

Anna B. Warner, 1858

Felix Bartholdy Mendelssohn, 1809-1847

1. We would see Je - sus; for the shad - ows length- en
2. We would see Je - sus, the great rock foun - da - tion
3. We would see Je - sus; oth - er lights are pal - ing,
4. We would see Je - sus; yet the spir - it lin - gers
5. We would see Je - sus; this is all we're need - ing;

A - cross the lit - tle land-scape of our life;
Where - on our feet were set by sov - 'reign grace;
Which for long years we have re - joiced to see;
Round the dear ob - jects it has loved so long,
Strength, joy, and will - ing - ness come with the sight;

We would see Je - sus, our weak faith to strength-en,
Nor life nor death, with all their ag - i - ta - tion,
The bless -ings of our pil - grim - age are fail - ing;
And earth from earth can scarce un - clasp its fin - gers;
We would see Je - sus, dy - ing, ris - en, plead - ing;

For the last wea - ri - ness, the fi - nal strife.
Can thence re - move us, if we see His face.
We would not mourn them, for we go to Thee.
Our love to Thee makes not this love less strong.
Then wel - come day, and fare - well mor - tal night.

343 How Oft, O Father, My Heart Is Burning

YEARNING 10 10, 9 9

Oscar R. Overby, 1931

Norwegian Folk-Tune
Arr. Oscar R. Overby, 1931

1. How oft, O Fa - ther, my heart is burn - ing
   With bit - ter pain and with sa - cred yearn - ing, When I have wan - dered so far a - stray, But seek re - turn - ing at close of day, But seek re - turn - ing at close of day.

2. A - kin to sol - ace, all peace sur - pass - ing,
   Is that re - turn when the mists are mass - ing. Se - cure a - gain in Thy fa - ther - fold I know no an - guish, but grace un - told, I know no an - guish, but grace un - told.

3. So let my spir - it, O Lord, be burn - ing
   In cease - less quest, and with sa - cred yearn - ing, That when sur - round - ed by sin I roam, I shall not stray but be guid - ed home, I shall not stray but be guid - ed home.

307

344 In Heaven Is Joy and Gladness

IN HEAVEN IS JOY 7 6 8L.

Johan Nordal Brun, 1786
Tr. O. H. Smeby, 1910

Norwegian Folk-Tune

1. In heav'n is joy and glad-ness, But while I so - journ here,
2. I do not strive for pleas-ures That fools pur-sue on earth,
3. For I shall see my Je - sus, He is my hope and stay;

So of - ten, bow'd in sad - ness, I shed the bit - ter tear.
I sow in tears for treas - ures That have more last - ing worth.
The cross that me op - press - es A - non He takes a - way.

Here ills, al - way pre - vail - ing, Dis - tress the Sav - ior's bride;
If, when my jour - ney end - eth, The sheaves I gath - er in,
Then noth - ing more shall grieve me, And no ad - ver - si - ty

Here mirth is lost in wail - ing; In heav'n but joys a - bide.
The bliss the fool pre - tend- eth I do not yearn to win.
Shall of my joy be - reave me; Soon I shall Je - sus see.

345 O Land of Our King!

O LAND OF OUR KING 5 11,11 11,11 5

Nicolai F. S. Grundtvig, 1783 - 1872
Tr. S. D. Rodholm

Ludvig M. Lindeman, 1812 - 1887

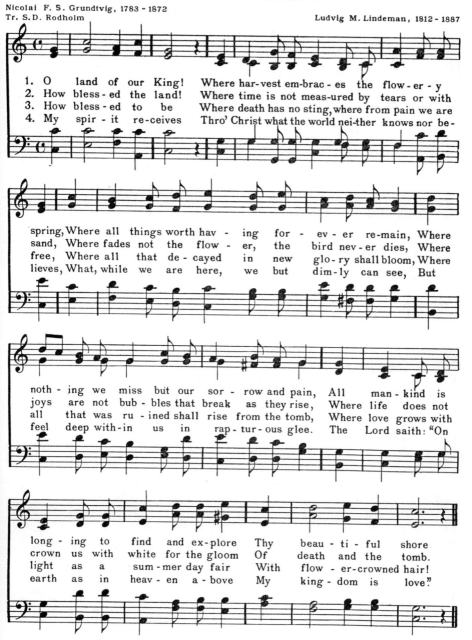

1. O land of our King! Where har-vest em-brac - es the flow-er-y
2. How bless-ed the land! Where time is not meas-ured by tears or with
3. How bless-ed to be Where death has no sting, where from pain we are
4. My spir - it re-ceives Thro' Christ what the world nei-ther knows nor be-

spring, Where all things worth hav - ing for - ev - er re-main, Where
sand, Where fades not the flow - er, the bird nev - er dies, Where
free, Where all that de - cayed in new glo - ry shall bloom, Where
lieves, What, while we are here, we but dim-ly can see, But

noth - ing we miss but our sor - row and pain, All man - kind is
joys are not bub - bles that break as they rise, Where life does not
all that was ru - ined shall rise from the tomb, Where love grows with
feel deep with-in us in rap - tur - ous glee. The Lord saith: "On

long - ing to find and ex-plore Thy beau - ti - ful shore
crown us with white for the gloom Of death and the tomb.
light as a sum - mer day fair With flow - er-crowned hair!
earth as in heav - en a - bove My king - dom is love."

346 Lead, Kindly Light, Amid th' Encircling Gloom

LUX BENIGNA 10 4,10 4,10 10

John H. Newman, 1833   John B. Dykes, 1868

1. Lead, kind-ly Light, a-mid th'en-cir-cling gloom,   Lead Thou me   on.
2. I   was not   ev - er thus, nor pray'd that Thou   Shouldst lead me   on;
3. So long Thy pow'r hath blest me, sure it still   Will   lead   me   on,
4. Meantime a - long the nar-row, rug-ged path   Thy - self hast   trod,

The night is dark, and I am far   from   home,   Lead Thou me   on.
I loved to choose and see my path, but   now   Lead Thou me   on.
O'er moor and fen, o'er crag and tor-rent,   till   The night is   gone,
Lead, Savior, lead me home in child-like   faith,   Home to   my   God,

Keep Thou my   feet,   I   do not ask to   see
The   gar - ish   day   I   loved; and, spite of   fears,
And with the   morn   those an - gel fac - es   smile,
For   e'er to   rest   from   ev - 'ry earth - ly   strife

The dis - tant   scene,   one step e - nough   for   me
Pride ruled   my   will,   re - mem - ber   not   past   years.
Which I   have loved   long since, and   lost   a - while.
In   the   calm light   of   ev - er - last - ing   life.

347 Hark, Hark, My Soul

PILGRIMS 11 10 4L. and Chorus

Frederick W. Faber, 1854   Henry Smart, 1868

1. Hark, hark, my soul, an - gel - ic songs are swell-ing O'er earth's green fields, and
2. On - ward we go, for still we hear them sing-ing, "Come, weary souls, for
3. Far, far a - way, like bells at ev-'ning peal - ing, The voice of Je - sus
4. An - gels, sing on! your faith-ful watch-es keep-ing: Sing us sweet fragments

o-cean's wave-beat shore, How sweet the truth those blessed strains are tell-ing
Je - sus bids you come;" And thro' the dark, its ech-oes sweet-ly ring - ing,
sounds o'er land and sea, And lad-en souls by thou-sands meekly steal-ing,
of the songs a - bove; Till morn-ing's joy shall end the night of weep-ing,

CHORUS

Of that new life when sin shall be no more
The mu - sic of the Gos-pel leads us home
Kind Shep-herd, turn their wea-ry steps to Thee.   An-gels of Je-sus,
And life's long shad-ows break in cloud - less love

An - gels of light, Sing-ing to wel-come the pil-grims of the night

348 I'm a Pilgrim, and I'm a Stranger

I'M A PILGRIM 9 11, 10 10, 9 11

Mary S.B. Shindler, 1841

Oskar Ahnfelt, 1813-1882

1. I'm a pil - grim, and I'm a stran-ger, I can tar - ry, I can tar - ry but a night, Do not de - tain me, for I am go - ing To where the foun-tains are ev - er flow - ing I'm a pil - grim, and I'm a stran-ger, I can tar - ry, I can tar-ry but a night.

2. There the glo - ry is ev - er shin-ing; O my long-ing heart, my long-ing heart is there Here in this coun-try so dark and drear - y I long have wan-dered, for-lorn and wea - ry I'm a pil - grim, and I'm a stran-ger, I can tar - ry, I can tar-ry but a night.

3. Of the cit - y to which I'm go-ing My Re - deem-er, My Re-deem-er is the light; There is no sor - row nor an - y sigh - ing, Nor an - y sin - ning, nor an - y dy - ing Of the cit - y to which I'm go - ing My Re - deem - er, my Re - deem-er is the light.

See also:
Draw us to Thee in mind and heart, 215
When peace like a river, 213
Angels from the realms of glory, 127
In heav'n above, 433

V. Home, Childhood and Youth

1. Home
2. Childhood
3. Youth

349 'Mid Pleasures and Palaces

HOME, SWEET HOME 11 11 4L. and Chorus,

John Howard Payne, 1792 - 1852   H.R. Bishop, 1786 - 1855

1. 'Mid pleas-ures and pal - a - ces though we may roam, Be it ev - er so
2. I   gaze on the moon as I   tread the drear wild, And   feel that my
3. An   ex - ile from home, splendor daz-zles in vain, O   give me my

hum-ble, there's no   place like home   A   charm from the skies seems to
moth-er now   thinks of her child, As she looks on that moon from our
low-ly thatched cot-tage a - gain, The   birds sing-ing gai - ly, that

hal - low us there,   Which, seek thro' the world, is ne'er met with else-where.
own   cot-tage door, Thro' the wood-bine whose fragrance shall cheer me no more.
came at my   call, Give me them, and that peace of mind dear- er than all.

CHORUS

Home, home, sweet, sweet home, There's no place like home, O there's no place like home.

350 O Love Divine and Golden

EVARTS 7 6 8L.

John S. B. Monsell, 1862   Lowell Mason, 1841

1. O love di - vine and gold - en, Mys - ter-ious depth and height,
2. O love di - vine and ten - der, That through our homes dost move,
3. God bless these hands, u - nit - ed; God bless these hearts made one!

To thee the world be - hold - en, Looks up for life and light,
Veiled in the soft-ened splen-dor Of ho - ly house-hold love.
Un - sev - ered and un - blight - ed May they through life go on,

O love di - vine and gen - tle, The bless - er and the blest,
A throne with-out thy bless - ing Were la - bor with-out rest,
Here in earth's home pre - par - ing For the bright home a - bove,

Be - neath thy care pa - ren - tal The world lies down in rest.
And cot - tag - es pos - sess - ing Thy bless - ed - ness, are blest.
And there for - ev - er shar - ing Its joy where God is love.

351 O Happy Home, Where Thou Art Loved

ONE RADIANT MORN 11 10 4L

Carl J. P. Spitta, 1833

Composer Unknown

1. O hap - py home, where Thou art loved the dear - est,
Thou lov - ing Friend and Sav - ior of our race,
And where a - mong the guests there nev - er com - eth
One who can hold such high and hon - ored place!

2. O hap - py home, whose lit - tle ones are giv - en
To Thee, O Lord, in hum - ble faith and pray'r,
To Thee, their Friend, who from the heights of heav - en
Guides them, and guards with more than moth - er's care!

3. O hap - py home, where each one serves Thee low - ly,
What - ev - er his ap - point - ed work may be,
Till ev - 'ry com - mon task seems great and ho - ly,
When it is done, O Lord, as un - to Thee!

4. O hap - py home, where Thou art not for - got - ten
When joy is o - ver - flow - ing, full and free,
O hap - py home, where ev - 'ry wound - ed spir - it
Is brought, Phy - si - cian, Com - fort - er, to Thee.

5. And when at last all earth - ly toil is end - ed,
All meet Thee in the bless - ed home a - bove,
From whence Thou cam - est, where Thou hast as - cend - ed,—
Thine ev - er - last - ing home of peace and love.

317

352 Great God, We Praise Thy Gracious Care (Table Prayer)

OLD HUNDREDTH L.M.

John Cennick

Louis Bourgeois, 1551

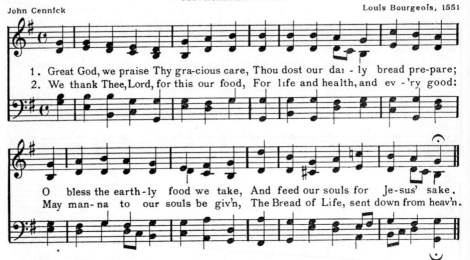

1. Great God, we praise Thy gra-cious care, Thou dost our dai - ly bread pre-pare;
2. We thank Thee, Lord, for this our food, For life and health, and ev -'ry good:

O   bless the earth-ly   food we take, And feed our souls for   Je-sus' sake.
May man- na to   our souls be giv'n, The Bread of Life, sent down from heav'n.

353 Our Table Now with Food Is Spread (Table Prayer)

OLD HUNDREDTH L.M.

Thomas Kingo, 1689
Tr. George Taylor Rygh, 1909

1. Our table now with food is spread,
   O God who givest daily bread,
   Bless these Thy gifts upon us so
   That strength of body they bestow.

2. O feed the hungry, God of love,
   Who sigh for bread to heaven above;
   Give to our land prosperity,
   And bless the earth, the sky, the sea!

3. Defend and bless our government,
   And give us all a mind content!
   O grant our souls the heavenly food
   Which Jesus purchased with His blood.

354 O Perfect Love

PERFECT LOVE 11 10 4L.

Dorothy Frances (Blomfield) Gurney, 1883

Joseph Barnby, 1889

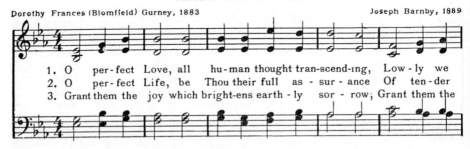

1. O   per-fect Love, all   hu-man thought tran-scend-ing, Low-ly we
2. O   per-fect Life, be   Thou their full   as - sur - ance Of   ten-der
3. Grant them the   joy which bright-ens earth - ly   sor - row; Grant them the

318

kneel in pray'r be-fore Thy throne, That theirs may be the love which knows no
char - i - ty and stead-fast faith, Of pa-tient hope, and qui-et, brave en -
peace which calms all earthly strife, And to life's day the glo-rious un-known

end - ing, Whom Thou for - ev - er-more dost join in one.
dur - ance, With child-like trust that fears nor pain nor death.
mor - row That dawns up - on e - ter-nal love and life.

355 O Blest the House, Whate'er Befall

C.C.L. von Pfeil, 1782
Tr. Catherine Winkworth, 1863

HARMONY GROVE L.M.

Henry K. Oliver, 1839

1. O blest the house, what-e'er be - fall, Where Je-sus Christ is all in all;
2. O blest that house where faith ye find, And all with - in have set their mind
3. O blest the par-ents who give heed Un - to their chil-dren's foremost need,
4. Blest such a house, it pros-pers well, In peace and joy the par-ents dwell,
5. Then here will I and mine to - day A sol-emn cov-'nant make and say:

Yea, if He were not dwell-ing there, How poor and dark and void it were!
To trust their God and serve Him still, And do, in all, His ho - ly will.
And wea-ry not of care or cost To them and heav'n shall none be lost
And in their chil-dren's lot is shown How rich-ly God can bless His own.
"Though all the world for-sake Thy word, I and my house will serve the Lord."

For *FAMILY DEVOTION,* see WORSHIP IN GENERAL, 1-77.

356 We Gather, We Gather, Dear Jesus, to Bring

ADESTE FIDELES 11 11 4L.

Anonymous

John F. Wade's Cantus Diversi, 1751

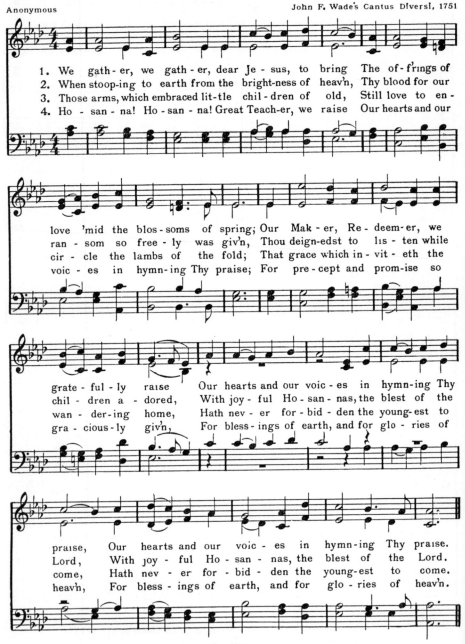

1. We gath-er, we gath-er, dear Je-sus, to bring The of-f'rings of
2. When stoop-ing to earth from the bright-ness of heav'n, Thy blood for our
3. Those arms, which embraced lit-tle chil-dren of old, Still love to en-
4. Ho-san-na! Ho-san-na! Great Teach-er, we raise Our hearts and our

love 'mid the blos-soms of spring; Our Mak-er, Re-deem-er, we
ran-som so free-ly was giv'n, Thou deign-edst to lis-ten while
cir-cle the lambs of the fold; That grace which in-vit-eth the
voic-es in hymn-ing Thy praise; For pre-cept and prom-ise so

grate-ful-ly raise Our hearts and our voic-es in hymn-ing Thy
chil-dren a-dored, With joy-ful Ho-san-nas, the blest of the
wan-der-ing home, Hath nev-er for-bid-den the young-est to
gra-cious-ly giv'n, For bless-ings of earth, and for glo-ries of

praise, Our hearts and our voic-es in hymn-ing Thy praise.
Lord, With joy-ful Ho-san-nas, the blest of the Lord.
come, Hath nev-er for-bid-den the young-est to come.
heav'n, For bless-ings of earth, and for glo-ries of heav'n.

357 The Wise May Bring Their Learning

MISSIONARY HYMN 7 6 8L

Anonymous, 1880   Lowell Mason, 1823

1 The wise may bring their learn-ing, The   rich may bring their wealth,
2. We'll bring Him hearts that love Him; We'll bring Him thank-ful praise,
3. We'll bring the lit - tle   du - ties We have to do each day;

And   some may bring their great-ness, And some bring strength and health,
And young souls meek-ly   striv-ing To walk in ho-ly ways.
We'll   try our best to please Him At home, at school, at play:

We,   too, would bring our treas-ures To   of - fer to the   King,
And these shall be the treas-ures We of - fer to the King,
And bet - ter are these treas-ures To of - fer to our King,

We   have no wealth or learn-ing; What shall we chil-dren bring?
And these are gifts that e - ven The poor-est child may bring
Than rich-est gifts with - out them; Yet these a child may bring

358 When, His Salvation Bringing

TOURS 7 6 6L.

John King, 1830

Berthold Tours, 1872

1 When, His sal - va - tion bring-ing, To Zi - on Je - sus came,
2. And since the Lord re - tain - eth His love for chil-dren still,
3. For should we fail pro - claim - ing Our great Re - deem-er's praise,

The chil-dren all stood sing - ing, Ho - san - nas to His name;
Tho' now as King He reign-eth On Zi - on's heav'n-ly hill,
The stones, our si - lence sham-ing, Would their Ho - san - nas raise.

Nor did their zeal of - fend Him, But as He rode a - long,
We'll flock a - round His ban - ner, Who sits up - on His throne,
But shall we on - ly ren - der The trib - ute of our words?

He let them still at - tend Him, And smiled to hear their song.
And cry a - loud, "Ho - san - na To Da - vid's roy - al Son."
No; while our hearts are ten - der, They too shall be the Lord's.

359 I Think When I Read That Sweet Story

SWEET STORY 11 8, 11 9

Jemima Luke, 1841   English Melody

1. I think when I read that sweet story of old,
How Jesus was here among men,
And called little children as lambs to His fold,
I should like to have been with them then.

2. I wish that His hands had been placed on my head,
His arm had been thrown around me,
That I might have seen His kind look when He said,
"Let the little ones come unto Me."

3. Yet still to His footstool in pray'r I may go,
And ask for a share in His love;
And if I thus earnestly seek Him below,
I shall see Him and hear Him above.

4. A beautiful place He has gone to prepare
For all who are washed and for-giv'n;
And many dear children shall be with Him there,
For of such is the kingdom of heav'n.

5. But thousands and thousands who wander and fall,
Ne'er heard of that heavenly home;
I wish they could know there is room for them all,
And that Jesus has bid them to come.

360 There's a Friend for Little Children

FRIEND 7 6 8L.

Albert Midlane, ca. 1860

Felix Bartholdy-Mendelssohn, 1809-1847

1. There's a Friend for lit - tle chil-dren, A - bove the bright blue sky,
2. There's a rest for lit - tle chil-dren, A - bove the bright blue sky,
3. There's a home for lit - tle chil-dren, A - bove the bright blue sky,
4. There are crowns for lit - tle chil-dren, A - bove the bright blue sky,
5. There are songs for lit - tle chil-dren, A - bove the bright blue sky,

A Friend who nev - er chang - es, Whose love will nev - er die.
Who love the bless-ed Sav - ior, And to the Fa - ther cry.
Where Je - sus reigns in glo - ry, A home of peace and joy;
And all who look to Je - sus Shall wear them by and by;
And harps of sweet-est mu - sic, And hymns of vic - to - ry:

Un - like our friends by na - ture, Who change with chang-ing years,
A rest from ev - 'ry troub - le, From sin and dan - ger free;
No home on earth is like it, Nor can with it com - pare,
Yea, crowns of bright-est glo - ry Which He shall sure be - stow
And all a - bove is pleas-ure, And found in Christ a - lone;

This Friend is al - ways wor - thy The pre-cious name He bears,
There ev - 'ry lit - tle pil - grim Shall rest e - ter - nal - ly,
For ev - 'ry one is hap - py, Nor can be hap - pier there,
On all who loved the Sav - ior And walked with Him be - low,
Lord, grant Thy lit - tle chil - dren, To know Thee as their own,

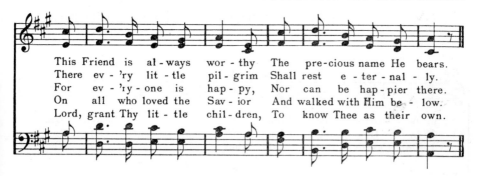

This Friend is al - ways wor - thy   The pre-cious name He bears.
There ev - 'ry lit - tle pil - grim   Shall rest e - ter - nal - ly.
For ev - 'ry - one is hap - py,   Nor can be hap - pier there.
On all who loved the Sav - ior   And walked with Him be - low.
Lord, grant Thy lit - tle chil - dren,   To know Thee as their own.

361 Savior, Like a Shepherd Lead Us

REGENT SQUARE 8 7 6L.

Dorothy Ann Thrupp, 1838

Henry Smart, 1867

1. Sav - ior, like a shep-herd lead us, Much we need Thy ten - der care;
2. We are Thine; do Thou be-friend us, Be the Guard-ian of our way;
3. Thou hast prom-ised to re-ceive us, Poor and sin - ful though we be;
4. Ear - ly let us seek Thy fav - or; Ear - ly let us do Thy will;

In Thy pleas-ant pas-tures feed us; For our use Thy folds pre-pare:
Keep Thy flock, from sin de-fend us, Seek us when we go a - stray:
Thou hast mer - cy to re-lieve us, Grace to cleanse, and pow'r to free:
Bless-ed Lord and on - ly Sav-ior, With Thy love our bos - oms fill:

Bless - ed Je - sus, bless - ed Je - sus, Thou hast bought us, Thine we are.
Bless - ed Je - sus, bless - ed Je - sus, Hear the chil - dren when they pray.
Bless - ed Je - sus, bless - ed Je - sus, Ear - ly let us turn to Thee.
Bless - ed Je - sus, bless - ed Je - sus, Thou hast loved us, love us still.

325

362 Around the Throne of God in Heaven

CHILDREN'S PRAISES 8 6, 8 6, 6 7

Anne H. Shepherd, 1835, alt.   Henry E. Matthews, 1854

1. A - round the throne of God in heav'n Great
2. In flow - ing robes of spot - less white See
3. On earth they sought the Sav - ior's grace, On

hosts of chil - dren stand, Whose sins are all by
ev - 'ry one ar - rayed; They dwell in ev - er -
earth they loved His name; So now they see His

grace for - giv'n, A ho - ly, hap - py band, Sing-ing,
last - ing light And joys that nev - er fade, Sing-ing,
bless - ed face, And stand be - fore the Lamb, Sing-ing,

"Glo - ry, glo - ry, Glo - ry be to God on high."
"Glo - ry, glo - ry, Glo - ry be to God on high."
"Glo - ry, glo - ry, Glo - ry be to God on high."

363 Away in a Manger, No Crib for His Bed

AWAY IN A MANGER 11 11 4L.

Martin Luther, 1530

Carl Mueller

1. A - way in a man - ger, no crib for His bed,
2. The cat - tle are low - ing, the poor ba - by wakes,
3. Be near me, Lord Je - sus, I ask Thee to stay

The lit - tle Lord Je - sus laid down His sweet head;
But lit - tle Lord Je - sus, no cry - ing He makes.
Close by me for - ev - er, and love me, I pray.

The stars in the sky looked down where He lay,
I love Thee, Lord Je - sus, look down from the sky,
Bless all the dear chil - dren in Thy ten - der care,

The lit - tle Lord Je - sus, a - sleep on the hay.
And stay by my cra - dle till morn - ing is nigh.
And fit us for heav - en to live with Thee there.

364 I Love to Hear the Story

WHAT JOY TO REACH 7 6, 7 6, 8 8, 7 6

Emily Huntington Miller, 1867

Norwegian Folk-Tune
Arr. Oscar R. Overby

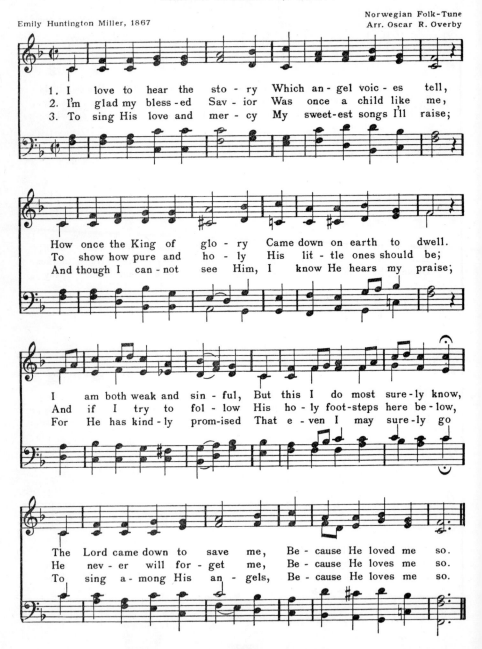

1. I love to hear the sto - ry Which an - gel voic - es tell,
2. I'm glad my bless -ed Sav - ior Was once a child like me,
3. To sing His love and mer - cy My sweet-est songs I'll raise;

How once the King of glo - ry Came down on earth to dwell.
To show how pure and ho - ly His lit - tle ones should be;
And though I can - not see Him, I know He hears my praise;

I am both weak and sin - ful, But this I do most sure - ly know,
And if I try to fol - low His ho - ly foot-steps here be - low,
For He has kind - ly prom-ised That e - ven I may sure - ly go

The Lord came down to save me, Be - cause He loved me so.
He nev - er will for - get me, Be - cause He loves me so.
To sing a - mong His an - gels, Be - cause He loves me so.

365 Jesus, Rule My Thoughts and Guide Me

LORD VICTORIOUS 8 7 8L.

Author Unknown
Tr. V. E. Boe, 1931

J.A. Freylinghausen's Gesangbuch, 1704

1. Je - sus, rule my thoughts and guide me, Je - sus, let me
walk with Thee, That what - e'er on earth be - tide me,
God's own lov - ing child I be. Let me with each
heart - pul - sa - tion Seek my Lord to glo - ri - fy;
Let me en - ter Thy sal - va - tion When in Thy blest name I die.

366 Thy Little Ones, Dear Lord, Are We

THY LITTLE ONES 8 8 4L.

Hans Adolf Brorson, 1732
Tr. Mrs. Harriet R. Spaeth, 1898

J. A. P. Schulz, 1747-1800
Arr. John Dahle, 1912

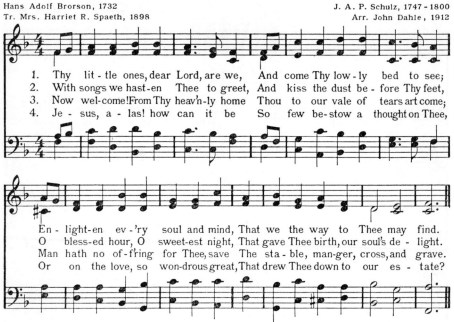

1. Thy lit-tle ones, dear Lord, are we, And come Thy low-ly bed to see;
2. With songs we hast-en Thee to greet, And kiss the dust be-fore Thy feet,
3. Now wel-come! From Thy heav'n-ly home Thou to our vale of tears art come;
4. Je-sus, a-las! how can it be So few be-stow a thought on Thee,

En-light-en ev-'ry soul and mind, That we the way to Thee may find.
O bless-ed hour, O sweet-est night, That gave Thee birth, our soul's de-light.
Man hath no of-f'ring for Thee, save The sta-ble, man-ger, cross, and grave.
Or on the love, so won-drous great, That drew Thee down to our es-tate?

5. O draw us wholly to Thee, Lord,
Do Thou to us Thy grace accord,
True faith and love to us impart,
That we may hold Thee in our heart.

6. Keep us, howe'er the world may lure,
In our baptismal covenant pure;
That every yearning thought may be
Directed only unto Thee:

7. Until at last we, too, proclaim,
With all Thy saints, Thy glorious name;
In Paradise our songs renew,
And praise Thee as the angels do.

8. We gather round Thee, Jesus dear,
So happy in Thy presence here;
Grant us, our Savior, every one,
To stand in heaven before Thy throne.

367 Shepherd of Tender Youth

Clement of Alexandria, ca. 220
Tr. Henry M. Dexter, 1846

OLIVET 6 6 4, 6 6 6 4

Lowell Mason, 1832

1. Shep-herd of ten-der youth, Guid-ing in love and truth,
2. Thou art our ho-ly Lord, O all-sub-du-ing Word,
3. Thou art the great High Priest; Thou hast pre-pared the feast
4. Ev-er be near our side, Our Shep-herd and our Guide,
5. So now, un-til we die, Sound we Thy prais-es high,

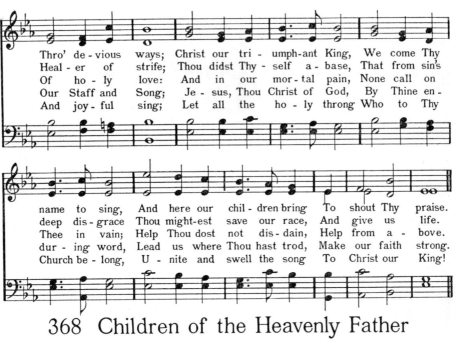

Thro' de - vious	ways;	Christ our tri - umph-ant	King,	We come Thy
Heal - er of	strife;	Thou didst Thy - self a - base,	That from sin's
Of ho - ly	love:	And in our mor - tal pain,	None call on
Our Staff and	Song;	Je - sus, Thou Christ of God,	By Thine en -
And joy - ful	sing;	Let all the ho - ly throng	Who to Thy

name to sing,	And here our chil - dren bring	To shout Thy	praise.
deep dis - grace	Thou might-est save our race,	And give us	life.
Thee in vain;	Help Thou dost not dis - dain,	Help from a - bove.
dur - ing word,	Lead us where Thou hast trod,	Make our faith strong.
Church be - long,	U - nite and swell the song	To Christ our King!

368 Children of the Heavenly Father

CHILDREN OF THE HEAVENLY FATHER L. M.

Carolina Sandell Berg, 1832-1903
Tr. E. W. Olson

Swedish Folk-Tune

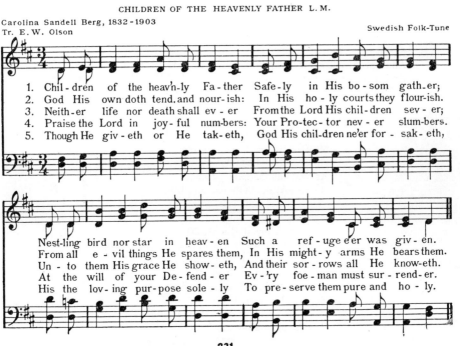

1. Chil - dren of the heav'n-ly Fa - ther Safe - ly in His bo - som gath-er;
2. God His own doth tend.and nour-ish: In His ho - ly courts they flour-ish.
3. Neith-er life nor death shall ev - er From the Lord His chil-dren sev - er;
4. Praise the Lord in joy-ful num-bers: Your Pro-tec-tor nev - er slum-bers.
5. Though He giv-eth or He tak-eth, God His chil-dren ne'er for - sak - eth,

Nest-ling bird nor star in heav - en Such a ref - uge e'er was giv - en.
From all e - vil things He spares them, In His might-y arms He bears them.
Un - to them His grace He show-eth, And their sor - rows all He know-eth.
At the will of your De - fend - er Ev - 'ry foe - man must sur - rend-er.
His the lov-ing pur-pose sole - ly To pre - serve them pure and ho - ly.

369 How Glad I Am Each Christmas Eve

CHRISTMAS EVE C.M.

Marie Wexelsen
Tr. P. A. Sveeggen, 1931

1. How glad I am each Christ-mas Eve! The night of Je - sus' birth;
2. The lit - tle child in Beth - le - hem, He was a king in - deed;
3. He dwells a - gain in heav - en's realm, The Son of God to - day;
4. How glad I am each Christ-mas Eve! His prais- es then I sing;
5. Then moth- er trims the Christ-mas tree, And fills the room with light.

Then like the sun the Star shone forth, And an - gels sang on earth.
He came from His high state in heav'n, Down to a world in need.
But He knows all the lit - tle ones, And hears them when they pray.
He o - pens then for ev - 'ry child The pal - ace of the King.
She says that so the Star shone forth And made the dark world bright.

6. She says the Star is shining still,
And never will grow dim;
And if it shines upon my way,
It leads me up to Him.

7. And so I love each Christmas Eve,
And I love Jesus too;
And that He loves me in return,
I know so well is true.

See also:

For the beauty of the earth, 245
My God, is any hour so sweet, 29
All glory, laud and honor, 34
As wide as the skies, 292
Be ye joyful, earth and sky, 129
There is a name, 143
My God, how wonderful Thou art, 19
The Lord's my shepherd, 207
As the sunflower turns in the morning, 54
There is a green hill far away, 174
My Jesus, I love Thee, 216
O how beautiful the sky, 148
Beautiful Savior, 6
Precious Child, so sweetly sleeping, 137
I ought to love my Savior, 372

370 Faith of Our Fathers, Living Still

ST. CATHERINE L. M. 6L.

Frederick W. Faber, 1849, alt.

Henri F. Hemy, 1865
Alt. J. G. Walton, 1871

1. Faith of our fa - thers, liv - ing still In spite of dun-geon, fire and sword, O how our hearts beat high with joy When-e'er we hear that glo - rious word: Faith of our fa - thers, ho - ly faith, We will be true to thee till death.

2. Our fa - thers, chained in pris - ons dark, Were still in heart and con - science free; And blest would be their chil - dren's fate If they, like them, should die for thee: Faith of our

3. Faith of our fa - thers! God's great pow'r Shall win all na - tions un - to thee; And thro' the truth that comes from God Man - kind shall then in - deed be free: Faith of our

4. Faith of our fa - thers, we will love Both friend and foe in all our strife, And preach thee, too, as love knows how By kind - ly words and vir - tuous life: Faith of our

371 Arise, Arise, United Youth

ALL SAINTS C M. 8L

C. K. Solberg, 1910   Henry S. Cutler, 1872

1. A - rise, a - rise, u - nit - ed youth Of our be - lov - ed Church!
2. Be - neath the ban-ner of the Cross, With - in our Church-'s fold,
3. Now bless us, Lord, that we may stand U - nit - ed, strong and true

Be guid - ed by God's pre - cious Truth In all your fu - ture search!
We seek to serve our com-mon cause, As did the saints of old;
To serve Thee here with heart and hand In all we find to do!

Come, here and now re - new your vow To serve your Lord and God,
In faith and pray'r we brave - ly dare To face our fierc - est foe,
Help us, we pray, up - on our way To ev - er trust in Thee,

And by His grace go forth to trace The path your fa - thers trod!
For, if we fight in God's own might, Suc - cess He will be - stow
And grant us pow'r each day and hour To win the vic - to - ry!

372 I Ought to Love My Savior

LORELEI 7 6 8L.

Anonymous

Friedrich Silcher, 1789-1860

1. I ought to love my Sav - ior; No earth - ly friend can be
2. He left His home in glo - ry To save my soul from death;
3. It is but ver - y lit - tle For Him that I can do;
4. And when I reach the man - sion He has pre - pared for me,

So lov - ing, kind, and faith - ful As He has been to me.
And now in all life's dan - gers He still sus - tains my breath.
Then let me seek to serve Him My earth - ly jour - ney through;
'Twill be my grate-ful pleas- ure My Sav - ior's face to see;

Be - fore my lips could ut - ter His sweet and pre - cious name,
I lay me down and slum- ber All through the hours of night,
And with-out sigh or mur- mur, To do His ho - ly will,
And 'mid the an - gels' mu - sic, Which then will greet my ear,

Un - til the pres-ent mo - ment, His love has been the same.
And wake a - gain in safe - ty To hail the morn-ing light.
And in my dai - ly du - ties, His wise com - mand ful - fill.
How eag - er - ly I'll lis - ten My Sav - ior's voice to hear.

335

373 Christian Leaguers, Rally

ST. GERTRUDE 6 5 8L. and Chorus

C. K Solberg, 1903   Arthur S. Sullivan, 1871

1. Chris-tian Lea-guers, ral - ly At the Lord's com - mand,
2. On we march to bat - tle, Fac - ing hosts of sin;
3. On - ward then, ye Lea - guers, Led by Christ, our Lord,

'Neath the cross of Je - sus Let us take our stand.
They are strong and ma - ny, But we hope to win:
Trust - ing in His prom - ise, Use in faith your sword,

Pledg-ing life - long ser - vice From our days of youth, Whol-ly con - se -
Je - sus is the Lead-er Of our roy - al band; By His grace we'll
Fight till eve of bat - tle, Soon the war will cease, Soon the word of

CHORUS

crat - ed To the cause of Truth.
con - quer At His safe com - mand.   For -ward, Chris-tian Lea-guers,
tri - umph Brings e - ter - nal Peace.

336

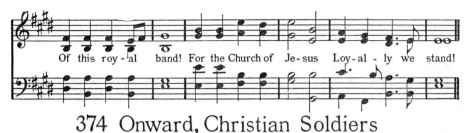

Of this roy-al band! For the Church of Je-sus Loy-al-ly we stand!

374 Onward, Christian Soldiers

Sabine Baring Gould, 1865   ST. GERTRUDE

1. Onward, Christian soldiers,
    Marching as to war,
    With the cross of Jesus
    Going on before:
    Christ,the Royal Master,
    Leads against the foe;
    Forward into battle,
    See, His banners go.

3. Crowns and thrones may perish,
    Kingdoms rise and wane,
    But the Church of Jesus
    Constant will remain;
    Gates of hell can never
    'Gainst that Church prevail;
    We have Christ's own promise,
    And that cannot fail.

CHORUS   Onward,Christain soldiers,
               Marching as to war,
               With the cross of Jesus
               Going on before.

2. Like a mighty army
    Moves the Church of God;
    Brothers, we are treading
    Where the saints have trod;
    We are not divided,
    All one body we,
    One in hope and doctrine,
    One in charity

4. Onward, then, ye people,
    Join our happy throng,
    Blend with ours your voices
    In the triumph song;
    Glory, laud, and honor
    Unto Christ,the King;
    This thro' countless ages
    Men and angels sing.

375 Begin, My Tongue, Some Heavenly Theme

MANOAH C.M.

Isaac Watts, 1707   Arr. from Gioacchino A. Rossini, 1851

1. Be-gin, my tongue,some heav'n-ly theme, And speak some bound-less thing;
2. O tell His won-dr,ous faith-ful-ness, And sound His pow'r a-broad;
3. His ver-y word of grace is strong As that which built the skies;
4. O might I hear Thy heav'n-ly tongue But whis-per "Thou art mine,"

The might-y works, or might-ier name, Of our e-ter-nal King.
And sing the prom-ise of His grace, The love and truth of God.
The voice that rolls the stars a-long Speaks all the prom-is-es.
Those gen-tle words should raise my song To notes al-most di-vine.

337

376 My Church, My Church, My Dear Old Church

ELLACOMBE C. M. D

German, 1784

1. My church! My church! My dear old church! My fa-thers' and my own!
2. My church! My church! My dear old church! My glo-ry and my pride!
3. My church! My church! My dear old church! I love her an-cient name;
4. My church! My church! I love my church! For she ex-alts my Lord!

On Proph-ets and A-pos-tles built, And Christ the cor-ner-stone!
Firm in the faith Im-man-uel taught, She holds no faith be-side.
And God for-bid, a child of hers Should ev-er do her shame!
She speaks, she breathes, she teach-es not But from His writ-ten word;

All else be-side, by storm or tide, May yet be o-ver-thrown:
Up-on this rock, 'gainst ev-'ry shock, Tho' gates of hell as-sail,
Her moth-er-care I'll ev-er share; Her child I am a-lone,
And if her voice bids me re-joice, From all my sins re-leased,

But not my church, my dear old church, My fa-thers' and my own!
She stands se-cure, with prom-ise sure, "They nev-er shall pre-vail."
Till He who gave me to her arms Shall call me to His own.
'Tis through th' a-ton-ing sac-ri-fice, And Je-sus is the Priest.

377 Savior, While My Heart Is Tender

RIPLEY 8 7 8L.

John Burton, 1850   Gregorian Chant Arr. Lowell Mason, 1839

1. Sav - ior, while my heart is ten - der, I would yield that heart to Thee;
2. Send me, Lord, where Thou wilt send me, On - ly do Thou guide my way,
3. May this sol - emn con - se - cra - tion Nev - er once for - got - ten be;

All my pow'rs to Thee sur - ren - der, Thine and on - ly Thine to be.
May Thy grace thro' life at - tend me, Glad - ly then shall I o - bey
Let it know no rev - o - ca - tion, Reg - is - tered, con-firmed by Thee.

Take me now, Lord Je-sus, take me, Let my youth-ful heart be Thine,
Let me do Thy will, or bear it, I would know no will but Thine,
Thine I am, O Lord, for - ev - er To Thy ser - vice set a - part;

Thy de - vot - ed ser-vant make me, Fill my soul with love di - vine.
Shouldst Thou take my life, or spare it, I that life to Thee re - sign.
Suf - fer me to leave Thee nev - er, Seal Thine im - age on my heart.

378 I Would Gather Treasures in Heaven

HEAVENLY TREASURES 9 8 4L

Oscar R. Overby, 1931

Norwegian Folk- Tune
Arr. Oscar R. Overby, 1931

In slow tempo

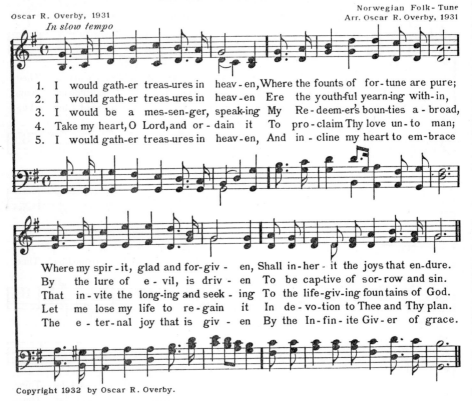

1. I would gath-er treas-ures in heav - en, Where the founts of for- tune are pure;
2. I would gath-er treas-ures in heav - en Ere the youth-ful yearn-ing with- in,
3. I would be a mes-sen-ger, speak-ing My Re - deem-er's boun-ties a - broad,
4. Take my heart, O Lord, and or - dain it To pro - claim Thy love un - to man;
5. I would gath-er treas-ures in heav - en, And in - cline my heart to em-brace

Where my spir - it, glad and for-giv - en, Shall in - her - it the joys that en-dure.
By the lure of e - vil, is driv - en To be cap-tive of sor- row and sin.
That in - vite the long-ing and seek - ing To the life-giv-ing foun tains of God.
Let me lose my life to re - gain it In de - vo-tion to Thee and Thy plan.
The e - ter-nal joy that is giv - en By the In-fin - ite Giv - er of grace.

Copyright 1932 by Oscar R. Overby.

379 How Shall the Young Secure Their Hearts

AZMON C. M

Isaac Watts, 1719

G. Gläser, 1828
Arr. Lowell Mason, 1839

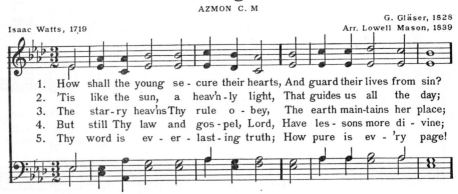

1. How shall the young se - cure their hearts, And guard their lives from sin?
2. 'Tis like the sun, a heav'n - ly light, That guides us all the day;
3. The star-ry heav'ns Thy rule o - bey, The earth main-tains her place;
4. But still Thy law and gos - pel, Lord, Have les - sons more di - vine;
5. Thy word is ev - er - last - ing truth; How pure is ev - 'ry page!

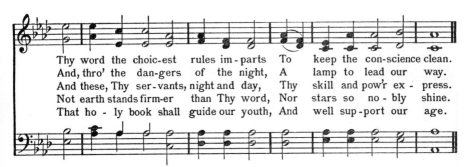

Thy word the choic-est rules im-parts To keep the con-science clean.
And, thro' the dan-gers of the night, A lamp to lead our way.
And these, Thy ser-vants, night and day, Thy skill and pow'r ex - press.
Not earth stands firm-er than Thy word, Nor stars so no - bly shine.
That ho - ly book shall guide our youth, And well sup-port our age.

380 I Know a Flower So Fair and Fine

FLOWER OF LOVE 8 7, 8 4 7

Nicolai F. S. Grundtvig, 1783 - 1872
Tr. Olav Lee, 1919

F. Melius Christiansen, 1919

1. I know a flow'r so fair and fine, So fra - grant
2. This flow'r so fair and fine is love. God's hand with
3. Up - on this earth but wild it grows; Not so in

and so cheer - ing; With life - blood clear as pur - est wine,
art it mould - ed. Un - seen on earth, but not a - bove,
new earth's E - den, Where stream of life se - rene - ly flows;

And leaf - let fine Like rose - leaves all ap - pear - ing.
Is growth of love, Till fair it is un - fold - ed.
It buds and blows, De - light - ful fra - grance breath - ing.

381 Summer Suns Are Glowing

RUTH 6 5 8L.

William W. How, 1871

Samuel Smith, 1870

1. Sum - mer suns are glow - ing O - ver land and sea;
2. God's free mer - cy stream - eth O - ver all the world,
3. Lord, up - on our blind - ness, Thy pure ra - diance pour;
4. We will nev - er doubt Thee, Tho' Thou veil Thy light;

Hap - py light is flow - ing Boun - ti - ful and free;
And His ban - ner gleam - eth Ev - 'ry - where un - furled;
For Thy lov - ing - kind - ness Make us love Thee more.
Life is dark with - out Thee, Death with Thee is bright.

Ev - 'ry - thing re - joic - es In the mel - low rays;
Broad and deep and glo - rious As the heav'n a - bove,
And when clouds are drift - ing Dark a - cross our sky,
Light of light! Shine o'er us On our pil - grim way;

All earth's thou - sand voic - es Swell the psalm of praise.
Shines in might vic - to - rious His e - ter - nal love.
Then, the veil up - lift - ing, Fa - ther, be Thou nigh.
Go Thou still be - fore us To the end - less day.

382 On Our Way Rejoicing

HERMAS 6 5 8L. and Chorus

John S. B. Monsell, 1863   Frances R. Havergal, 1872

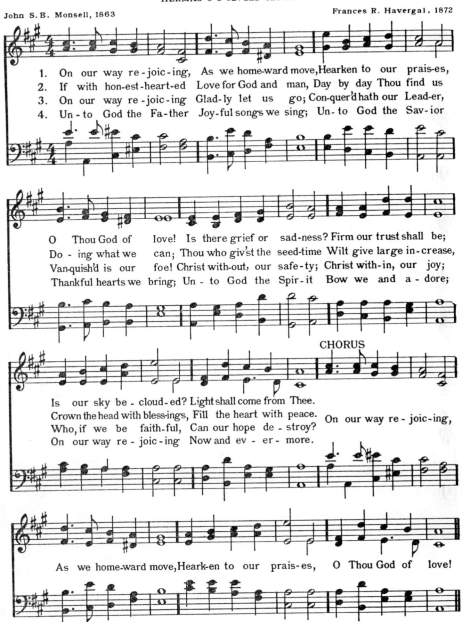

1. On our way re-joic-ing, As we home-ward move, Hearken to our prais-es,
2. If with hon-est-heart-ed Love for God and man, Day by day Thou find us
3. On our way re-joic-ing Glad-ly let us go; Con-quer'd hath our Lead-er,
4. Un-to God the Fa-ther Joy-ful songs we sing; Un-to God the Sav-ior

O Thou God of love! Is there grief or sad-ness? Firm our trust shall be;
Do-ing what we can; Thou who giv'st the seed-time Wilt give large in-crease,
Van-quish'd is our foe! Christ with-out, our safe-ty; Christ with-in, our joy;
Thankful hearts we bring; Un-to God the Spir-it Bow we and a-dore;

CHORUS

Is our sky be-cloud-ed? Light shall come from Thee.
Crown the head with bless-ings, Fill the heart with peace.   On our way re-joic-ing,
Who, if we be faith-ful, Can our hope de-stroy?
On our way re-joic-ing Now and ev-er-more.

As we home-ward move, Heark-en to our prais-es, O Thou God of love!

383 Lord of Spirits, I Surrender

LORD OF SPIRITS 8 7, 8 7, 8 8 8

Johan S.C. Welhaven, 1807-1873
Tr. George Taylor Rygh

F. A. Reissiger

1. Lord of spir - its, I sur - ren - der For Thy use Thy gifts to me: O but show Thy mer - cy ten - der When my song no more shall be; More and more my heart's a - flut - ter With the thots I may not ut - ter, While life's rid - dle great I pon - der.

2. Let my laur - els in ob - liv - ion Turn to dust, I shall re - joice If my soul, re - newed, is giv - en There to sing with sa - cred voice, If, in ac - cents pure and glo - rious, I may join the hymn vic - to - rious At Thy throne to harps of heav - en.

See also:

VI. Missions

1. Home

2. Foreign

3. Jewish

4. Stewardship

5. Brotherhoods

384 Hark, the Voice of Jesus Calling

RIPLEY 8 7 8L.

Daniel March, 1868, alt.

Gregorian Chant
Arr. Lowell Mason, 1839

1. Hark! the voice of Je-sus call-ing, "Who will go and work to day?
2. If you can-not cross the o-cean, And the hea-then lands ex-plore,
3. If you can-not be a watch-man, Stand-ing high on Zi-on's wall,
4. Let none hear you id-ly say-ing, "There is noth-ing I can do,"

Fields are white, and har-vests wait-ing, Who will bear the sheaves a-way?"
You can find the hea-then near-er, You can help them at your door.
Point-ing out the path to heav-en, Of-f'ring life and peace to all;
While the souls of men are dy-ing, And the Mas-ter calls for you.

Loud and long the Mas-ter call-eth, Rich re-ward He of-fers thee:
If you can-not give your thou-sands, You can give with will-ing might;
With your pray'rs and with your boun-ties You can do what heav'n de-mands;
Take the task He gives you glad-ly, Let His work your pleas-ure be;

Who will an-swer, glad-ly say-ing, "Here am I; send me, send me"?
And the least you do for Je-sus Will be pre-cious in His sight.
You can be like faith-ful Aa-ron, Hold-ing up the pro-phet's hands.
An-swer quick-ly when He call-eth: "Here am I; send me, send me."

347

385 Jesus, Master, Son of God

HORTON 7 7 4L.

Joseph Augustus Seiss, 1899

C. von Wartensee, 1780

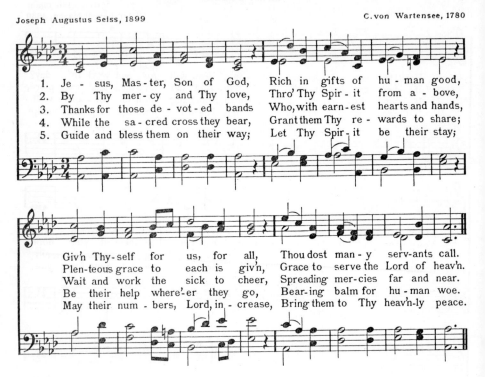

1. Je - sus, Mas - ter, Son of God, Rich in gifts of hu - man good,
2. By Thy mer - cy and Thy love, Thro' Thy Spir - it from a - bove,
3. Thanks for those de - vot - ed bands Who, with earn - est hearts and hands,
4. While the sa - cred cross they bear, Grant them Thy re - wards to share;
5. Guide and bless them on their way; Let Thy Spir - it be their stay;

Giv'n Thy - self for us, for all, Thou dost man - y serv - ants call.
Plen - teous grace to each is giv'n, Grace to serve the Lord of heav'n.
Wait and work the sick to cheer, Spreading mer - cies far and near.
Be their help where' - er they go, Bear - ing balm for hu - man woe.
May their num - bers, Lord, in - crease, Bring them to Thy heav'n - ly peace.

386 Saints of God, the Dawn Is Brightening

EASTER MORROW 8 7 6L.

Mary H. Maxwell, 1840

Ludvig M. Lindeman, 1812 - 1887

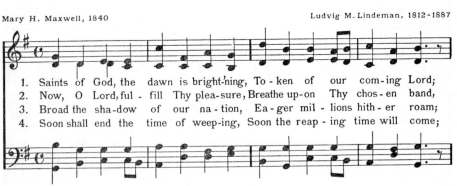

1. Saints of God, the dawn is bright - 'ning, To - ken of our com - ing Lord;
2. Now, O Lord, ful - fill Thy plea - sure, Breathe up - on Thy chos - en band,
3. Broad the sha - dow of our na - tion, Ea - ger mil - lions hith - er roam;
4. Soon shall end the time of weep - ing, Soon the reap - ing time will come;

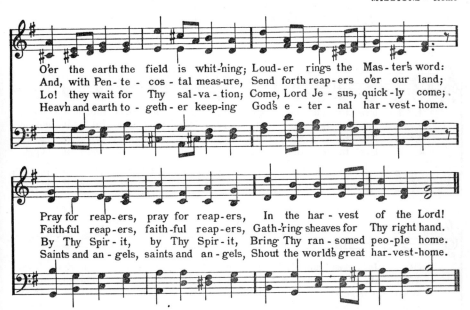

O'er the earth the field is whit-'ning; Loud-er rings the Mas-ter's word:
And, with Pen-te-cos-tal meas-ure, Send forth reap-ers o'er our land;
Lo! they wait for Thy sal-va-tion; Come, Lord Je-sus, quick-ly come;
Heav'n and earth to-geth-er keep-ing God's e-ter-nal har-vest-home.

Pray for reap-ers, pray for reap-ers, In the har-vest of the Lord!
Faith-ful reap-ers, faith-ful reap-ers, Gath-'ring sheaves for Thy right hand.
By Thy Spir-it, by Thy Spir-it, Bring Thy ran-somed peo-ple home.
Saints and an-gels, saints and an-gels, Shout the world's great har-vest-home.

387 Where Cross the Crowded Ways of Life

GERMANY L. M.

Frank Mason North, 1903

William Gardiner's Sacred Melodies, 1815

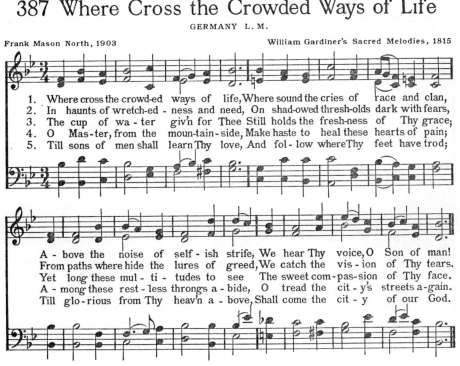

1. Where cross the crowd-ed ways of life, Where sound the cries of race and clan,
2. In haunts of wretch-ed-ness and need, On shad-owed thresh-olds dark with fears,
3. The cup of wa-ter giv'n for Thee Still holds the fresh-ness of Thy grace;
4. O Mas-ter, from the moun-tain-side, Make haste to heal these hearts of pain;
5. Till sons of men shall learn Thy love, And fol-low where Thy feet have trod;

A-bove the noise of self-ish strife, We hear Thy voice, O Son of man!
From paths where hide the lures of greed, We catch the vis-ion of Thy tears.
Yet long these mul-ti-tudes to see The sweet com-pas-sion of Thy face.
A-mong these rest-less throngs a-bide, O tread the cit-y's streets a-gain.
Till glo-rious from Thy heav'n a-bove, Shall come the cit-y of our God.

388 I Love to Tell the Story

I LOVE TO TELL THE STORY 7 6 8L. and Chorus

Katherine Hankey, 1866   William G. Fischer, 1869

1. I love to tell the sto - ry Of un - seen things a - bove,
2. I love to tell the sto - ry; More won - der - ful it seems
3. I love to tell the sto - ry; 'Tis pleas-ant to re - peat
4. I love to tell the sto - ry; For those who know it best

Of Je - sus and His glo - ry, Of Je - sus and His love.
Than all the gold - en fan - cies Of all our gold - en dreams.
What seems, each time I tell it, More won - der - ful - ly sweet.
Seem hun - ger - ing and thirst-ing To hear it, like the rest.

I love to tell the sto - ry, Be - cause I know 'tis true;
I love to tell the sto - ry, It did so much for me;
I love to tell the sto - ry, For some have nev - er heard
And when, in scenes of glo - ry, I sing the new, new song,

It sat - is - fies my long-ings As noth - ing else could do.
And that is just the rea - son I tell it now to thee.
The mes - sage of sal - va - tion From God's own ho - ly Word.
'Twill be the old, old sto - ry, That I have loved so long.

CHORUS

I love to tell the sto-ry, 'Twill be my theme in glo-ry

To tell the old, old sto-ry Of Je-sus and His love.

389 Look from Thy Sphere of Endless Day

CANONBURY L. M.

William Cullen Bryant, 1840, alt.   Robert Schumann, 1839

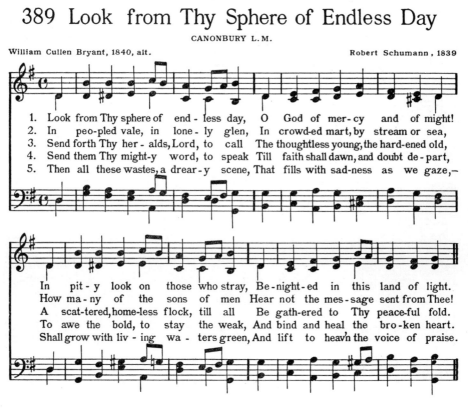

1. Look from Thy sphere of end-less day, O God of mer-cy and of might!
2. In peo-pled vale, in lone-ly glen, In crowd-ed mart, by stream or sea,
3. Send forth Thy her-alds, Lord, to call The thoughtless young, the hard-ened old,
4. Send them Thy might-y word, to speak Till faith shall dawn, and doubt de-part,
5. Then all these wastes, a drear-y scene, That fills with sad-ness as we gaze,—

In pit-y look on those who stray, Be-night-ed in this land of light.
How ma-ny of the sons of men Hear not the mes-sage sent from Thee!
A scat-tered, home-less flock, till all Be gath-ered to Thy peace-ful fold.
To awe the bold, to stay the weak, And bind and heal the bro-ken heart.
Shall grow with liv-ing wa-ters green, And lift to heav'n the voice of praise.

351

390 Our Country's Voice Is Pleading

MISSIONARY HYMN 7 6 8L.

Maria Frances Anderson, 1848

Lowell Mason, 1823

1. Our coun-try's voice is plead-ing, Ye men of God, a - rise!
2. The love of Christ un - fold-ing, Speed on from east to west,

His prov - i - dence is lead - ing, The land be - fore you lies;
Till all, His cross be - hold - ing, In Him are ful - ly blest.

O'er it the day has bright-ened, The prom - ise clothes the soil;
Great Au - thor of sal - va - tion, Haste, haste the glo - rious day

Wide fields for har - vest whit - ened, In - vite the reap-ers' toil.
When we, a ran-somed na - tion, Thy scep-ter shall o - bey.

See also:

O wonderful words of the gospel, 258

There is a sea of mercy, 255

391 The Morning Light Is Breaking

WEBB 7 6 8L.

Samuel F. Smith, 1832

George J. Webb, 1837

1. The morn-ing light is break-ing, The dark-ness dis-ap-pears;
2. See hea-then na-tions bend-ing Be-fore the God we love,
3. Blest riv-er of sal-va-tion, Pur-sue thy on-ward way;

The sons of earth are wak-ing, To pen-i-ten-tial tears;
And thou-sand hearts a-scend-ing In grat-i-tude a-bove;
Flow thou to ev-'ry na-tion, Nor in thy rich-ness stay:

Each breeze that sweeps the o-cean Brings ti-dings from a-far
While sin-ners, now con-fess-ing, The gos-pel call o-bey,
Stay not till all the low-ly Tri-umph-ant reach their home;

Of na-tions in com-mo-tion, Pre-pared for Zi-on's war.
And seek the Sav-ior's bless-ing, A na-tion in a day.
Stay not till all the ho-ly Pro-claim, "The Lord is come."

392 O Zion, Haste, Thy Mission High Fulfilling

PROCLAMATION 11 10 4L. and Chorus

Mary A Thompson, 1870   James Walck, 1876

1. O Zi - on, haste, thy mis-sion high ful - fill - ing, To tell to all the
2. Be - hold how ma - ny thou-sands still are ly - ing Bound in the dark-some
3. Pro-claim to ev - 'ry peo - ple, tongue, and na - tion That God, in whom they
4. Give of thy sons to bear the mes - sage glo-rious; Give of thy wealth to
5. He comes a - gain: O Zi - on, ere thou meet Him, Make known to ev - 'ry

world that God is Light; That He who made all na - tions is not will - ing
pris - on-house of sin, With none to tell them of the Sav - ior's dy ing,
live and move, is Love: Tell how He stooped to save His lost cre - a - tion,
speed them on their way; Pour out thy soul for them in pray'r vic - to - rious;
heart His sav - ing grace; Let none whom He hath ran-somed fail to greet Him,

CHORUS

One soul should per - ish, lost in shades of night:
Or of the life He died for them to win.
And died on earth that man might live a - bove. Pub-lish glad ti - dings;
And all thou spend-est Je - sus will re - pay.
Thro' thy neg - lect, un - fit to see His face.

ti - dings of peace; Ti - dings of Je - sus, re - demp-tion and re - lease.

354

393 From Greenland's Icy Mountains

MISSIONARY HYMN 7 6 8L.

Reginald Heber, 1819   Lowell Mason, 1823

1. From Green-land's i - cy moun-tains, From In - dia's cor- al strand,
2. Can we, whose souls are light - ed With wis - dom from on high,
3. Waft, waft, ye winds, His sto - ry, And you, ye wa - ters, roll,

Where Af - ric's sun - ny foun - tains Roll down their gold - en sand;
Can we to men be - night - ed The lamp of life de - ny?
Till, like a sea of glo - ry, It spreads from pole to pole;

From ma - ny an an - cient riv - er, From ma - ny a palm - y plain,—
Sal - va - tion, O sal - va - tion! The joy - ful sound pro - claim
Till o'er our ran-somed na - ture The Lamb for sin - ners slain,

They call us to de - liv - er Their land from er - ror's chain.
Till each re - mot - est na - tion Has learned Mes-si - ah's name.
Re - deem-er, King, Cre - a - tor, In bliss re-turns to reign.

394 Shepherd of One Fold Is He

TOPLADY 7 7 6L

Jeremiah Eames Rankin, 1828-1904

Thomas Hastings, 1830

1. Shep-herd of one fold is He, Je - sus, Lamb of Cal - va - ry!
2. All are pre-cious in His sight, Par-thian, Mede and El - a - mite,
3. Won-ders in the heav'n a - bove, Won-ders of re - deem-ing love;
4. This same Je - sus who once died, God has sealed and glo - ri - fied;

When He drank the gar-den's cup, From the earth was lift - ed up,
Crete, A - ra - bian, Jew, and Greek, They shall yet one lan-guage speak;
Won-ders on the earth be - neath, Dy - ing love has con-quered death:
All ye scat-tered ones and lost, Now re - ceive the Ho - ly Ghost;

When His work of love was done, 'Twas to draw all in - to one.
Oth - er tongue than that of earth,— Speech of a ce - les - tial birth.
Who on Je - sus' name shall call Shall be saved,—each one and all.
Shep-herd of one fold is He, Je - sus, Lamb of Cal - va - ry.

395 O Lord Our God, Arise

THATCHER S.M.

Ralph Wardlaw, 1800

Arr. from George Frederick Händel, 1732

1. O Lord our God, a - rise, The cause of truth main - tain;
2. Thou Prince of Life, a - rise, Nor let Thy con - quests cease:
3. Thou Ho - ly Ghost, a - rise, Ex - ert Thy quick - 'ning pow'r,
4. All men on earth, a - rise, To God the Sav - ior sing;

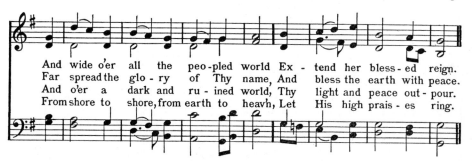

And wide o'er all the peo-pled world Ex - tend her bless-ed reign.
Far spread the glo - ry of Thy name, And bless the earth with peace.
And o'er a dark and ru - ined world, Thy light and peace out - pour.
From shore to shore, from earth to heav'n, Let His high prais - es ring.

396 Lost in the Night

LOST IN THE NIGHT 11 11, 11 5 5

Translation of a Norwegian rendering
of a Finnish Song, by Olav Lee, 1929

Finnish Folk-Tune

1. Lost in the night doth the heath-en yet lan-guish, Long-ing for morn-ing the dark-ness to van-quish, Plain-tive-ly heav-ing a sigh full of an - guish: Will not day come soon? Will not day come soon?

2. Must he be vain - ly a - wait-ing the mor-row? Shall we who have it no light let him bor - row? Giv - ing no heed to his bur - den of sor-row: Will you help us soon? Will you help us soon?

3. Sor - row-ing broth - er, in dark-ness yet dwell-ing, Dawned hath the day of a ra - diance ex - cel - ling, Death's dread-ed dark - ness ev - er dis-pel - ling: Christ is com-ing soon! Christ is com-ing soon!

4. Light o'er the land of the heath-en is beam-ing, Riv - ers of life through its des - erts are stream-ing. Mil - lions yet sigh for the Sav - ior re - deem-ing: Come and save us soon! Come and save us soon!

397 Speed Thy Servants, Savior, Speed Them

HERE BEHOLD ME 8.7 6L.

Thomas Kelly, 1820

Darmstadt-Gesangbuch, 1698

1. Speed Thy serv-ants, Sav-ior, speed them, Rul-er of the winds and waves.
2. Friends and home, and all for-sak-ing, Lord, they go at Thy com-mand,
3. When no fruit ap-pears to cheer them, And they seem to toil in vain,
4. In the midst of op-po-si-tion Let them trust, O Lord, in Thee;

They were bound, but Thou hast freed them; Now they go to free the slaves.
As their stay Thy prom-ise tak-ing, While they trav-erse sea and land:
Then in mer-cy, Lord, draw near them, Then their sink-ing hopes sus-tain.
When suc-cess at-tends their mis-sion, Let Thy ser-vants hum-ble be;

Be Thou with them, be Thou with them, 'Tis Thine arm a-lone that saves.
O be with them, O be with them, Lead them safe-ly by the hand.
Thus sup-port-ed, thus sup-port-ed, Let their zeal re-vive a-gain.
Nev-er leave them, nev-er leave them, Till Thy face in heav'n they see!

398 Lord of the Harvest, Hear

SCHUMANN S. M.

Charles Wesley, 1742

Arr. from Robert Schumann, 1810-1856

1. Lord of the har-vest, hear Thy need-y serv-ants' cry;
2. On Thee we hum-bly wait, Our wants are in Thy view;
3. A-noint and send forth more In-to Thy Church a-broad,
4. O let them spread Thy name, Their mis-sion ful-ly prove;

358

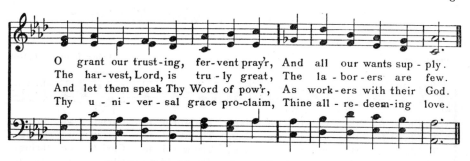

O grant our trust-ing, fer-vent pray'r, And all our wants sup - ply.
The har-vest, Lord, is tru - ly great, The la - bor-ers are few.
And let them speak Thy Word of pow'r, As work-ers with their God.
Thy u - ni - ver - sal grace pro-claim, Thine all - re- deem-ing love.

399 Hail to the Brightness

WESLEY 11 10, 4L.

Thomas Hastings, 1832

Lowell Mason, 1830

1. Hail to the bright-ness of Zi - on's glad morn-ing, Joy to the
2. Hail to the bright-ness of Zi - on's glad morn-ing, Long by the
3. Lo, in the des - ert rich flow-ers are spring-ing, Streams ev - er
4. See, from all lands, from the isles of the o - cean, Praise to Je -

lands that in dark-ness have lain! Hush'd be the ac - cents of
proph - ets of Is - rael fore - told; Hail to the mil - lions from
co - pious are glid - ing a - long; Loud from the moun-tain - tops
ho - vah as - cend - ing on high; Fall'n are the en - gines of

sor-row and mourning, Zi - on in tri-umph be-gins her mild reign.
bond-age re-turn-ing! Gen - tiles and Jews the blest vi - sion be - hold.
ech-oes are ring-ing, Wastes rise in ver-dure and min-gle in song.
war and com-mo-tion, Shouts of sal - va-tion are rend-ing the sky.

400 Christ for the World We Sing

ITALIAN HYMN 6 6 4, 6 6 6 4

Samuel Wolcott, 1869

Felice de Giardini, 1769

1. Christ for the world we sing; The world to Christ we bring,
2. Christ for the world we sing; The world to Christ we bring,
3. Christ for the world we sing; The world to Christ we bring,
4. Christ for the world we sing; The world to Christ we bring,

With lov-ing zeal; The poor, and them that mourn, The faint and
With fer-vent pray'r; The way-ward and the lost, By rest-less
With one ac-cord; With us the work to share, With us re-
With joy-ful song; The new-born souls, whose days, Re-claimed from

o-ver-borne, Sin-sick and sor-row-worn, Whom Christ doth heal.
pas-sion tossed, Re-deemed, at count-less cost, From dark de-spair.
proach to dare, With us the cross to bear, For Christ our Lord.
er-ror's ways, In-spired with hope and praise, To Christ be-long.

See also:

401 Lord, Thine Ancient People See

LAST HOPE 7 7 4L.

E. Harland, 1855

Louis M. Gottschalk, 1867
Arr. Edwin P. Parker, 1836

1. Lord, Thine an-cient peo-ple see, Cap-tive still in dark-ness bound;
2. Still the veil is on their heart: Rend it, Lord, at length in twain;
3. Let Thy love their blind-ness heal; God of Is-rael, hear our pray'r;
4. Harp of Ju-dah, long un-strung, Sound at length the Sav-ior's praise;

Let Thy gos-pel set them free, Let them hear its joy-ful sound
Bid their un-be-lief de-part, Bring them to Thy fold a-gain.
Let Thy grace their par-don seal, Still Thy cove-nant let them share.
Jew and Gen-tile, old and young, Loud the glad Ho-san-na raise

402 O That the Lord's Salvation

ABIDE IN GRACE 7 6 4L.

Henry F. Lyte, 1834

Melchior Vulpius, 1609

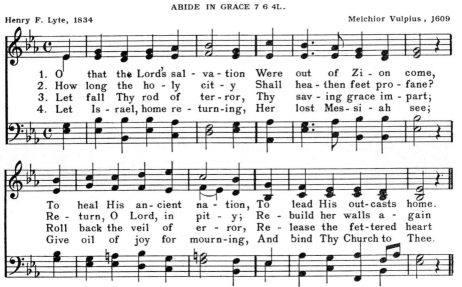

1. O that the Lord's sal-va-tion Were out of Zi-on come,
2. How long the ho-ly cit-y Shall hea-then feet pro-fane?
3. Let fall Thy rod of ter-ror, Thy sav-ing grace im-part;
4. Let Is-rael, home re-turn-ing, Her lost Mes-si-ah see;

To heal His an-cient na-tion, To lead His out-casts home.
Re-turn, O Lord, in pit-y; Re-build her walls a-gain
Roll back the veil of er-ror, Re-lease the fet-tered heart
Give oil of joy for mourn-ing, And bind Thy Church to Thee.

361

403 Unchanging God, Hear from Eternal Heaven

EVENTIDE 10 10 4L

Samuel J. Stone, 1855   William H. Monk, 1861

1 Un - chang-ing God, hear from e - ter - nal heav'n: We plead Thy
2. Out of our faith in Thee, who canst not lie, Out of our
3. Bring Thy be - lov - ed back, Thine Is - ra - el, Thine own e -
4. Fa - ther of mer - cies! these the long a - stray, These in soul-

gifts of grace, for - ev - er giv'n, Thy call, with - out re -
heart's de - sire, goes up the cry, From hope's sweet vi - sion
lect who from Thy fa - vor fell, But not from Thine e -
blind-ness now the far - a - way, These are not a - liens,

pent-ance, call-ing still, The sure e - lec-tion of Thy sov-'reign will
of the thing to be, From love to those who still are loved by Thee.
lec - tion! O for-give, Speak but the word, and, lo! the dead shall live.
but Thy sons of yore, O, by Thy Fa-ther-hood, re - store, re - store!

5. Breathe on Thy church, that it may greet the day,
    Stir up her will to toil, and teach, and pray,
    Till Zionward again salvation come,
    And all her outcast children are at home

6. Triune Jehovah, Thine the grace and pow'r,
    Thine all the work, its past, its future hour;
    O Thou, who failest not, Thy gifts fulfill,
    And crown the calling of Thy changeless will.

See also:

Hail to the brightness of Zion's glad morning, 399

404 We Give Thee But Thine Own

SCHUMANN S. M.

William W. How, 1864

Arr. from Robert Schumann, 1810 -1856

1. We give Thee but Thine own, What-e'er the gift may be: All
2. May we Thy boun-ties thus As stew-ards true re - ceive, And
3. O hearts are bruised and dead, And homes are bare and cold, And
4. And we be - lieve Thy word, Though dim our faith may be, What-

that we have is Thine a - lone, A trust, O Lord, from Thee.
glad - ly, as Thou bless-est us, To Thee our first-fruits give.
lambs for whom the Shep-herd bled Are stray-ing from the fold.
e'er for Thine we do, O Lord, We do it un - to Thee.

405 O God of Mercy, God of Might

JUST AS I AM 8 8, 8 6

Godfrey Thring, 1877

Joseph Barnby, 1883

1. O God of mer - cy, God of might, In love and pit - y in - fi - nite,
2. And Thou who cam'st on earth to die, That fall-en man might live there-by,
3. Teach us the les - son Thou hast taught, To feel for those Thy blood hath bought,
4. For all are breth-ren, far and wide, Since Thou, O Lord, for all hast died;

Teach us, as ev - er in Thy sight, To live our life to Thee.
O hear us, for to Thee we cry; In hope, O Lord, to Thee.
That ev - 'ry word, and deed, and thought, May work a work for Thee.
Then teach us, what-so - e'er be - tide, To love them all in Thee.

363

406 Take My Life and Let It Be

CONSECRATION 7 7 4L.

Frances R. Havergal, 1874

William H. Havergal, 1874

1. Take my life, and let it be Con-se-crat-ed, Lord, to Thee;
2. Take my hands, and let them move With the im-pulse of Thy love:

Take my mo-ments and my days,—Let them flow in cease-less praise.
Take my feet and let them be Swift and beau-ti-ful for Thee.

3. Take my voice, and let me sing
Always, only for my King;
Take my lips, and let them be
Filled with messages from Thee

4. Take my silver and my gold,—
Not a mite would I withhold;
Take my intellect, and use
Ev'ry pow'r as Thou dost choose.

5. Take my will and make it Thine;
It shall be no longer mine;
Take my heart, it is Thine own;
It shall be Thy royal throne.

6. Take my love; my Lord, I pour
At Thy feet its treasure store;
Take myself, and I will be
Ever, only, all for Thee.

See also:

Lord of Spirits, I surrender, 383

407 The Voice of God Is Calling

WEBB 7 6 8L.

John Haynes Holmes, 1913   George J. Webb, 1837

1. The voice of God is call-ing Its sum-mons un-to men;
2. I hear My peo-ple cry-ing In cot and mine and slum;
3. We heed, O Lord, Thy sum-mons, And an-swer, here are we!
4. From ease and pleas-ure save us, From pride of place ab-solve;

As once He spoke of Zi-on, So now He speaks a-gain.
No field or mart is si-lent, No cit-y street is dumb.
Send us up-on Thine er-rand, Let us Thy serv-ants be.
Purge us of low de-sire, Lift us to high re-solve.

Whom shall I send to suc-cor My peo-ple in their need?
I see my peo-ple fall-ing In dark-ness and de-spair,
Our strength is dust and ash-es, Our years a pass-ing hour,
Take us, and make us ho-ly, Teach us Thy will and way,

Whom shall I send to loos-en The bonds of lust and greed?
Whom shall I send to shat-ter The fet-ters which they bear?
But Thou canst use our weak-ness, To mag-ni-fy Thy pow'r.
Speak, and be-hold! we an-swer, Com-mand, and we o-bey!

408 How Good It Is for Brethren

ALL GLORY, LAUD 7 6 4L.

F. G. Wetzel
Tr. H. Brueckner, 1918

Ludvig M. Lindeman, 1812-1887

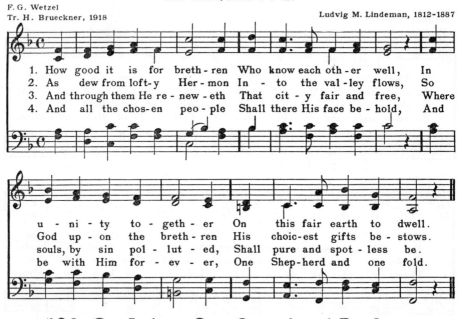

1. How good it is for breth - ren Who know each oth - er well, In
2. As dew from loft- y Her - mon In - to the val - ley flows, So
3. And through them He re - new - eth That cit - y fair and free, Where
4. And all the chos- en peo - ple Shall there His face be - hold, And

u - ni - ty to - geth - er On this fair earth to dwell.
God up - on the breth - ren His choic- est gifts be - stows.
souls, by sin pol - lut - ed, Shall pure and spot - less be.
be with Him for - ev - er, One Shep-herd and one fold.

409 Go, Labor On; Spend and Be Spent

ERNAN L. M.

Horatius Bonar, 1843

Lowell Mason, 1850

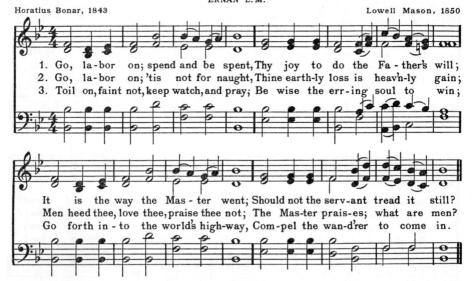

1. Go, la - bor on; spend and be spent, Thy joy to do the Fa - ther's will;
2. Go, la - bor on; 'tis not for naught, Thine earth-ly loss is heav'n-ly gain;
3. Toil on, faint not, keep watch, and pray; Be wise the err-ing soul to win;

It is the way the Mas - ter went; Should not the serv-ant tread it still?
Men heed thee, love thee, praise thee not; The Mas-ter prais-es; what are men?
Go forth in - to the world's high-way, Com-pel the wan-d'rer to come in.

See also: Saints of God, the dawn is brightening, 386. Our country's voice is pleading, 390

VII. National

410 My Country! 'Tis of Thee

AMERICA 6 6 4, 6 6 6 4

Samuel F. Smith, 1830   Henry Carey, 1743

1. My coun-try! 'tis of thee, Sweet land of lib-er-ty,
2. My na-tive coun-try, thee, Land of the no-ble, free,
3. Let mu-sic swell the breeze, And ring from all the trees
4. Our fa-thers' God, to Thee, Au-thor of lib-er-ty,

Of thee I sing: Land where my fa-thers died, Land of the
Thy name I love; I love thy rocks and rills, Thy woods and
Sweet free-dom's song; Let mor-tal tongues a-wake, Let all that
To Thee we sing: Long may our land be bright With free-dom's

Pil-grims' pride, From ev-'ry moun-tain-side Let free-dom ring.
tem-pled hills, My heart with rap-ture thrills Like that a-bove.
breathe par-take, Let rocks their si-lence break, The sound pro-long.
ho-ly light; Pro-tect us by Thy might, Great God, our King.

411 God Bless Our Native Land

TUNE: AMERICA

Charles T. Brooks, 1834
John S. Dwight, 1844

1. God bless our native land,
Firm may she ever stand,
Through storm and night;
When the wild tempests rave,
Ruler of wind and wave,
Do Thou our country save
By Thy great might.

2. For her our prayers shall rise
To God, above the skies;
On Him we wait;
Thou who art ever nigh,
Guarding with watchful eye,
To Thee aloud we cry,
God save the state.

412 O Thou before Whose Presence

AURELIA 7 6 8L.

Samuel J. Stone, 1889

Samuel S. Wesley, 1864

1. O Thou be - fore whose pres - ence Naught e - vil may come in,
2. Fierce is our sub - tle foe - man: The forc - es at his hand
3. So hast Thou wrought a - mong us The great things that we see:
4. Lead on, O Love and Mer - cy, O Pur - i - ty and Pow'r,

Yet who dost look in mer - cy Down on this world of sin;
With woes that none can num - ber De - spoil the pleas - ant land;
For things that are we thank Thee, And for the things to be.
Lead on till peace e - ter - nal Shall close this bat - tle - hour:

O give us no - ble pur - pose To set the sin - bound free,
All they who war a - gainst them, In strife so keen and long,
For bright hope is up - lift - ing Faint hands and fee - ble knees,
Till all who prayed and strug - gled To set their breth - ren free,

And Christ - like ten - der pi - ty To seek the lost for Thee.
Must in their Sav - ior's ar - mor Be strong - er than the strong.
To strive be - neath Thy bless - ing For great - er things than these.
In tri - umph meet to praise Thee, Most Ho - ly Trin - i - ty.

413 O Beautiful for Spacious Skies

MATERNA C. M. D.

Katharine Lee Bates, 1893-1910

Samuel A. Ward, 1847-1903

1. O beau-ti-ful for spa-cious skies, For am-ber waves of grain,
2. O beau-ti-ful for pil-grim feet Whose stern im-pas-sioned stress
3. O beau-ti-ful for he-roes proved In lib-er-at-ing strife,
4. O beau-ti-ful for pa-triot dream That sees be-yond the years

For pur-ple moun-tain maj-es-ties A-bove the fruit-ed plain.
A thor-ough-fare for free-dom beat A-cross the wil-der-ness.
Who more than self their coun-try loved, And mer-cy more than life.
Thine al-a-bas-ter cit-ies gleam Un-dimmed by hu-man tears.

A-mer-i-ca! A-mer-i-ca! God shed His grace on thee,
A-mer-i-ca! A-mer-i-ca! God mend thine ev-'ry flaw,
A-mer-i-ca! A-mer-i-ca! May God thy gold re-fine
A-mer-i-ca! A-mer-i-ca! God shed His grace on thee,

And crown thy good with broth-er-hood From sea to shin-ing sea.
Con-firm thy soul in self-con-trol, Thy lib-er-ty in law.
Till all suc-cess be no-ble-ness, And ev-'ry gain di-vine.
And crown thy good with broth-er-hood From sea to shin-ing sea.

414 O Say, Can You See, by the Dawn's Early Light

STAR-SPANGLED BANNER Irregular

Francis Scott Key, 1814

John Stafford Smith, ca. 1778

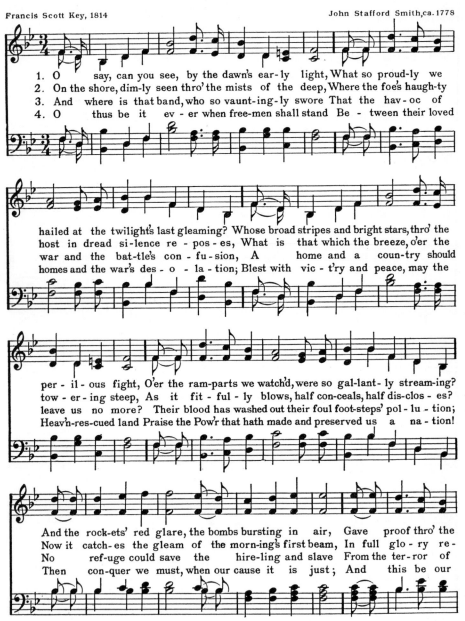

1. O say, can you see, by the dawn's ear-ly light, What so proud-ly we hailed at the twilight's last gleaming? Whose broad stripes and bright stars, thro' the per-il-ous fight, O'er the ram-parts we watch'd, were so gal-lant-ly stream-ing? And the rock-ets' red glare, the bombs bursting in air, Gave proof thro' the

2. On the shore, dim-ly seen thro' the mists of the deep, Where the foe's haugh-ty host in dread si-lence re-pos-es, What is that which the breeze, o'er the tow-er-ing steep, As it fit-ful-ly blows, half con-ceals, half dis-clos-es? Now it catch-es the gleam of the morn-ing's first beam, In full glo-ry re-

3. And where is that band, who so vaunt-ing-ly swore That the hav-oc of war and the bat-tle's con-fu-sion, A home and a coun-try should leave us no more? Their blood has washed out their foul foot-steps' pol-lu-tion; No ref-uge could save the hire-ling and slave From the ter-ror of

4. O thus be it ev-er when free-men shall stand Be-tween their loved homes and the war's des-o-la-tion; Blest with vic-t'ry and peace, may the Heav'n-res-cued land Praise the Pow'r that hath made and preserved us a na-tion! Then con-quer we must, when our cause it is just; And this be our

night that our flag was still there. O say, does that star-spangled
flect - ed, now shines on the stream: 'Tis the star-span-gled ban-ner; O
flight or the gloom of the grave. And the star-span-gled ban-ner in
mot - to: "In God is our trust!" And the star-span-gled ban-ner in

ban - ner yet wave O'er the land of the free, and the home of the brave?
long may it wave O'er the land of the free, and the home of the brave.
tri-umph doth wave O'er the land of the free, and the home of the brave.
tri-umph shall wave O'er the land of the free, and the home of the brave.

415 In Days of Yore, from Britain's Shore*

MAPLE LEAF FOR EVER

Alexander Muir
Arr. Lawrence J. Munson, 1915

1. In days of yore, from Brit - ain's shore, Wolf, the daunt - less
2. At Queens-town Heights and Lun - dy's Lane, Our brave fa - thers,
3. Our fair Do - min - ion now ex - tends From Cape Race to
4. On mer - ry Eng - land's far - famed land May kind Heav - en

he - ro, came, And plant - ed firm Bri - tan - nia's flag, On Can -
side by side, For free - dom, homes, and loved ones dear, Firm-ly
Noot-ka Sound; May peace for ev - er be our lot, And
sweet-ly smile; God bless old Scot-land ev - er more, And

*Printed here at the request of Canadians

a - da's fair do - main.   Here may it wave, our boast, our pride,
stood and no - bly died;   And those dear rights which they main-tained,
plen-teous store a - bound;   And may those ties of love be ours
Ire - land's Em-'rald Isle!   Then swell the song both loud and long,

And joined in love to - geth-er!   The This - tle, Sham-rock,
We swear to yield them nev - er!   Our watch-word ev - er
Which dis - cord can - not sev - er,   And flour - ish green o'er
Till rocks and for - est quiv - er,   God save our King and

Rose, en - twine, The Ma - ple Leaf for ev - er!
more shall be, The Ma - ple Leaf for ev - er!
Free - dom's home, The Ma - ple Leaf for ev - er!
Heav - en bless The Ma - ple Leaf for ev - er!

CHORUS

The Ma - ple Leaf, our em - blem dear, The Ma - ple Leaf for ev - er!

God save our King, and Heav-en bless The Ma-ple Leaf for ev-er!

416 O God, beneath Thy Guiding Hand

DUKE STREET L. M.

Leonard Bacon, 1845

John Hatton, d. 1793

1. O God, be-neath Thy guid - ing hand Our ex - iled
2. Thou heard, well-pleased, the song, the pray'r; Thy bless-ing
3. Laws, free-dom, truth, and faith in God Came with those
4. And here Thy name, O God of love, Their chil-dren's

fa - thers crossed the sea; And when they trod the
came, and still its pow'r Shall on - ward thro' all
ex - iles o'er the waves; And where their pil - grim
chil - dren shall a - dore, Till these e - ter - nal

win - try strand, With pray'r and psalm they wor-shiped Thee.
a - ges bear The mem-'ry of that ho - ly hour.
feet have trod, The God they trust - ed guards their graves.
hills re - move, And spring a - dorns the earth no more.

375

417 God Save Our Gracious King*

AMERICA 6 6 4, 6 6 6 4

Henry Carey, 1743

1. God save our gra - cious King, Long live our
2. O Lord our God, a - rise, Scat - ter his
3. Thy choic - est gifts in store On him be

no - ble King, God save the King: Send him vic -
en - e - mies, And make them fall: Con - found their
pleased to pour; Long may he reign: May he de -

to - ri - ous, Hap - py and glo - ri - ous,
pol - i - tics; Frus - trate their knav - ish tricks;
fend our laws, And ev - er give us cause

Long to reign o - ver us, God save the King.
On him our hopes we fix; God save us all.
To sing with heart and voice, God save the King.

* Printed here at the request of Canadians.

See also:

Lord of our life, 14

Faith of our fathers, 370

VIII. Last Things

418 Despair Not, O Heart, in Thy Sorrow

DESPAIR NOT, O HEART 9 9 4L.

Aurelius C. Prudentius, ca. 413
Peder J. Hegelund, 1586
Tr. O. T. Sanden, 1909

4th Century? 1542

1. De - spair not, O heart, in thy sor - row, But hope from God's
2. The bo - dy is shroud-ed in mourn-ing; The gar - lands, the
3. A dear - ly be - loved one hath left us; God hath in His
4. When dawn-eth the glo - ri - ous mor - row, This bo - dy, that

prom - is - es bor - row; Be - ware, in thy sor - row, of
cas - ket a - dorn - ing, Are em - blems of hope that be -
wis - dom be - reft us; But He will not leave us for -
we view with sor - row, A glo - ri - fied form shall be

sin - ning, For death is of life the be - gin - ning.
tok - en, O Death, that thy pow - er is brok - en.
sak - en,— We know that the dead shall a - wak - en.
giv - en, Re - stored to its spir - it in heav - en.

5. The seed that in springtime is planted,
   Is hid in the ground; but if granted
   A measure of sunshine and showers,
   Will spring into fruitage and flowers.

6. O Christ, our souls' Maker and Lover;
   When time and earth's travail are over,
   Thou closest the grave's mournful story,
   And callest Thine own to Thy glory.

419 Asleep in Jesus! Blessed Sleep

LORD JESUS CHRIST, BE PRESENT NOW L.M.
(See No. 421)

Margaret Mackay, 1832

Cantionale Sacrum, Gotha, 1654
Arr. F. Melius Christiansen, 1907

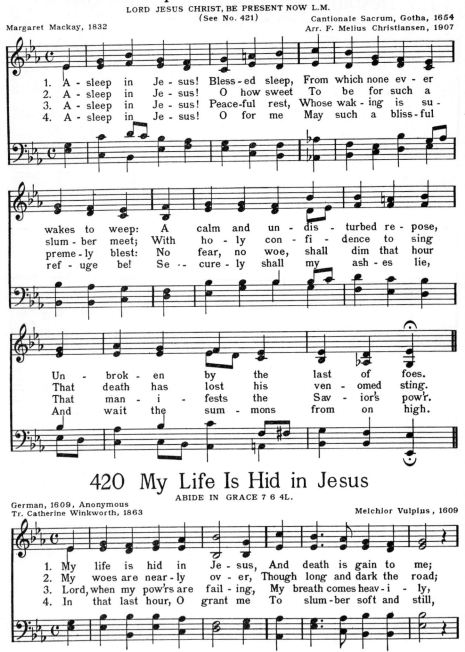

1. A - sleep in Je - sus! Bless - ed sleep, From which none ev - er
2. A - sleep in Je - sus! O how sweet To be for such a
3. A - sleep in Je - sus! Peace-ful rest, Whose wak - ing is su -
4. A - sleep in Je - sus! O for me May such a bliss - ful

wakes to weep: A calm and un - dis - turbed re - pose,
slum - ber meet; With ho - ly con - fi - dence to sing
preme - ly blest: No fear, no woe, shall dim that hour
ref - uge be! Se - cure - ly shall my ash - es lie,

Un - brok - en by the last of foes.
That death has lost his ven - omed sting.
That man - i - fests the Sav - ior's pow'r.
And wait the sum - mons from on high.

420 My Life Is Hid in Jesus

ABIDE IN GRACE 7 6 4L.

German, 1609, Anonymous
Tr. Catherine Winkworth, 1863

Melchior Vulpius, 1609

1. My life is hid in Je - sus, And death is gain to me;
2. My woes are near - ly ov - er, Though long and dark the road;
3. Lord, when my pow'rs are fail - ing, My breath comes heav - i - ly,
4. In that last hour, O grant me To slum - ber soft and still,

Then, when-so-e'er He pleas - es; I meet it will-ing-ly.
My sin His mer-its cov - er, And I have peace with God.
And words are un-a - vail-ing, O hear my sighs to Thee!
No doubts to vex or haunt me, Safe an-chored on Thy will.

421 Asleep in Jesus, Blessed Sleep

ASLEEP IN JESUS L.M.
(See No. 419)

Margaret Mackay, 1832   Ole Bull

1. A - sleep in Je - sus! Bless - ed sleep, From which none
2. A - sleep in Je - sus! O how sweet To be for
3. A - sleep in Je - sus! Peace - ful rest, Whose wak - ing
4. A - sleep in Je - sus! O for me May such a

ev - er wakes to weep; A calm and un-dis-turbed re - pose,
such a slum - ber meet; With ho - ly con-fi-dence to sing
is su - preme-ly blest: No fear, no woe,shall dim that hour
bliss-ful ref - uge be! Se - cure-ly shall my ash-es lie,

Un - brok - en by the last of foes, last of foes.
That death has lost his ven - omed sting, ven-omed sting.
That man - i - fests the Sav - ior's pow'r, Sav-ior's pow'r.
And wait the sum-mons from on high, from on high.

422 As Sinks beneath the Ocean

AS SINKS BENEATH THE OCEAN 7 6,7 6,7 6,7 6 7

Sigvald Skavlan
Tr. Olav Lee

F. Melius Christiansen

1. As sinks be-neath the o - cean The sun at ev - en-tide, E'en so the soul whose por-tion Is Christ, in Him doth hide. Ab-solved thro' faith it rest-eth With - in His wounds' re-treat, And mer - cy hav-ing tast - ed It death can

2. O death, I do not fear thee, Though dark thy sha - dow be, Thy sting is gone, and near me The o - pen heav'n I see. Where is, O grave, thy boot - y? 'Tis in the hand of God; How does such vic - t'ry suit thee? Crushed is thy

3. As ris - es from the o - cean The sun in bright ar - ray With beau - ty for its por - tion To lead the new - born day, So shall I rise all glo-rious His crown-ed bride to be Who rose o'er death vic - tor - ious, To share His

382

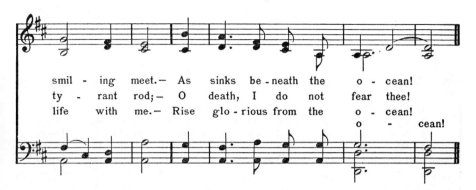

smil - ing meet. — As sinks be - neath the o - cean!
ty - rant rod; — O death, I do not fear thee!
life with me. — Rise glo - rious from the o - cean!
o - cean!

423 Tender Shepherd, Thou Hast Stilled

JESUS CHRIST, MY SURE DEFENCE 7 8, 7 8, 7 7

J. W. Meinhold, 1835   German, 1656

1. Ten-der Shep-herd, Thou hast stilled Now Thy lit - tle lamb's brief weep-ing:
2. In this world of pain and care, Lord, Thou wouldst no long - er leave it:
3. O Lord Je - sus, grant that we There may live where it is liv - ing,

Ah, how peace-ful, pale and mild, In its nar - row bed 'tis sleep-ing!
To Thy heav'n-ly mead-ows fair Lov - ing - ly Thou dost re - ceive it.
And the bliss-ful pas-tures see That its heav'n-ly food are giv - ing;

And no sigh of an-guish sore Heaves that lit - tle bo - som more.
Clothed in robes of spot - less white, Now it dwells with Thee in light.
Then the gain of death we'll prove, Though Thou take what most we love.

424 Come, Lord, Thyself with Thine Abounding Grace

EVENTIDE 10 10 4L.

Hallgrimur Petursson, 1614-1674
Tr. C. V. Pilcher

William Henry Monk, 1861

1. Come, Lord, Thy - self with Thine a - bound - ing grace;
Mine ut - most depth of need Thine eyes can trace:
Thou, Lord, through life's long way my guard and guide,
Let not Thy pil - grim's last tired foot - steps slide.

2. Up - on my sight dark dawns the ris - ing day;
Faint fall the sounds of earth, and far a - way:
None, none can aid; by death's lone nar - row door,
I pass be - yond man's help for - ev - er - more.

3. None, none can aid but Thou, Al - might - y Lord;
I stay me on Thine ev - er - last - ing word;
Let earth de - cay, heav'n's far - flung glo - ries pale,
Je - ho - vah's plight - ed word can nev - er fail.

4. With - in th' e - ter - nal arms I sink to rest;
Washed in the stream that flow'd from Je - sus' breast:
The life Thou gav - est, Fa - ther, now de - fend;
In - to Thy hands my spir - it I com - mend.

5. Let the last psalm my dy - ing voice can raise,
Ex - tol Thy lov - ing - kind - ness, hymn Thy praise:
Let the first notes my wak - ing lips can frame
A - mid th' e - ter - nal glo - ry laud Thy name.

425 Praise God, This Hour of Sorrow

O BREAD OF LIFE 7 7 6, 7 7 8

Johann Heerman, 1634
Hans Adolf Brorson, 1714
Tr. O.H. Smeby, 1904

Heinrich Isaac, 1490

1. Praise God, this hour of sor - row Shall bring a bright-er mor - row:
2. I was on earth your treas-ure; When now I know but pleas - ure
3. When ye shall see me near-ing The throne of God, ap - pear - ing
4. Ye both shall rue the sad-ness That made you weep, and glad - ness
5. Fare - well, I now must leave you; The grief this day doth give you

I go to Par - a - dise. My moth-er dear and fa - ther, When
Ye weep in bit - ter woe; Be - lieve, what-e'er be - tid - eth, God's
A - dorned and crown'd a bride, My palms of vic - t'ry swing-ing, 'Midst
E'er in your hearts shall reign. Who fol-lows where God guid - eth, And
Soon oth-ers, too, shall bear. Be ye to God com - mend - ed; In

round my grave you gath - er, Lay me to rest with songs of praise.
love in all a - bid - eth, And soon your tears shall cease to flow.
Hal - le - lu - jahs ring - ing, In beau-teous grace the Lamb be - side:
takes what He pro - vid - eth, Shall know sur-cease from all his pain.
heav'n all woe is end - ed, And we shall meet in glo - ry there.

See also:

426 Wake, Awake, for Night Is Flying

WAKE, AWAKE Irregular

Philipp Nicolai, 1599
Tr. William Cook, 1871, alt.

Philipp Nicolai, 1599

One beat to the half-note.

1. Wake, a - wake, for night is fly - ing: The
2. Zi - on hears the watch-men sing - ing, Her
3. Hear Thy praise, O Lord, as - cend - ing From

watch-men on the heights are cry - ing, A - wake, Je - ru - sa - lem, a - rise!
heart with deep de-light is spring-ing, At once she wakes, she hastes a-way:
tongues of men and an - gels, blend-ing With harp and lute and psal-ter - y.

Mid-night's sol-emn hour is toll - ing, His char-iot wheels are near-er
Forth her Bride-groom hast-ens glo - rious, In grace ar-rayed, by truth vic -
By Thy pearl - y gates in won - der We stand, and swell the voice of

roll - ing; He comes; prepare, ye vir-gins wise. Rise up; with will-ing feet
to - rious; Her grief is joy, her night is day: All hail, in-car-nate Lord,
thun-der, In bursts of chor-al mel - o - dy: To mor-tal eyes and ears

Go   forth, the Bridegroom meet;   Hal - le - lu - jah!   Bear thro' the night
Our crown, and our re - ward!   Hal - le - lu - jah!   We haste a - long,
What glo - ry now ap - pears!   Hal - le - lu - jah!   We raise the song,

your well-trimmed light,   Speed forth to join the mar - riage rite.
in   pomp of song,   And glad-some join the mar - riage throng.
we   swell the throng,   To praise Thee ag - es all   a - long.

427 Great King of Kings, Why Dost Thou Stay

ALMSGIVING 8 8, 8 4

Horatius Bonar, 1868   John B. Dykes, 1865

1. Great King of kings, why dost Thou stay, Why tar-riest Thou up -
2. Life in its   full - ness is with Thee, Life in its ho - ly
3. Earth is still wait - ing for the day, When old things shall have
4. O King of glo - ry, King of peace, Bid all these storms and

on Thy way, Why lin-gers the ex - pect - ed day? Thy kingdom come!
lib - er - ty; From death and chains this world set free; Thy kingdom come!
pass'd a - way, And all be clad in new ar - ray: Thy kingdom come!
tu - mults cease, Bring in Thy reign of right - eous-ness; Thy kingdom come!

428 The Day Is Surely Drawing Near

ALL GLORY BE TO THEE 8 7, 8 7, 8 8 7

Bartholomaus Ringwaldt, ca. 1565, alt.
Tr. Peter A. Peter

Val. Schumann's Geistliche Lieder, 1539
Nicolaus Decius? 1539

1. The day is sure-ly draw-ing near, When He, the Lord's A-noint-ed,
2. Then woe to those who scorn'd the Lord, And sought but car-nal pleas-ures,
3. O Christ, my In-ter-ces-sor be, And for Thy death and mer-it
4. Lord Je-sus Christ, do not de-lay, O hast-en our sal-va-tion!

Will with great maj-es-ty ap-pear, As Judge of all ap-
Who here de-spised His pre-cious word, And loved their earth-ly
De-clare my name from judg-ment free, With all who life in-
We oft-en trem-ble on our way, In fear and trib-u-

point-ed. No more the gos-pel call is heard To
treas-ures, With shame and trem-bling they shall stand, And
her-it; That with my breth-ren I may stand With
la-tion. Then hear us when we cry to Thee: Come,

turn from sin and heed God's word: The day of grace is end-ed.
at the Judg-e's stern com-mand De-part from Him for-ev-er.
Thee in heav'n, our fa-ther-land, Which Thou for us hast pur-chased.
might-y Judge, come, make us free From ev-'ry e-vil. A-men!

429 When Jesus Comes in Glory

AURELIA 7 6 8L

Samuel Martin Miller, 1922

Samuel S. Wesley, 1864

1. When Je-sus comes in glo - ry, As Lord and King of kings,
2. His voice like rush-ing wa - ters Will reach with might-y sound
3. And we who are be - liev - ing And His ap - pear-ing love,
4. O hast - en Thine ap - pear-ing, Thou Bright and Morn-ing Star!

O what a won-drous sto - ry The bless-ed Bi - ble brings:
In - to the deep-est quar-ters Of all cre - a - tion round;
Shall know we are re - ceiv - ing His glo - ry from a - bove;
Lord, may we soon be hear - ing The trum-pet sound a - far;

His face will shine like sun - light, His head be white as snow,
And at this won-drous greet - ing The dead in Christ shall rise,
His res - ur - rec -tion pow - er Will raise us to the place
Thy peo-ple all are yearn-ing To be Thy rap-tured bride,

His eyes like flam-ing fire - light, His feet like brass a - glow.
Their Lord and Sav -ior meet - ing In glo - ry in the skies.
Where we that won-drous ho - ur Shall see Him face to face.
And at Thine own re - turn - ing Be caught up to Thy side.

430 O Son of God, We Wait for Thee

BADEN 8 7, 8 7, 8 7 7

Philip F. Hiller, 1767
Tr. Joseph A. Seiss, 1890

Severus Gastorius, 1675

1. O Son of God, we wait for Thee, We long for Thine ap-
2. We wait for Thee 'mid toil and pain, In wear-i-ness and
3. We wait for Thee; here Thou hast won Our hearts to hope and
4. We wait for Thee; soon Thou wilt come, The time is swift-ly

pear - ing, We know Thou sit-test on the throne, And
sigh - ing; But glad that Thou our guilt hast borne, And
du - ty; But while our spir-its feel Thee near, Our
near - ing; In this we al-so do re-joice, And

we Thy name are bear - ing. Who trusts in Thee may joy-ful be,
can-celled it by dy - ing. Hence, cheer-ful-ly may we with Thee
eyes would see Thy beau - ty; We fain would be at rest with Thee
long for Thine ap - pear - ing, O bliss 'twill be when Thee we see,

And see Thee, Lord, de-scend - ing To bring us bliss un-end - ing.
Take up our cross and bear it, Till we re-lief in-her - it.
In peace and joy su-per - nal, In glo-rious life e-ter - nal.
Home-ward Thy peo-ple bring - ing, With trans-port and with sing - ing!

See also: Rejoice all ye believers, 113. Hark! ten thousand harps and voices, 219

431 Jerusalem the Golden

EWING 7 6 8L.

Bernard de Morlaix, ca. 1145
Tr. John Mason Neale, 1851

Alexander Ewing, 1853

1. Je - ru - sa - lem the gold - en, With milk and hon - ey blest,
2. They stand, those halls of Zi - on, All ju - bi - lant with song,
3. There is the throne of Da - vid; And there from care re - leased,
4. O sweet and bless - ed coun - try, The home of God's e - lect!

Be - neath thy con - tem - pla - tion Sink heart and voice op - prest,
And bright with many an an - gel, And all the mar - tyr throng;
The shout of them that tri - umph, The song of them that feast;
O sweet and bless - ed coun - try That ea - ger hearts ex - pect!

I know not, O I know not, What joys a - wait us there,
The Prince is ev - er in them, The day - light is se - rene,
And they who with their Lead - er Have con - quered in the fight,
In mer - cy, Je - sus, bring us To that dear land of rest;

What ra - dian - cy of glo - ry, What bliss be - yond com - pare.
The pas - tures of the bless - ed Are decked in glo - rious sheen.
For ev - er and for ev - er Are clad in robes of white.
Who art, with God, the Fa - ther And Spir - it ev - er blest.

391

432 How Blessed Is the Host in White

BLESSED HOST 8 6. 8 6, 8 8, 8 6

Olav Lee

Folk-Tune
Arr. Oscar R. Overby, 1932

1. How bless - ed is the host in white Whom Je - sus
2. They hun - ger not, they thirst no more, No heat shall

made His own, To serve the Lord is their de - light,
strike them there. The Lamb who go - eth them be - fore

To wor - ship at His throne. He spreads in new Je -
For all their wants doth care. To where the liv - ing

ru - sa - lem His ta - ber - na - cle o - ver them, And there se -
wa - ters flow They with their Shep - herd glad - ly go, And He who

cure from harm they dwell; Their bliss no tongue can tell.
on the throne ap - pears Shall wipe a - way their tears.

433 In Heaven Above, in Heaven Above

IN HEAVEN ABOVE 8 6, 8 6, 8 8 6

Laurentius Laurentii, 1573-1655
Tr William Maccall, 1868

Norwegian Folk-Tune

1. In heav'n a - bove, in heav'n a - bove, Where God, our Fa - ther, dwells;
2. In heav'n a - bove, in heav'n a - bove, What glo - ry deep and bright!
3. In heav'n a - bove, in heav'n a - bove, No tears of pain are shed:
4. In heav'n a - bove, in heav'n a - bove, God hath a joy pre - pared,

How bound-less there the bless-ed - ness! No tongue its great-ness tells:
The splen-dor of the noon-day sun Grows pale be - fore its light:
For naught can yon - der fade or die; Life's ful - ness round is spread,
Which mor - tal ear had nev - er heard, Nor mor - tal vis - ion shared,

There face to face, and full and free, For - ev - er,
The heav'n - ly light that ne'er goes down, A - round whose
And like an o - cean, joy o'er - flows, And with im -
Which nev - er en - tered mor - tal breast, By mor - tal

ev - er - more we see — Our God, the Lord of hosts!
ra - diance clouds ne'er frown, Is God, the Lord of hosts.
mor - tal mer - cy glows Our God, the Lord of hosts.
lips was ne'er ex - pressed, O God, the Lord of hosts!

434 Behold the Host Arrayed in White

GREAT WHITE HOST 8 8, 4 4 6 15L.

Hans Adolf Brorson, ca. 1760
Tr. Carl Doving, 1909

Norwegian Folk-Tune
Arr. Edvard Grieg, 1843-1907

1. Be - hold the host ar - rayed in white, Like thou-sand snow- clad
2. On earth de-spised, be - neath the rod, They thro' the fire of
3. O hap - py saints for - ev - er blest! Hail, ye who have at -

moun-tains bright, With palms they stand—Who are this band Be -
tri - als trod, Now clothed in white, They dwell in light, Are
tained your rest! Faith - ful to death Ye kept the faith Though

fore the throne of light? These are the ran-somed throng, the same
kings and priests to God; How of - ten in the e - vil day
ye were sore op - prest; The world ye did re - nounce of yore,

That from the trib - u - la - tion came And in the flood Of
They here be - low did weep and pray, But, con - flicts past, Bro't
The pre-cious seed ye weep-ing bore, Now reap the joy With-

Je - sus blood Are cleansed from guilt and shame, And now ar-rayed in
home at last, God wiped their tears a - way; No hun-ger there, nor
out al - loy In bliss for - ev - er - more; Lift up your voice, wave

robes made white They God are serv - ing day and night, And
thirst they know, No scorch-ing sun doth work them woe, The
palms a - gain, And swell the ev - er - last-ing song: All

an - thems swell Where God doth dwell 'Mid an - gels in the height.
Lamb them feeds, Him - self them leads Where liv - ing foun - tains flow.
glo - ry be, O God, to Thee, And to the Lamb be - long.

See also:

O land of our King, 345

One radiant morn, 337

There many shall come, 157 or 158

What joy to reach the harbor, 330

From all Thy saints in warfare, 240

Dayspring of eternity, 52

I see Thee standing, 220

In heaven is joy and gladness, 344

I know of a sleep in Jesus' name, 331

O happy day, 62

Orders of Service

The Order of Morning Service I

The Order of Morning Service II

The Holy Communion Service

The Order of Afternoon or Evening Service

The Order of Evening Service

The Order of Church School Service

The Order of Morning Service I

ORGAN PRELUDE

OPENING PRAYER

Minister, or Assistant:

O Lord, our Maker, Redeemer, and Comforter, we are assembled in Thy presence to hear Thy holy word. We pray Thee so to open our hearts by Thy Holy Spirit, that through the preaching of Thy word we may be taught to repent of our sins, to believe on Jesus in life and in death, and to grow day by day in grace and holiness. Hear us for Christ's sake. Amen.

OPENING HYMN

CONFESSION OF SIN

Minister:

Let us bow before the Lord and confess our sins:
Almighty God, our Maker and Redeemer, we poor sinners confess unto Thee that we are by nature sinful and unclean, and that we have sinned against Thee by thought, word and deed. Wherefore we flee for refuge to Thine infinite mercy, seeking and imploring Thy grace, for the sake of our Lord Jesus Christ. Amen.

Or,

O most merciful God, who hast given Thine only-begotten Son to die for us, have mercy upon us, and for His sake grant us remission of all our sins; and by Thy Holy Spirit increase in us true knowledge of Thee, and of Thy will, and true obedience to Thy word, to the end that by Thy grace we may come to everlasting life, through Jesus Christ, our Lord. Amen.

KYRIE

Congregation, or Minister and Congregation responsively:

O God the Father in heaven, have mercy upon us!

O God the Son, Redeemer of the world, have mercy upon us!

O God the Holy Ghost, true Comforter, have mercy upon us!

399

ABSOLUTION

Minister:

Almighty God, our heavenly Father, hath had mercy upon us, and hath given His only Son to die for us, and for His sake forgiveth us all our sins. To them that believe on His name He giveth power to become the sons of God, and hath promised them His Holy Spirit. He that believeth and is baptized shall be saved.

Grant this, Lord, unto us all.

GLORIA (May be omitted during Lent)

Minister Chants or Says:

Glo - ry be to God in the high - est,

Congregation responds, singing:

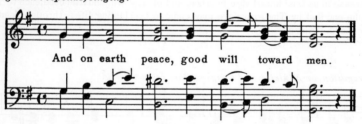

And on earth peace, good will toward men.

THE COLLECT (The congregation shall rise and stand until the Epistle is read)

Minister Chants or Says: *Congregation responds:*

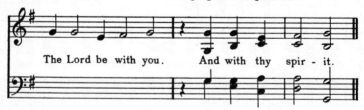

The Lord be with you.   And with thy spir - it.

Minister Chants or Says:

Let us all pray:

The Collect for the day follows here, after which the congregation responds:

400

Congregation:

THE EPISTLE, OR LESSON

Minister reads the Epistle or Lesson for the day

(Here the service may be shortened by going directly to the Confession of Faith)

HYMN OR SPECIAL MUSIC

THE GOSPEL (The congregation shall rise and stand until the Creed has been said)

Minister reads the Gospel

Congregation responds by singing:

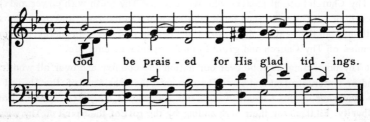

CONFESSION OF FAITH -- THE APOSTLES' CREED

Minister:

Let us confess our holy Faith:

Minister and congregation:

I believe in God the Father Almighty, Maker of heaven and earth.
And in Jesus Christ, His only Son, our Lord; Who was conceived by the Holy Ghost;
Born of the Virgin Mary; Suffered under Pontius Pilate; Was crucified, dead and
buried; He descended into hell; The third day He rose again from the dead; He a-
scended into heaven, And sitteth on the right hand of God the Father Almighty; From
thence He shall come to judge the quick and the dead.
I believe in the Holy Ghost; The Holy Christian Church, the Communion of Saints;
The Forgiveness of sins; The Resurrection of the body; And the Life everlasting.

Congregation: (This *Amen* may be said or sung)

A - - - - men.

HYMN

SERMON, Closing with the

Gloria Patri:

Glory be to the Father, and to the Son, and to the Holy Ghost; as it was in the be-
ginning, is now, and ever shall be, world without end. Amen.

Then may be said

The General Prayer:

Everlasting and merciful God, we beseech Thee in the name of our Lord Jesus Christ:

Look in mercy upon Thy Church. Protect it and sanctify it by Thy truth. May Thy
word be taught in its purity and Thy sacraments be rightly administered. Grant unto Thy Church faithful pastors who will declare Thy truth with power and shall live
according to Thy will. Send forth laborers into Thy harvest, and open the door of
faith unto all the heathen and unto the people of Israel. In mercy remember the
enemies of Thy Church and grant to them repentance unto life.

Let Thy protecting hand be over our nation and country and over all who travel by
land or water. Protect and bless Thy servants, the President of the United States,
the Governor of this Commonwealth, our Judges and Magistrates, and all others in
authority. Fit them for their high calling by the gift of the Spirit of Thy wisdom and
fear, that we may lead a quiet and peaceable life, in all godliness and honesty.

According to Thy promise, O God, be Thou the Defender of the widow and the Fa -
ther of the orphan. Relieve and comfort the sick and the sorrowful. Graciously help
those who are assaulted by the devil and who are in peril of death. Be the strength
of those who are suffering for the sake of Christ's name. Grant that we may live
together in peace and prosperity. Bestow upon us good and seasonable weather.
And bless us with upright Christian counsel in all that we undertake.

Especially do we commend to Thy care and keeping this Thy congregation which
Thou hast bought with a great price. Keep from us all offenses, and bind us together in the unity of Thy holy love. Grant that the little ones who are baptized in
Thy name may be brought up in Thy fear. (Bestow the power of renunciation and
faith upon the hearts of the young who are to be confirmed in their baptismal covenant.) And at Thy table give unto those who there commune with Thee peace and
life everlasting.

Be merciful, O God, unto all men, according to Thy great love in Christ Jesus, our Lord. And, when our final hour shall come, grant us a blessed departure from this world, and, on the last day, a resurrection to Thy glory. Amen.

The Lord's Prayer:

Our Father who art in heaven; Hallowed be Thy name; Thy kingdom come; Thy will be done on earth, as it is in heaven; Give us this day our daily bread; And forgive us our trespasses, as we forgive those who trespass against us; And lead us not into temptation; But deliver us from evil: For Thine is the kindgom, and the power, and the glory, forever and ever. Amen.

The Apostolic Benediction:

The grace of the Lord Jesus Christ, and the love of God, and the communion of the Holy Ghost be with you all. Amen.

HYMN OR CHOIR ANTHEM

At this place the *Announcements* may be made, after which an *Offertory* may be played and the *Offerings* gathered.

HOLY BAPTISM may then be administered, before and after which a baptismal hymn shall be sung.

HOLY COMMUNION -- When Holy Communion is celebrated, continue from here to A on page 412.

For *Public Confession and Absolution,* see Altar Book.

COLLECT FOR THE WORD (The congregation shall stand)

Minister Chants or Says: *Congregation responds:*

The Lord be with you. And with thy spir - it.

Minister Chants or Says:

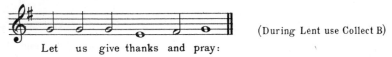

Let us give thanks and pray: (During Lent use Collect B)

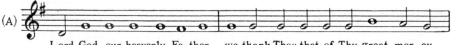

(A) Lord God, our heavenly Fa-ther, we thank Thee, that of Thy great mer- cy

403

Thou hast given us Thy ho - ly and bless-ed word by which Thou dost al -

so a - mong us gath - er Thy Chris-tian Church. We hum-bly en-treat Thee,

grant us Thy Ho - ly Spir-it, that we may re-ceive Thy word with thank -

ful hearts, and live ac - cord-ing there-to, and ev - er in-crease in Chris-

tian faith, and hope, and love, and at last ob-tain e - ter - nal sal -

va-tion: Through Je-sus Christ, Thy be-lov-ed Son, who liv-eth and reign - eth

with Thee and the Ho - ly Ghost, ev - er one God, world with-out end.

(Lenten Collect)

(B) We thank Thee, Lord God the Fa - ther, that Thou didst give

Thine on - ly be - got - ten Son, that who - so - ev - er be - liev -

eth on Him shall not per - ish, but have ev - er - last - ing life.

We thank Thee, Lord Je-sus Christ, that Thou hast borne in Thy sa-cred bod - y

all our sins, and by Thy blood hast blot-ted out all our trans-gres-sions.

We thank Thee, Lord the Ho - ly Ghost, that Thou hast wrought in our hearts such faith,

that we know noth-ing where-in to trust for sal - va - tion, save Je - sus Christ

and Him cru - ci - fied. Grant us, O God, Thy grace, that we may per - fect - ly

be-lieve that all our sins are for-giv - en, for the sake of the pas-sion

and death of Je - sus Christ, and so en -light - en us by Thy Ho - ly

Spir - it, that, in the power of our Re-deem-er's death, we may day by

day put off sin, and nev - er for-sake the Lord Je - sus, un - til we

see Him face to face in life e - ter - nal We ask it all in Christ's name

Congregation:

A - - - - men

THE ORDER OF MORNING SERVICE I

BENEDICTION

Minister Chants or Says: *Congregation responds:*

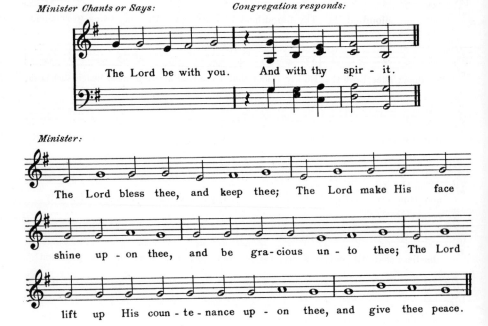

The Lord be with you.   And with thy spir - it.

Minister:

The Lord bless thee, and keep thee; The Lord make His face shine up - on thee, and be gra - cious un - to thee; The Lord lift up His coun - te - nance up - on thee, and give thee peace.

Congregation:

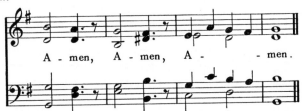

A - men, A - men, A - - men.

CLOSING HYMN

CLOSING PRAYER

Minister, or Assistant:

O Lord, we render unto Thee our heartfelt thanks that Thou hast taught us what Thou wouldst have us believe and do. Help us, O God, by Thy Holy Spirit for the sake of Jesus Christ to keep Thy word in pure hearts, that we thereby may be strengthened in faith, perfected in holiness, and comforted in life and death. Amen.

ORGAN POSTLUDE

Morning Service II

The Order of Morning Service II

OPENING HYMN

CONFESSION OF SIN

Minister:

Let us bow before the Lord and confess our sins.

Almighty God, our Maker and Redeemer, we poor sinners confess unto Thee that we are by nature sinful and unclean, and that we have sinned against Thee in thought, word and deed. Wherefore we flee for refuge to Thine infinite mercy and beseech Thee for Christ's sake, grant us remission of all our sins, and by Thy Holy Spirit increase in us true knowledge of Thee and of Thy will and true obedience to Thy word, to the end that by Thy grace we may come to everlasting life, through Jesus Christ, our Lord. Amen.

KYRIE

Congregation sings:

O God the Father in heaven, have mercy upon us!

O God the Son, Redeemer of the world, have mercy upon us!

O God the Holy Ghost, true Comforter, have mercy upon us!

COLLECT

SCRIPTURE LESSON, after which the

Congregation sings:

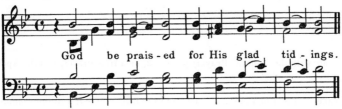

God be prais - ed for His glad tid - ings.

CONFESSION OF FAITH

Minister:

Let us confess our holy Faith.

Minister and Congregation:

I believe in God the Father Almighty, Maker of heaven and earth.

And in Jesus Christ, His only Son, our Lord; Who was conceived by the Holy Ghost; Born of the Virgin Mary; Suffered under Pontius Pilate; Was crucified, dead and buried; He descended into hell; The third day He rose again from the dead; He ascended into heaven; And sitteth on the right hand of God the Father Almighty; From thence He shall come to judge the quick and the dead.

I believe in the Holy Ghost; The holy Christian Church, the Communion of Saints; The Forgiveness of sins; The Resurrection of the body; And the Life everlasting. Amen.

GLORIA PATRI

CHARLES MEINEKE

Glo-ry be to the Fa-ther, and to the Son, and to the Ho - ly Ghost; As it was in the be-ginning, is now, and ev-er shall be, world with-out end. A-men, A - men.

CHOIR ANTHEM

ANNOUNCEMENTS

OFFERTORY

HYMN

SERMON, closing with the General Prayer, page 402, or a free Prayer, and the Apostolic Benediction·

> The grace of the Lord Jesus Christ, and the love of God, and the communion of the Holy Ghost, be with you all. Amen.

HYMN

COMMUNION -- See page 414, B, for Communion Service

BAPTISM

THE LORD'S PRAYER

In unison·

> Our Father who art in heaven, Hallowed be Thy name; Thy kingdom come; Thy will be done on earth, as it is in heaven; Give us this day our daily bread; And forgive us our trespasses, as we forgive those who trespass against us; And lead us not into temptation; But deliver us from evil: For Thine is the kingdom, and the power, and the glory, for ever. Amen.

BENEDICTION

Minister:

> The Lord bless thee, and keep thee,
> The Lord make His face shine upon thee, and be gracious unto thee,
> The Lord lift up His countenance upon thee, and give thee peace. Amen.

Congregation sings:

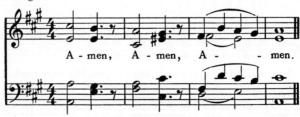

A - men, A - men, A - men.

CLOSING HYMN

The Holy Communion Service

Holy Communion

For *Confession* and *Absolution,* see Altar Book

COMMUNION HYMN, or the following PREFACE

Minister chants or says: *Congregation rises and responds:*

The Lord be with you.   And with thy spir - it.

Minister:

Lift up your hearts un - to the Lord.

Congregation:

We lift up our hearts un - to the Lord.

Minister:

Let us give thanks un - to the Lord our God.

Congregation:

It is meet and right so to do.

Minister, turning to the Altar:

It is tru - ly meet, right and sal - u - ta - ry, that we should

at all times, and in all plac - es, give praise un - to Thee, Ho - ly Lord,

Al - might - y Fa - ther, Ev - er - last - ing God, through Je - sus Christ our Lord;

There - fore with An - gels and Arch - an - gels, and with all the

com - pa - ny of heav - en, we laud and mag - ni - fy Thy

glo - rious Name; ev - er - more prais - ing Thee, and say - ing:

SANCTUS

Congregation:

Ho - ly, ho - ly, ho - ly, Lord, God of Sa - ba - oth.

Heaven and earth are full of Thy glo - ry. Ho - san - na

413

in the high - est. Bless - ed is He that com - eth in the name of the Lord. Ho - san - na in the high - est.

Ⓑ

EXHORTATION BEFORE COMMUNION

The Communicants gather about the Altar and remain standing.

Minister:

Dear friends in Christ! In order that you may receive this holy Sacrament worthily it becomes you diligently to consider what you must now believe and do. From the words of Christ: "This is my Body, which is given for you"; "This is my Blood, which is shed for you for the remission of sins"; you should believe that Jesus Christ is Himself present with His Body and Blood, as the words declare. From Christ's words, "For the remission of sins", you should, in the next place, believe that Jesus Christ bestows upon you His Body and Blood to confirm unto you the remission of all your sins. And, finally, you should do as Christ commands you when He says: "Take, eat"; "Drink ye all of it"; and, "This do in remembrance of me".

If you believe these words of Christ, and do as He therein has commanded, then you have rightly examined yourselves and may worthily eat Christ's Body and drink His Blood for the remission of your sins.

You should, also, unite in giving thanks to Almighty God, the Father of our Lord Jesus Christ, for so great a gift, and should love one another with a pure heart, and thus, with the whole Christian Church, have comfort and joy in Christ our Lord. To this end may God the Father grant you His grace; through the same, our Lord Jesus Christ. Amen.

Or,

Dearly Beloved! Forasmuch as we purpose to come to the Holy Supper of our Lord Jesus Christ, it becometh us diligently to examine ourselves, as St. Paul exhorteth us. For this Holy Sacrament hath been instituted for the special comfort and strengthening of those who humbly confess their sins, and who hunger and thirst after righteousness.

But if we thus examine ourselves, we shall find nothing in us but only sin and death, from which we can in no wise set ourselves free. Therefore our Lord Jesus Christ hath had mercy upon us and hath taken upon Himself our nature, that so He might fulfill for us the whole will and law of God, and for us and for our deliverance suffer death and all that we by our sins have deserved. And to the end that we should the more confidently believe this, and be strengthened by our faith in a cheerful obedience to His holy will, He hath instituted the Holy Sacrament of His Supper, in which He feedeth us with His Body, and giveth us to drink of His Blood.

Therefore whoso eateth of this bread, and drinketh of this cup, firmly believing the words of Christ, dwelleth in Christ, and Christ in him, and hath eternal life.

We should also do this in remembrance of Him, of His death, and how He was delivered for our offences, and raised again for our justification. And with hearts filled with gratitude for so great a salvation, we should take up our cross and follow Him, and, according to His commandment, love one another even as He hath loved us. For we are all one bread and one body, even as we are partakers of this one bread and drink of this one cup.

LORD'S PRAYER, Communicants kneel

Minister chants or says:

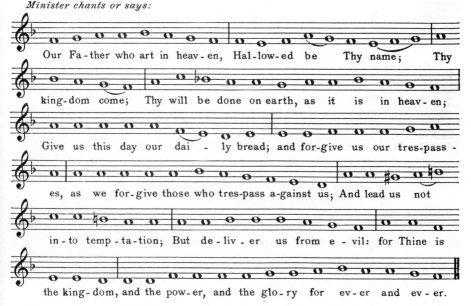

Our Fa-ther who art in heav-en, Hal-low-ed be Thy name; Thy king-dom come; Thy will be done on earth, as it is in heav-en; Give us this day our dai - ly bread; and for-give us our tres-pass-es, as we for-give those who tres-pass a-gainst us; And lead us not in-to temp-ta-tion; But de-liv-er us from e-vil: for Thine is the king-dom, and the pow-er, and the glo-ry for ev-er and ev-er.

Congregation:

A - - - - men.

WORDS OF INSTITUTION

Minister chants or says:

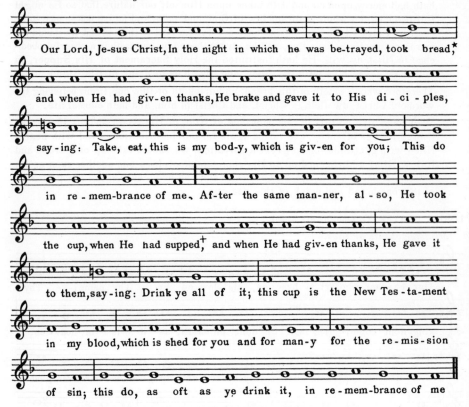

Our Lord, Je-sus Christ, In the night in which he was be-trayed, took bread,*

and when He had giv-en thanks, He brake and gave it to His di - ci - ples,

say - ing: Take, eat, this is my bod-y, which is giv-en for you; This do

in re - mem-brance of me. Af-ter the same man-ner, al - so, He took

the cup, when He had supped,+ and when He had giv-en thanks, He gave it

to them, say - ing: Drink ye all of it; this cup is the New Tes - ta-ment

in my blood, which is shed for you and for man-y for the re - mis - sion

of sin; this do, as oft as ye drink it, in re - mem-brance of me

★ Here he takes the Plate with the Bread in his hand
✚ Here he takes the Cup in his hand.

DISTRIBUTION, A Communion Hymn may be sung during the Distribution

Minister gives the Bread to the Communicants, saying to each one:

This is the true Body of Christ.

He then gives the Cup to the Communicants, saying to each one:

This is the true Blood of Christ.

Minister, when Distribution is ended, says:

Our crucified and risen Lord, Jesus Christ, who now hath bestowed upon you His holy Body and Blood, whereby He hath made full satisfaction for all your sins, strengthen and preserve you in the true faith unto everlasting life. Peace be with you. Amen.

HYMN OF THANKSGIVING

COLLECT OF THANKSGIVING

Minister chants or says: *Congregation responds:*

The Lord be with you. And with thy spir - it..

Minister:

Let us give thanks and pray: We thank Thee, Lord God Al - might - y,

that Thou hast vouch-safed to re - fresh us with these Thy sal - u -

tar - y gifts; and we be- seech Thee, of Thy mer - cy, to strength-

en us through the same, in faith to - ward Thee, in fer- vent love

to - ward one an - oth - er; through Je - sus Christ, Thy Son, our Lord.

Congregation:

A - men.

417

THE HOLY COMMUNION SERVICE

BENEDICTION

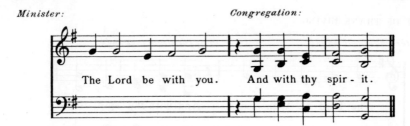

Minister: *Congregation:*

The Lord be with you.   And with thy spir - it.

Minister:

The Lord bless thee, and keep thee; The Lord make His face shine up - on thee, and be gra-cious un - to thee; The Lord lift up His coun - te - nance up - on thee, and give thee peace.

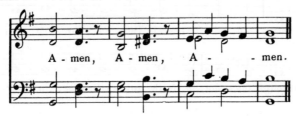

Congregation:

A - men, A - men, A - - men.

CLOSING HYMN

CLOSING PRAYER

Minister, or assistant:

O Lord, we render unto Thee our heartfelt thanks that Thou hast taught us what Thou wouldst have us believe and do. Help us, O God, by Thy Holy Spirit for the sake of Jesus Christ to keep Thy word in pure hearts, that we thereby may be strengthened in faith, perfected in holiness and comforted in life and death. Amen.

ORGAN POSTLUDE

The Afternoon or Evening Service
The Evening Service
The Church School Service

The Order of Afternoon or Evening Service
(Short Form)

INTROIT

Minister:

In the Name of the Father, and of the Son, and of the Holy Ghost.   Amen.

HYMN

VERSICLE

How amiable are Thy tabernacles, O Lord of hosts! My soul longeth, yea, even fainteth for the courts of the Lord. For a day in Thy courts is better than a thousand (Ps. 84: 1, 2, 10). One thing have I desired of the Lord, that will I seek after; that I may dwell in the house of the Lord all the days of my life, to behold the beauty of the Lord, and to inquire in His temple (Ps. 27: 4).

PRAYER

Almight and most merciful God, we are now assembled in Thy presence to hear all that shall be spoken in Thy name and by Thy command. We pray Thee: grant that we may receive Thy word with true devotion and faithfully keep it. Remove from us all vain and sinful thoughts, and open our hearts by Thy Holy Spirit, that through the preaching of Thy blessed word we may be made truly to know Thy will, and to conform our lives thereto, to the praise and glory of Thy holy name, and to the salvation of our souls; through Jesus Christ our Lord and Savior. Amen.

SCRIPTURE LESSON

GLORIA PATRI

Glo - ry be to the Fa - ther, and to the Son, and to the Ho - ly Ghost! As it

420

was in the be - gin - ning, is now, and

ev - er shall be: World with-out end, A - men.

HYMN

SERMON, preceded by a short prayer

THE LORD'S PRAYER

> Our Father who art in heaven; Hallowed be Thy name; Thy kingdom come; Thy
> will be done on earth, as it is in heaven; Give us this day our daily bread; And
> forgive us our trespasses, as we forgive those who trespass against us; And
> lead us not into temptation; But deliver us from evil: For Thine is the kingdom,
> and the power, and the glory, for ever and ever. Amen.

HYMN

BENEDICTION

Minister:

> The grace of the Lord Jesus Christ, and the love of God, and the communion of
> the Holy Ghost, be with you all. Amen.

Congregation shall then offer silent prayer

421

The Order of Evening Service

HYMN

SALUTATION

Minister, before the Altar:

Grace be unto you, and peace from God our Father, and from the Lord Jesus Christ. Amen.

O come, let us worship and bow down; let us kneel before the Lord our Maker, for He is our God.

CONFESSION OF SIN

Minister, kneeling:

O most merciful God and Father, whose grace endureth from generation to generation! Thou art patient and long-suffering, and forgivest all who are truly penitent their sins and their transgressions Look with compassion upon Thy people and hear their supplications. We poor sinners confess unto Thee that we are by nature sinful and unworthy of Thy goodness and love. Against Thee have we sinned and done wickedness in Thy sight. Remember not our transgressions; have mercy upon us; help us, O God, our Savior! For Thy name's sake grant us remission of all our sins and save us. Give us the grace of Thy Holy Spirit that we may amend our sinful lives and obtain with Thee everlasting life; through Thy Son Jesus Christ our Lord. Amen.

Minister, standing:

The blood of Jesus Christ cleanseth us from all sin. He that believeth, and is baptized, shall be saved. Grant us, O Lord, this salvation.

GLORIA PATRI, Congregation shall rise and remain standing to the end of the Creed

Minister and Congregation sing:

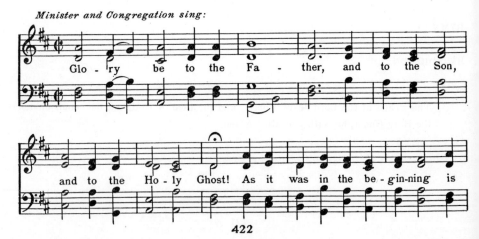

Glo-ry be to the Fa-ther, and to the Son, and to the Ho-ly Ghost! As it was in the be-gin-ning is

422

now, and ev-er shall be: World with-out end, A - men.

SCRIPTURE LESSON

CONFESSION OF FAITH — THE APOSTLES' CREED

Minister and Congregation:

I believe in God the Father Almighty, Maker of heaven and earth.

And in Jesus Christ, His only Son, our Lord; Who was conceived by the Holy Ghost; Born of the Virgin Mary; Suffered under Pontius Pilate; was crucified, dead, and buried; He decended into hell; The third day He rose again from the dead; He ascended into heaven, and sitteth on the right hand of God the Father Almighty; From thence He shall come to judge the quick and the dead.

I believe in the Holy Ghost; The Holy Christian Church, the Communion of Saints; The Forgiveness of sins; The Resurrection of the body; And the Life everlasting. Amen.

CHOIR ANTHEM, OR HYMN

SERMON

Announcements may be made here, followed by the

Apostolic Benediction:

The grace of the Lord Jesus Christ, and the love of God, and the communion of the Holy Ghost, be with you all. Amen.

OFFERTORY

SALUTATION

Minister chants or says: *Congregation rises and sings:*

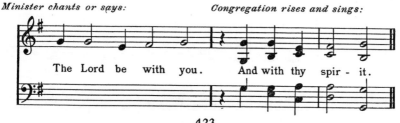

The Lord be with you.   And with thy spir - it.

THE ORDER OF EVENING SERVICE

Minister:

Let us pray.

O Lord, our heavenly Father, watch over us and protect us from all evil; and grant that we may this night rest secure under Thy care. Preserve and bless Thy Church and our government. Look in tender mercy upon them that are in sickness, in need, or in danger. Have mercy upon all men. And finally, when our last evening shall come, let us depart in peace; through Jesus Christ, Thy Son, our Lord.

Congregation sings:

A - - - - - men.

THE LORD'S PRAYER

In unison

Our Father who art in heaven; Hallowed be Thy name; Thy kingdom come; Thy will be done on earth, as it is in heaven; Give us this day our daily bread; And forgive us our trespasses, as we forgive those who trespass against us; And lead us not into temptation; But deliver us from evil: For Thine is the kingdom, and and the power, and the glory, for ever and ever. Amen.

THE NUNC DIMITTIS may then be sung:

Lord, now let-test Thou Thy ser - vant de - part in peace, Ac - cord - ing to Thy word; For mine eyes have seen Thy Sal - va - tion, Which Thou hast pre-pared be-fore the face of all peo - ple:

A light to light-en the Gen - tiles, And the glo-ry of Thy peo-ple Is-ra-el. Glo-ry be to the Fa - ther, and to the Son, and to the Ho-ly Ghost: As it was in the be-gin-ning, is now, and ev-er shall be, World with-out end. A - men.

BENEDICTION

Minister:

Bow your heads to God and receive the benediction.

The Lord bless thee, and keep thee,
The Lord make His face shine upon thee, and be gracious unto thee,
The Lord lift up His countenance upon thee, and give thee peace.
In the Name of the Father, and of the Son, and of the Holy Ghost.

Congregation sings:

A - men, A - men, A - - men.

The Order of Church School Service

SUPERINTENDENT:

In the Name of the Father, and of the Son, and of the Holy Ghost. Amen.

HYMN

SCRIPTURE SELECTION

GLORIA PATRI   CHARLES MEINEKE

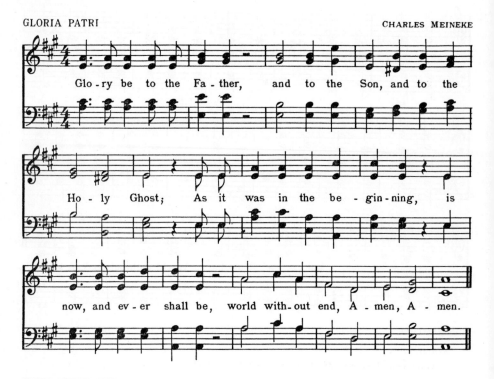

Glo - ry be to the Fa - ther, and to the Son, and to the Ho - ly Ghost; As it was in the be - gin - ning, is now, and ev - er shall be, world with - out end, A - men, A - men.

SUPERINTENDENT:

Let us confess our holy Faith.

SCHOOL:

I believe in God the Father Almighty, Maker of heaven and earth.

And in Jesus Christ His only Son, our Lord; Who was conceived by the Holy Ghost; Born of the Virgin Mary; Suffered under Pontius Pilate; Was crucified, dead, and buried; He descended into hell; The third day He rose again from the dead; He ascended into heaven, And sitteth on the right hand of God the Father Almighty; From thence He shall come to judge the quick and the dead.

I believe in the Holy Ghost; The Holy Christian Church, the Communion of Saints; The Forgiveness of sins; The Resurrection of the body; And the Life everlasting. Amen.

Or,

SUPERINTENDENT:

Let us repeat the Ten Commandments.

SCHOOL.

I am the Lord, thy God: Thou shalt have no other gods before Me.

Thou shalt not take the Name of the Lord thy God in vain; for the Lord will not hold him guiltless that taketh His Name in vain.

Remember the Sabbath day, to keep it holy.

Honor thy father and thy mother, that it may be well with thee, and thou mayest live long on the earth.

Thou shalt not kill.

Thou shalt not commit adultery.

Thou shalt not steal.

Thou shalt not bear false witness against thy neighbor.

Thou shalt not covet thy neighbor's house.

Thou shalt not covet thy neighbor's wife, nor his manservant, nor his maidservant, nor his cattle, nor anything that is his.

(If both the Commandments and Creed are used, the Commandments should be repeated first)

PRAYER, concluding with the

LORD'S PRAYER, in unison:

Our Father who art in heaven; Hallowed be Thy name; Thy kingdom come; Thy will be done on earth, as it is in heaven; Give us this day our daily bread; And forgive us our trespasses, as we forgive those who trespass against us; And lead us not into temptation; But deliver us from evil: For Thine is the kingdom, and the power, and the glory, for ever and ever. Amen.

HYMN

ANNOUNCEMENTS

LESSON PERIOD

In large schools, where there is no general assembly in closing, each department may use the following closing service. Where each class closes individually, one of the closing prayers may be used.

427

CLOSING

HYMN

REPORTS

SCHOOL, in unison:

> O Jesus, I beseech Thee
> Thou would'st my heart prepare,
> And late and early teach me
> To be Thy temple fair.
> From vanities, O lead me,
> From all the worldly wise,
> That I may know and need Thee —
> Such wisdom will suffice.
>
> Or,
>
> Seal my heart with Thine impressure,
> Jesus, King and God of grace,
> That no pain or earth-born pleasure
> Shall Thine image there efface.
> Let this imprint, Lord, abide:
> Jesus Christ, the Crucified,
> Is my life, my firm foundation,
> All my glory and salvation.

"The Lord watch between me and thee when we are absent one from another."

DOXOLOGY

Praise God from whom all bless-ings flow; Praise Him all crea-tures here be - low;

Praise Him a-bove, ye heaven-ly host: Praise Fa-ther, Son, and Ho - ly Ghost.

The Order of Baptismal Service in Cases of Emergency

When a new-born child is in danger of death, the Minister should be promptly called to baptize it. In such case he shall use as much of the common Order for Baptism as the circumstances allow. But where the danger is very great, and no Minister is within reach, the father of the child, or some other Christian man or woman, may baptize it. But they shall not do so except in extreme necessity, when the following Order may be used:

In the Name of the Father, and of the Son, and of the Holy Ghost. Amen.

Jesus said: "All authority hath been given unto me in heaven and on earth. Go ye therefore, and make disciples of all the nations, baptizing them into the name of the Father, and of the Son, and of the Holy Spirit: teaching them to observe all things whatsoever I commanded you: and lo, I am with you always, even unto the end of the world" (Matt. 28:18-20 A. S.).

Let us pray.

Our Father, who art in heaven; Hallowed be Thy Name; Thy kingdom come; Thy will be done on earth, as it is in heaven; Give us this day our daily bread; And forgive us our trespasses, as we forgive those who trespass against us; And lead us not into temptation; But deliver us from evil; For Thine is the kingdom, and the power, and the glory, for ever and ever. Amen.

He who performs the Baptism shall pour water on the child's head three times and say:

N. (The name of the child), I baptize thee in the Name of the Father, and of the Son, and of the Holy Spirit. Amen.

Let us pray.

Almighty and most merciful God and Father, we thank Thee that Thou hast granted to this child the new birth in Holy Baptism with its washing away of all sin, and hast made it Thy child, and an heir to Thy heavenly kingdom. If it be Thy will to preserve this child alive and to restore it to health, we humbly beseech Thee to defend and keep it in this grace, that, according to all Thy good pleasure, it may be faithfully and savingly brought up to the praise and honor of Thy holy Name. But if Thou wilt take it out of this world, and receive it unto Thyself, grant unto Thy servants grace to be still and know that Thou art God. Thou, God the Father, hast created it; Thou, God the Son, hast redeemed it; Thou, God the Holy Ghost, hast regenerated it; Into Thy hands we commit this child. Amen.

This being done, it is not to be doubted that the child is truly baptized.

Such Baptism, whether the child live or die, is to be reported to the Minister, who shall inquire whether the child was properly baptized with water, in the Name of the Father, and of the Son, and of the Holy Ghost, which are the two main things to constitute a proper Christian Baptism, and if he so find, he shall approve it as a true Christian Baptism, and enter the same in the records of the Church.

If the child continue to live, it is to be brought to the church, that the Minister may publicly confirm the Baptism thus administered under necessity.

PRAYERS FOR THE OPENING
OF CHURCH SCHOOL

Prayers for the Opening of Church School

1. Precious Jesus, Friend of children, we thank Thee most heartily that Thou hast assembled us in our Sunday school on this Lord's Day to teach us out of Thy Holy Word what Thou wouldst have us to believe and do. Praise be to Thee for the promise that where two or three are gathered together in Thy name there Thou wilt be in the midst of them. Be Thou present with us now and bless abundantly the instruction given that we may learn to know Thee better in Thy saving love; that we may be drawn closer to Thee as our Savior from sin, and that we may be filled with a desire to serve Thee better. Bless our pastor, our teachers, our parents and all who are near and dear to us. Bless our Church and our country, and touch by Thy Holy Spirit the hearts of all, that they might love Thee who died to save us from sin and eternal death. Help us to live all our days as true Christians and children of our Heavenly Father, and forgive us our many sins. All this we ask for Jesus' sake. Amen.

2. Dear Lord God, Father, Son, and Holy Spirit, we lift up our voices in gratitude and praise for Thy great goodness toward us. Thou hast given us life and health and strength and all things needful for body and soul. We thank Thee that we have been received into fellowship with Jesus Christ through Holy Baptism. Help us, dear Lord, to keep close to Jesus and to please Him by trusting in Him and serving Him. Give us always the needed strength to resist temptations, and when we do sin against Thee, make us truly sorry and through grace grant us Thy pardon. Bless our Sunday school and help us all to render faithful service to our God. And may we obtain eternal life through Jesus Christ, our Savior. In Jesus' name we pray. Amen.

3. O Lord Jesus, Thou hast said that Thou art the Good Shepherd and we are glad to have the assurance that Thou knowest the lambs and the sheep of Thy pasture. As we gather to be instructed in Thy Word may we learn to know more of Thy saving love and watchful care. May we be numbered among those to whom Thou art the Good Shepherd, that we may serve Thee in constant obedience to Thy Word, and at last be found with those who come to Thy Heavenly home in glory. Forgive us our many sins and help us to give Thee all honor. We pray in Thy Holy Name. Amen.

4. Dear Lord God, we rejoice today that Thou hast sent Thy Holy Spirit into the world as the Comforter and the Spirit of truth. We thank Thee that Thou hast called us by the Gospel to be followers of the Lord Jesus Christ. We thank Thee that Thou art continually seeking to enlighten us by Thy gifts. And now we pray Thee, help us, as we are gathered here, to learn about Jesus and His love with true gladness of heart. Help us to believe the Word of God, never doubting Thy blessed promises. Take possession of our hearts and guide us by Thy wisdom so that we may give our lives to Jesus. In Jesus' Name and for His sake we pray. Amen.

5. O God in Heaven, we are tenderly invited to believe that Thou art really our Father and we Thy children, that we may come to Thee with our cares, our wants, our fears and our troubles even as we turn in confidence to parents here below. Our hearts are glad trusting Thee. Today we come to hear and learn the Word of such a God and Father; to see Thee in the face and form of our Lord and Savior Jesus Christ; to know by the Holy Spirit Thy truth and Thy love, which pass all knowledge.

Help all those who serve Thee for our well-being, father and mother, teachers at school and in church, good friends and good companions.

Help us to be disciples indeed hearing our Master's Word and keeping it. Help us to be true sons and daughters of our Father in Heaven. In Jesus' Name. Amen.

6. Lord Jesus, long ago the children heard Thee saying, "Suffer the little ones to come to me, and forbid them not, for of such is the Kingdom of Heaven." We also can hear Thee say it. Thanks, dear Jesus, for the invitation. But are we of the Kingdom of Heaven? We are not worthy of Thy Kingdom, so much of sin is in us. Thou knowest it. Make us again, by Thy grace, clean in the sight of God, and help us to be clean in thought, word, and act. Be Thou the unseen member of every class today, as in Thy Name we are together. Amen.

7. O Holy Spirit, all the deep things of God are known to Thee, and there is no secret thought or way in our hearts hid from Thee.

At our baptismal font, at our first prayer lesson, at our study of Thy Book, yea all the way Thou hast been calling us, enlightening us, bringing us to Christ our Savior again and again.

Help us, loving Spirit, that we may be true to Him; make our faith living and strong that we might trust Him more and more.

Make us strong in temptation, let us grow in knowledge, in holiness, in goodness, and, like Jesus, in the favor of God and fellowmen. In His Name. Amen.

8. Our Father, who art in heaven; Hallowed be Thy Name; Thy kingdom come; Thy will be done on earth, as it is in heaven; Give us this day our daily bread; And forgive us our trespasses, as we forgive those who trespass against us; And lead us not into temptation; But deliver us from evil; For Thine is the kingdom, and the power, and the glory, forever and ever. Amen.

Scripture Selections

For Responsive Reading

PSALM 1

Blessed is the man that walketh not in the counsel of the ungodly: **nor standeth in the way of sinners, nor sitteth in the seat of the scornful.**

But his delight is in the law of the Lord: **and in His law doth he meditate day and night.**

And he shall be like a tree planted by the rivers of water: **that bringeth forth his fruit in his season.**

His leaf also shall not wither: **and whatsoever he doeth shall prosper.**

The ungodly are not so: **but are like the chaff which the wind driveth away.**

Therefore the ungodly shall not stand in the judgment: **nor sinners in the congregation of the righteous.**

For the Lord knoweth the way of the righteous: **but the way of the ungodly shall perish.**

Psalm 2

Why do the heathen rage: **and the people imagine a vain thing?**

The kings of the earth set themselves, and the rulers take counsel together: **against the Lord and against His anointed, saying,**

Let us break their bands asunder: **and cast away their cords from us.**

He that sitteth in the heavens shall laugh: **the Lord shall have them in derision.**

Then shall He speak unto them in His wrath: **and vex them in His sore displeasure.**

Yet have I set my king: **upon my holy hill of Zion.**

I will declare the decree: **the Lord hath said unto me, Thou art my Son; this day have I begotten Thee.**

Ask of me, and I shall give Thee the heathen for Thine inheritance: **and the uttermost parts of the earth for Thy possession.**

Thou shalt break them with a rod of iron: **Thou shalt dash them in pieces like a potter's vessel.**

Be wise now therefore, O ye kings: **be instructed, ye judges of the earth.**

Serve the Lord with fear: **and rejoice with trembling.**

Kiss the Son, lest He be angry, and ye perish from the way, when His wrath is kindled but a little: **blessed are all they that put their trust in Him.**

PSALM 4

Hear me when I call, O God of my righteousness: **Thou hast enlarged me when I was in distress; have mercy upon me, and hear my prayer.**

O ye sons of men, how long will ye turn my glory into shame: **how long will ye love vanity and seek after leasing?**

But know that the Lord hath set apart him that is godly for Himself: **the Lord will hear when I call unto Him.**

Stand in awe, and sin not: **commune with your own heart upon your bed, and be still.**

Offer the sacrifices of righteousness: **and put your trust in the Lord.**

There be many that say, Who will shew us any good: **Lord, lift Thou** up the light of Thy countenance upon us.

Thou hast put gladness in my heart: more than in the time that their corn and their wine increased.

I will both lay me down in peace, and sleep: for Thou, Lord, only makest me dwell in safety.

PSALM 8

O Lord, our Lord, how excellent is Thy name in all the earth: who hast set Thy glory above the heavens.

Out of the mouth of babes and sucklings hast Thou ordained strength because of Thine enemies: that Thou mightest still the enemy and the avenger.

When I consider Thy heavens, the work of Thy fingers: the moon and the stars, which Thou hast ordained;

What is man, that Thou art mindful of him: and the son of man, that Thou visitest him?

For Thou hast made him a little lower than the angels: and hast crowned him with glory and honor.

Thou madest him to have dominion over the works of Thy hands: Thou hast put all things under his feet:

All sheep and oxen: yea, and the beasts of the field;

The fowl of the air, and the fish of the sea: and whatsoever passeth through the paths of the seas.

O Lord, our Lord: how excellent is Thy name in all the earth!

PSALM 13

How long wilt Thou forget me, O Lord? for ever: how long wilt Thou hide Thy face from me?

How long shall I take counsel in my soul having sorrow in my heart daily: how long shall mine enemy be exalted over me?

Consider and hear me, O Lord my God: lighten mine eyes, lest I sleep the sleep of death;

Lest mine enemy say, I have prevailed against him: and those that trouble me rejoice when I am moved.

But I have trusted in Thy mercy: my heart shall rejoice in Thy salvation.

I will sing unto the Lord: because He hath dealt bountifully with me.

PSALM 19:7-14

The law of the Lord is perfect, converting the soul: the testimony of the Lord is sure, making wise the simple.

The statutes of the Lord are right, rejoicing the heart: the commandment of the Lord is pure, enlightening the eyes.

The fear of the Lord is clean, enduring for ever: the judgments of the Lord are true and righteous altogether.

More to be desired are they than gold, yea, than much fine gold: sweeter also than honey and the honeycomb.

Moreover by them is Thy servant warned: and in keeping of them there is great reward.

Who can understand his errors: cleanse Thou me from secret faults.

Keep back Thy servant also from presumptuous sins; let them not have dominion over me: then shall I be upright and I shall be innocent from the great transgression.

Let the words of my mouth, and the meditations of my heart, be acceptable in Thy sight: O Lord, my Strength, and my Redeemer.

PSALM 23

The Lord is my shepherd: I shall not want.

He maketh me to lie down in green pastures: He leadeth me beside the still waters.

He restoreth my soul: He leadeth me in the paths of righteousness for His name's sake.

Yea, though I walk through the valley of the shadow of death, I will fear no evil: for Thou art with me; Thy rod and Thy staff they comfort me.

Thou preparest a table before me in the presence of mine enemies: Thou anointest my head with oil; my cup runneth over.

Surely goodness and mercy shall follow me all the days of my life: and I will dwell in the house of the Lord for ever.

PSALM 24

The earth is the Lord's, and the fulness thereof: the world, and they that dwell therein:

For He hath founded it upon the seas: and established it upon the floods.

Who shall ascend into the hill of the Lord: or who shall stand in His holy place?

He that hath clean hands, and a pure heart: who hath not lifted up his soul unto vanity, nor sworn deceitfully.

He shall receive the blessing from the Lord: and righteousness from the God of his salvation.

This is the generation of them that seek Him: that seek Thy face, O Jacob.

Lift up your heads, O ye gates; and be ye lift up, ye everlasting doors: and the King of glory shall come in.

Who is this King of glory: the Lord strong and mighty, the Lord mighty in battle.

Lift up your heads, O ye gates even lift them up, ye everlasting doors: and the King of glory shall come in.

Who is this King of glory: the Lord of hosts, He is the King of glory.

PSALM 32

Blessed is he whose transgression is forgiven: whose sin is covered.

Blessed is the man unto whom the Lord imputeth not iniquity: and in whose spirit there is no guile.

When I kept silence: my bones waxed old through my roaring all the day long.

For day and night Thy hand was heavy upon me: my moisture is turned into the drought of summer.

I acknowledged my sin unto Thee: and mine iniquity have I not hid.

I said, I will confess my transgressions unto the Lord: and Thou forgavest the iniquity of my sin.

For this shall every one that is godly pray unto Thee in a time when Thou mayest be found: surely in the floods of great waters they shall not come nigh unto him.

Thou art my hiding place; Thou shalt preserve me from trouble: Thou shalt compass me about with songs of deliverance.

I will instruct thee and teach thee in the way which thou shalt go: I will guide thee with mine eye.

Be ye not as the horse, or as the mule, which have no understanding: whose mouth must be held in with bit and bridle, lest they come near unto thee.

Many sorrows shall be to the wicked: but he that trusteth in the Lord, mercy shall compass him about.

Be glad in the Lord, and rejoice, ye righteous: and shout for joy, all ye that are upright in heart.

PSALM 42

As the hart panteth after the waterbrooks: so panteth my soul after Thee, O God.

My soul thirsteth for God; for the living God: when shall I come and appear before God?

My tears have been my meat day and night: while they continually say unto me, Where is thy God?

When I remember these things, I

pour out my soul in me: for I had gone with the multitude.

I went with them to the house of God, with the voice of joy and praise: with a multitude that kept holy day.

Why art thou cast down, O my soul? and why art thou disquieted within me? Hope thou in God: for I shall yet praise Him for the help of His countenance.

O my God, my soul is cast down within me: therefore will I remember Thee from the land of Jordan, and of the Hermonites, from the hill Mizar.

Deep calleth unto deep at the noise of Thy waterspouts: all Thy waves and Thy billows are gone over me.

Yet the Lord will command His lovingkindness in the daytime: and in the night His song shall be with me, and my prayer unto the God of my life.

I will say unto God my Rock, Why hast Thou forgotten me: why go I mourning because of the oppression of the enemy?

As with a sword in my bones, mine enemies reproach me: while they say daily unto me, Where is thy God?

Why art thou cast down, O my soul: and why art thou disquieted within me?

Hope thou in God: for I shall yet praise Him who is the health of my countenance, and my God.

PSALM 46

God is our refuge and strength: a very present help in trouble.

Therefore will not we fear, though the earth be removed: and though the mountains be carried into the midst of the sea;

Though the waters thereof roar and be troubled: though the mountains shake with the swelling thereof.

There is a river, the streams whereof shall make glad the city of God: the holy place of the tabernacles of the Most High.

God is in the midst of her; she shall not be moved: God shall help her, and that right early.

The heathen raged, the kingdoms were moved: He uttered His voice, the earth melted.

The Lord of hosts is with us: the God of Jacob is our refuge.

Come, behold the works of the Lord: what desolations He hath made in the earth.

He maketh wars to cease unto the end of the earth: He breaketh the bow, and cutteth the spear in sunder: He burneth the chariot in the fire.

Be still, and know that I am God: I will be exalted among the heathen, I will be exalted in the earth.

The Lord of hosts is with us: the God of Jacob is our refuge.

PSALM 51:1-13

Have mercy upon me, O God, according to Thy lovingkindness: according unto the multitude of Thy tender mercies, blot out my transgressions.

Wash me thoroughly from mine iniquity: and cleanse me from my sin.

For I acknowledge my transgressions: and my sin is ever before me.

Against Thee, Thee only, have I sinned, and done this evil in Thy sight: that Thou mightest be justified when Thou speakest, and be clear when Thou judgest.

Behold, I was shapen in iniquity: and in sin did my mother conceive me.

Behold, Thou desirest truth in the inward parts: and in the hidden part Thou shalt make me to know wisdom.

Purge me with hyssop, and I shall be clean: wash me, and I shall be whiter than snow.

Make me to hear joy and gladness: that the bones which Thou hast broken may rejoice.

Hide Thy face from my sins: and blot out all mine iniquities.

Create in me a clean heart, O God: and renew a right spirit within me.

Cast me not away from Thy presence: and take not Thy Holy Spirit from me.

Restore unto me the joy of Thy salvation: and uphold me with Thy free Spirit.

Then will I teach transgressors Thy ways: and sinners shall be converted unto Thee.

PSALM 84

How amiable are Thy tabernacles: O Lord of hosts!

My soul longeth, yea, even fainteth for the courts of the Lord: my heart and my flesh crieth out for the living God.

Yea, the sparrow hath found an house, and the swallow a nest for herself, where she may lay her young: even Thine altars, O Lord of hosts, my King and my God.

Blessed are they that dwell in Thy house: they will be still praising Thee.

Blessed is the man whose strength is in Thee: in whose heart are the ways of them.

Who passing through the valley of Baca make it a well: the rain also filleth the pools.

They go from strength to strength: every one of them in Zion appeareth before God.

O Lord of hosts, hear my prayer: give ear, O God of Jacob.

Behold, O God our shield: and look upon the face of Thine Anointed.

For a day in Thy courts is better than a thousand: I had rather be a doorkeeper in the house of my God, than to dwell in the tents of wickedness.

For the Lord God is a sun and a shield: the Lord will give grace and glory.

No good thing will He withhold from them that walk uprightly: O Lord of hosts, blessed is the man that trusteth in Thee.

PSALM 103:1-13

Bless the Lord, O my soul: and all that is within me, bless His holy name.

Bless the Lord, O my soul: and forget not all His benefits;

Who forgiveth all thine iniquities: who healeth all thy diseases;

Who redeemeth thy life from destruction: who crowneth thee with lovingkindness and tender mercies;

Who satisfieth thy mouth with good things: so that thy youth is renewed like the eagle's.

The Lord executeth righteousness and judgment: for all that are oppressed.

He made known His ways unto Moses: His acts unto the children of Israel.

The Lord is merciful and gracious: slow to anger and plenteous in mercy.

He will not always chide: neither will He keep His anger for ever.

He hath not dealt with us after our sins: nor rewarded us according to our iniquities.

For as the heaven is high above the earth: so great is His mercy toward them that fear Him.

As far as the east is from the west: so far hath He removed our transgressions from us.

Like as a father pitieth his children: so the Lord pitieth them that fear Him.

PSALM 119:9-16

Wherewithal shall a young man cleanse his way: by taking heed thereto according to Thy word.

With my whole heart have I sought Thee: **O let me not wander from Thy commandments.**

Thy word have I hid in mine heart: **that I might not sin against Thee.**

Blessed art Thou, O Lord: **teach me Thy statutes.**

With my lips have I declared: **all the judgments of Thy mouth.**

I have rejoiced in the way of Thy testimonies: **as much as in all riches.**

I will meditate in Thy precepts: **and have respect unto Thy ways.**

I will delight myself in Thy statutes: **I will not forget Thy word.**

PSALM 121

I will lift up mine eyes unto the hills: **from whence cometh my help.**

My help cometh from the Lord: **which made heaven and earth.**

He will not suffer thy foot to be moved: **He that keepeth thee will not slumber.**

Behold, He that keepeth Israel: **shall neither slumber nor sleep.**

The Lord is thy keeper: **the Lord is thy shade upon thy right hand.**

The sun shall not smite thee by day: **nor the moon by night.**

The Lord shall preserve thee from all evil: **He shall preserve thy soul.**

The Lord shall preserve thy going out, and thy coming in: **from this time forth, and even for evermore.**

PSALM 139:1-12 and 23, 24

O Lord, Thou hast searched me, and known me:

Thou knowest my downsitting and mine uprising; Thou understandest my thought afar off.

Thou compassest my path and my lying down: **and art acquainted with all my ways.**

For there is not a word in my tongue: **but, lo, O Lord, Thou knowest it altogether.**

Thou hast beset me behind and before: **and laid Thine hand upon me.**

Such knowledge is too wonderful for me: **it is high, I cannot attain unto it.**

Whither shall I go from Thy Spirit: **or whither shall I flee from Thy presence?**

If I ascend up into heaven, Thou art there: **if I make my bed in hell, behold, Thou art there.**

If I take the wings of the morning: **and dwell in the uttermost parts of the sea;**

Even there shall Thy hand lead me: **and Thy right hand shall hold me.**

If I say, Surely the darkness shall cover me: **even the night shall be light about me.**

Yea, the darkness hideth not from Thee, but the night shineth as the day: **the darkness and the light are both alike to Thee.**

Search me, O God, and know my heart: **try me, and know my thoughts.**

And see if there be any wicked way in me: **and lead me in the way everlasting.**

PROVERBS 2:1-9

My son, if thou wilt receive my words, and hide my commandments with thee:

So that thou incline thine ear unto wisdom, and apply thine heart to understanding;

Yea, if thou criest after knowledge, and liftest up thy voice for understanding;

If thou seekest her as silver, and searchest for her as for hid treasures;

Then shalt thou understand the fear of the Lord, and find the knowledge of God:

For the Lord giveth wisdom, out of His mouth cometh knowledge and understanding.

He layeth up sound wisdom for the righteous: **He is a buckler to them that walk uprightly.**

He keepeth the paths of judgment, and preserveth the way of His saints:

Then shalt thou understand righteousness, and judgment, and equity; yea, every good path.

ECCLESIASTES 12:1-7

Remember now thy Creator in the days of thy youth: **while the evil days come not, nor the years draw nigh, when thou shalt say, I have no pleasure in them;**

While the sun, or the light, or the moon, or the stars, be not darkened: **nor the clouds return after the rain;**

In the day when the keepers of the house shall tremble, and the strong men shall bow themselves: **and the grinders cease because they are few, and those that look out of the windows be darkened.**

And the doors shall be shut in the streets, when the sound of the grinding is low: **and he shall rise up at the voice of the bird, and all the daughters of music shall be brought low;**

Also when they shall be afraid of that which is high, and fears shall be in the way, and the almond tree shall flourish, and the grasshopper shall be a burden, and desire shall fail: **because man goeth to his long home, and the mourners go about the streets;**

Or ever the silver cord be loosed, or the golden bowl be broken: **or the pitcher be broken at the fountain, or the wheel broken at the cistern.**

Then shall the dust return to the earth as it was: **and the spirit shall return unto God who gave it.**

ISAIAH 53:3-6

He is despised and rejected of men; a man of sorrows, and acquainted with grief: and we hid as it were our faces from Him; He was despised, and we esteemed Him not.

Surely He hath borne our griefs, and carried our sorrows: yet we did esteem Him stricken, smitten of God, and afflicted.

But He was wounded for our transgressions, He was bruised for our iniquities: the chastisement of our peace was upon Him; and with His stripes we are healed.

All we, like sheep, have gone astray; we have turned every one to his own way; and the Lord hath laid on Him the iniquity of us all.

ISAIAH 55:6-11

Seek ye the Lord while He may be found, call ye upon Him while He is near.

Let the wicked forsake his way, and the unrighteous man his thoughts: and let him return unto the Lord, and He will have mercy upon him: and to our God, for He will abundantly pardon.

For my thoughts are not your thoughts, neither are your ways my ways, saith the Lord.

For as the heavens are higher than the earth, so are my ways higher than your ways, and my thoughts than your thoughts.

For as the rain cometh down, and the snow, from heaven, and returneth not thither, but watereth the earth, and maketh it bring forth and bud, that it may give seed to the sower, and bread to the eater;

So shall my word be that goeth forth out of my mouth: it shall not return unto me void; but it shall accomplish that which I please, and it shall prosper in the thing whereto I sent it.

MATTHEW 5:3-10

Blessed are the poor in spirit: for theirs is the kingdom of heaven.

Blessed are they that mourn: for they shall be comforted.

Blessed are the meek: for they shall inherit the earth.

Blessed are they which do hunger and thirst after righteousness: for they shall be filled.

Blessed are the merciful: for they shall obtain mercy.

Blessed are the pure in heart: for they shall see God.

Blessed are the peacemakers: for they shall be called the children of God.

Blessed are they which are persecuted for righteousness' sake: for theirs is the kingdom of heaven.

MATTHEW 5:13-16

Ye are the salt of the earth: but if the salt have lost his savor, wherewith shall it be salted? it is thenceforth good for nothing, but to be cast out, and to be trodden under foot of men.

Ye are the light of the world. A city that is set on an hill cannot be hid.

Neither do men light a candle, and put it under a bushel, but on a candlestick; and it giveth light unto all that are in the house.

Let your light so shine before men, that they may see your good works, and glorify your Father which is in heaven.

MATTHEW 6:19-23

Lay not up for yourselves treasures upon earth, where moth and rust doth corrupt, and where thieves break through and steal:

But lay up for yourselves treasures in heaven, where neither moth nor rust doth corrupt, and where thieves do not break through nor steal:

For where your treasure is, there will your heart be also.

The light of the body is the eye: if therefore thine eye be single, thy whole body shall be full of light.

But if thine eye be evil, thy whole body shall be full of darkness. If therefore the light that is in thee be darkness, how great is that darkness!

MATTHEW 28:18-20

And Jesus came to them and spake unto them, saying, All authority hath been given unto me in heaven and on earth.

Go ye, therefore, and make disciples of all the nations, baptizing them into the name of the Father and of the Son and of the Holy Spirit:

Teaching them to observe all things whatsoever I commanded you: and lo, I am with you always, even unto the end of the world.

LUKE 6:43-49

For a good tree bringeth not forth corrupt fruit; neither doth a corrupt tree bring forth good fruit.

For every tree is known by his own fruit: for of thorns men do not gather figs, nor of a bramble bush gather they grapes.

A good man out of the good treasure of his heart bringeth forth that which is good; and an evil man out of the evil treasure of his heart bringeth forth that which is evil: for of the abundance of the heart his mouth speaketh.

And why call ye me Lord, Lord, and do not the things which I say?

Whosoever cometh to me, and heareth my sayings, and doeth them, I will shew you to whom he is like:

He is like a man which built an house, and digged deep, and laid the foundation on a rock; and when the flood arose, the stream beat vehemently upon that house, and could not shake it; for it was founded upon a rock.

But he that heareth, and doeth not, is like a man that without a foundation built an house upon the earth: against which the stream did beat vehemently, and immediately it fell; and the ruin of that house was great.

JOHN 3:14-18

And as Moses lifted up the serpent in the wilderness, even so must the Son of man be lifted up:

That whosoever believeth in Him should not perish, but have eternal life.

For God so loved the world, that He gave His only begotten Son, that whosoever believeth in Him should not perish, but have everlasting life.

For God sent not His Son into the world to condemn the world; but that the world through Him might be saved.

He that believeth on Him is not condemned; but he that believeth not is condemned already, because he hath not believed in the name of the only begotten Son of God.

JOHN 14:1-6

Let not your heart be troubled: ye believe in God, believe also in me.

In my Father's house are many mansions: if it were not so, I would have told you. I go to prepare a place for you.

And if I go and prepare a place for you, I will come again, and receive you unto myself; that where I am, there ye may be also.

And whither I go ye know, and the way ye know.

Thomas saith unto Him, Lord, we know not whither Thou goest; and how can we know the way?

Jesus saith unto him, I am the way, the truth, and the life: no man cometh unto the Father, but by me.

JOHN 15:1-8

I am the true vine, and my Father is the husbandman.

Every branch in me that beareth not fruit He taketh away: and every branch that beareth fruit, He purgeth it, that it may bring forth more fruit.

Now ye are clean through the word which I have spoken unto you.

Abide in me, and I in you. As the branch cannot bear fruit of itself, except it abide in the vine; no more can ye, except ye abide in me.

I am the vine, ye are the branches. He that abideth in me, and I in him, the same bringeth forth much fruit: for without me ye can do nothing.

If a man abide not in me, he is cast forth as a branch, and is withered; and men gather them, and cast them into the fire, and they are burned.

If ye abide in me, and my words abide in you, ye shall ask what ye will, and it shall be done unto you.

Herein is my Father glorified, that ye bear much fruit; so shall ye be my disciples.

ROMANS 5:1-8

Therefore being justified by faith, we have peace with God through our Lord Jesus Christ:

By whom also we have access by faith into this grace wherein we stand, and rejoice in hope of the glory of God.

And not only so, but we glory in tribulations also: knowing that tribulation worketh patience;

And patience, experience; and experience, hope;

And hope maketh not ashamed; because the love of God is shed abroad in our hearts by the Holy Ghost, which is given unto us.

For when we were yet without strength, in due time Christ died for the ungodly.

For scarcely for a righteous man will one die; yet peradventure for a good man some would even dare to die.

But God commendeth His love toward us, in that, while we were yet sinners, Christ died for us.

ROMANS 8:31-39

What shall we then say to these things? If God be for us, who can be against us?

He that spared not His own Son, but delivered Him up for us all, how shall He not with Him also freely give us all things?

Who shall lay any thing to the charge of God's elect? It is God that justifieth.

Who is he that condemneth? It is Christ that died, yea rather, that is risen again, who is even at the right hand of God, who also maketh intercession for us.

Who shall separate us from the love of Christ? shall tribulation, or distress, or persecution, or famine, or nakedness, or peril, or sword?

As it is written, For Thy sake we are killed all the day long; we are accounted as sheep for the slaughter.

Nay, in all these things we are more than conquerors, through Him that loved us.

For I am persuaded that neither death, nor life, nor angels, nor principalities, nor powers, nor things present, nor things to come,

Nor height nor depth, nor any other creature, shall be able to separate us from the love of God, which is in Christ Jesus our Lord.

1 CORINTHIANS 13

Though I speak with the tongues of men and of angels, and have not charity, I am become as sounding brass, or a tinkling cymbal.

And though I have the gift of prophecy, and understand all mysteries, and all knowledge; and though I have all faith, so that I could remove mountains, and have not charity, I am nothing.

And though I bestow all my goods to feed the poor, and though I give my body to be burned, and have not charity, it profiteth me nothing.

Charity suffereth long, and is kind; charity envieth not; charity vaunteth not itself, is not puffed up.

Doth not behave itself unseemly, seeketh not her own, is not easily provoked, thinketh no evil;

Rejoiceth not in iniquity, but rejoiceth in the truth;

Beareth all things, believeth all things, hopeth all things, endureth all things.

Charity never faileth: but whether there be prophecies, they shall fail; whether there be tongues, they shall cease; whether there be knowledge, it shall vanish away.

For we know in part, and we prophesy in part.

But when that which is perfect is come, then that which is in part shall be done away.

When I was a child, I spake as a child, I understood as a child, I thought as a child; but when I became a man, I put away childish things.

For now we see through a glass, darkly; but then face to face: now I know in part; but then shall I know even as also I am known.

And now abideth faith, hope, charity, these three; but the greatest of these is charity.

PHILIPPIANS 2:5-11

Let this mind be in you, which was also in Christ Jesus:

Who, being in the form of God, thought it not robbery to be equal with God:

But made Himself of no reputation, and took upon Him the form of a servant and was made in the likeness of men:

And being found in fashion as a man He humbled Himself, and became obedient unto death, even the death of the cross.

Wherefore God also hath highly exalted Him, and given Him a name which is above every name:

That at the name of Jesus every knee should bow, of things in heaven, and things in earth, and things under the earth;

And that every tongue should confess that Jesus Christ is Lord, to the glory of God the Father.

PHILIPPIANS 4:4-8

Rejoice in the Lord alway: and again I say, Rejoice.

Let your moderation be known unto all men. The Lord is at hand.

Be careful for nothing; but in every thing by prayer and supplication with thanksgiving let your requests be made known unto God.

And the peace of God, which passeth all understanding, shall keep your hearts and minds through Christ Jesus.

Finally, brethren, whatsoever things are true, whatsoever things are honest, whatsoever things are just, whatsoever things are pure, whatsoever things are lovely, whatsoever things are of good report; if there be any virtue, and if there be any praise, think on these things.

1 JOHN 1:5-10

This then is the message which we have heard of Him, and declare unto you, that God is light, and in Him is no darkness at all.

If we say that we have fellowship with Him, and walk in darkness, we lie, and do not the truth:

But if we walk in the light, as He is in the light, we have fellowship one with another, and the blood of Jesus Christ His Son cleanseth us from all sin.

If we say that we have no sin, we deceive ourselves, and the truth is not in us.

If we confess our sins, He is faithful and just to forgive us our sins, and to cleanse us from all unrighteousness.

If we say that we have not sinned, we make Him a liar, and His word is not in us.

1 JOHN 2:15-17

Love not the world, neither the things that are in the world. If any man love the world, the love of the Father is not in him.

For all that is in the world, the lust of the flesh, and the lust of the eyes, and the pride of life, is not of the Father, but is of the world.

And the world passeth away, and the lust thereof: but he that doeth the will of God abideth for ever.

1 JOHN 3:1-5

Behold, what manner of love the Father hath bestowed upon us, that we should be called the sons of God: therefore the world knoweth us not, because it knew Him not.

Beloved, now are we the sons of God; and it doth not yet appear what we shall be: but we know that, when He shall appear, we shall be like Him; for we shall see Him as He is.

And every man that hath this hope in Him purifieth himself, even as He is pure.

Whosoever committeth sin transgresseth also the law: for sin is the transgression of the law.

And ye know that He was manifested to take away our sins; and in Him is no sin.

REVELATION 5:9-13

And they sung a new song, saying, Thou art worthy to take the book, and to open the seals thereof: for Thou wast slain, and hast redeemed us to God by Thy blood, out of every kindred, and tongue, and people, and nation;

And hast made us unto our God kings and priests: and we shall reign on the earth.

And I beheld, and I heard the voice of many angels round about the throne and the beasts and the elders: and the number of them was ten thousand times ten thousand, and thousands of thousands;

Saying with a loud voice, Worthy is the Lamb that was slain to receive power, and riches, and wisdom, and strength, and honour, and glory, and blessing.

And every creature which is in heaven, and on the earth, and under the earth, and such as are in the sea, and all that are in them, heard I saying, Blessing, and honour, and glory, and power, be unto Him that sitteth upon the throne, and unto the Lamb for ever and ever.

REVELATION 21:1-5

And I saw a new heaven and a new earth: for the first heaven and the first earth were passed away; and there was no more sea.

And I John saw the holy city, new Jerusalem, coming down from God out of heaven, prepared as a bride adorned for her husband.

And I heard a great voice out of heaven, saying, Behold, the tabernacle of God is with men, and He will dwell with them, and they shall be His people, and God Himself shall be with them, and be their God.

And God shall wipe away all tears from their eyes; and there shall be no more death, neither sorrow, nor crying, neither shall there be any more pain: for the former things are passed away.

And He that sat upon the throne said, Behold, I make all things new. And He said unto me, Write; for these words are true and faithful.

Prayers for Private Worship

Morning and Evening Prayers

Sunday Morning

O Lord, on whom the eyes of all do wait, remember every creature of Thine for good, and visit the world with Thy mercy, on this day of peace and rest; this is the day in which we will rejoice, and be glad, and praise Thy holy Name.

O Thou God of holiness and truth, who lookest not on the outward appearance, but on the heart, have mercy on us, and teach us this day to worship Thee in spirit and truth. Give unto all destitute flocks pastors after Thine own heart, bless Thou him who labors among us. Give us grace to enter Thy house with lowly and contrite hearts that we may confess our sins with godly sorrow; and give us understanding to speak Thy praise with joy and gladness. Hear, O Lord, in heaven, Thy dwelling place, the voice of our fervent prayers, and when Thou hearest, forgive.

Furthermore, we most humbly beseech Thee, give us Thy blessed Spirit, to renew our minds; to bring us to a right understanding of Thy Word; and to plant in us such a knowledge of Thy truth, that we may continue Thine for ever. O heavenly Father, who didst on this first day of the week bring again from the dead our Lord Jesus Christ, raise up our souls unto newness of life; make us perfect in every good work to do Thy will; and evermore work in us that which is well-pleasing in Thy sight, through the same our Savior Jesus Christ. Amen.

Sunday Evening

O Lord God, heavenly Father, suffer us again to gather ourselves together before Thee, and close this sacred day with prayer and praise, and let Thy holy Spirit be with us, for Jesus Christ's sake.

Another blessed opportunity has been given us of attending to the things which belong unto our peace. Oh, that we had used it as we ought! That we had this day served Thee better, and loved Thee more! Yet, weak and sinful as we are, merciful Lord, accept our services, and let us not retire to rest without Thy pardon and blessing; but let the precious blood of our Savior wash away our uncleanness, and do Thou look upon us as a reconciled Father in Jesus Christ.

Grant that the rest of this day may raise up in our hearts an earnest longing after that everlasting rest, which remaineth for the people of God! No eye hath seen, no ear hath heard, neither is any heart able to conceive the joys which Thou, O Lord, hast prepared for them that love Thee. Make us meet, we pray Thee, for that state of blessedness! Give us wisdom to find the strait gate, and guide us in the narrow way that leadeth unto life! Sanctify us in body and in soul; and lead us in the path of holiness, and prayer, and praise, to that glorious kingdom, where angels bless Thy name for evermore, and where Thou livest and reignest with Thy dearly beloved Son, and the Holy Ghost, one true and everlasting God, world without end. Amen.

Monday Morning

O merciful God, in whom we live, and move, and have our being, be with us this day, we beseech Thee, in the duties of our calling, and prosper with Thy blessing our handiwork. Strengthen us inwardly by the power of Thy grace, that we may be fervent in spirit, serving Thee, O Lord.

We most humbly beseech Thee to write Thy commandments in our hearts, that we may fulfill the royal law of the Scriptures, of loving our neighbors as ourselves, and doing unto all men as we would they should do unto us. Uphold us by Thy Spirit that we may never be tempted to envy, or to covet any man's goods; make us to rejoice in the prosperity of the prosperous, and to feel for the afflictions of the afflicted, knowing that we ourselves may soon be afflicted and tried.

And now, O Lord, since another day of rest is gone, and the cares of a new week lie before our path, guide us in safety along the narrow way of life, and defend us from the temptations of the world, of the devil, and of our own hearts. And grant, we entreat Thee, that, enjoying the fruits of our labors here, we may acknowledge Thy goodness, and glorify Thy holy Name, and finally be received into Thy heavenly kingdom, for the sake of Jesus, our Lord. Amen.

Monday Evening

Most gracious Lord, and merciful Father, we, Thy sinful creatures, humble ourselves before Thy Divine Majesty, beseeching Thee to forgive the sins which we have committed this day, and all the days of our lives. Not for our own righteousness, not for anything that we have done, do we claim Thy forgiveness, O Lord; but we draw nigh to the throne of Thy mercy, in the Name of our Savior Jesus Christ! For His sake, O heavenly Father, even for the sake of the bitter sufferings which He endured on the cross, be merciful to us, whom He has redeemed with His most precious blood! O cast not away us whom Thou hast permitted to be called Christians, after the Name of Thy well-beloved Son. Forsake us not; leave us not to ourselves; but continually assist and strengthen us and especially be Thou our defense this night.

O Lord, mercifully grant that every member of this family may be found among the number of them that shall be saved! Give us all grace to lead godly and innocent lives! Let faith, and hope, and charity, dwell in our hearts and guide us in all our ways! And so order our steps through this vain and transitory world, that we may attain to Thine everlasting glory in heaven, through Jesus Christ our Lord. Amen.

Tuesday Morning

Blessed be the Lord, who hath preserved us from the perils of the night past! Our help is in the Name of the Lord, who hath made both heaven and earth! Blessed be the Name of our Lord, from henceforth, and forevermore.

O heavenly Father, we beseech Thee to look with a merciful eye upon this family which Thou hast brought to see the light of another day: Support and guide us; hold us up, and save us, that we come not under Thy displeasure for transgressing this day any of Thy laws. Thou, Lord, hast appointed us a way to walk in and commanded that we should not turn aside to the right hand or to the left. As Thou hast commanded, even so give us grace to do! Let us not follow our own will, nor the will of other men; let us not obey the world, nor the desires of our own sinful hearts: but do Thou make us diligent to consider always beforehand what we shall speak, and what we shall do; do Thou govern and direct our ways, that we may walk in the paths of Thy righteousness: and make every one of us, in thought, word, and work, to seek Thy honor and glory, the everlasting welfare of all around us, and the good of our own souls.

And now, O gracious Lord God, we humbly commend ourselves, and all whom we ought specially to remember in our prayers, to Thy mercies in Christ Jesus. May Thy Spirit carry on the work of Thy grace among the children of men. Increase and sanctify Thy whole church. Send forth the glad tidings of great joy to heathen lands. Bless all Thy messengers. Comfort all Thine afflicted, strengthen the weak. Succor the poor and needy. Be with us all, O Lord, in Thy holy Spirit, through Thy Son Jesus Christ, our only Redeemer and Mediator. Amen.

Tuesday Evening

O Lord our God, we come unto Thee for quiet and repose after the labors and cares of the day; commending our bodies and souls to Thy fatherly protection, and praising Thy holy Name for the mercies which have followed us to the present hour. And yet with sorrow and confusion of face, we acknowledge that we have not served Thee, as we ought to have done. So frail is our nature, so weak our flesh, so evil our desires from the day of our birth that we cannot of ourselves do anything good in Thy sight. We have sinned; we have done amiss; and if Thou wert strict to mark iniquity, which of us, O Lord, could stand? But there is mercy with Thee, that Thou mayest be feared! Vouchsafe then, most loving Father, to send us Thy holy Spirit to subdue our evil passions, and create in our hearts pure and good desires; fill us with holy affections, and so renew us in spirit, that we may die unto the old Adam, and henceforth live unto Thee in newness of life.

O Thou good Shepherd, who didst lay down Thy life for Thy sheep, preserve us this night from all evil; and take us, and all who are near and dear to us, under Thy gracious care, and refresh our weary souls with supplies of godly strength, as may enable us to serve Thee in holiness and righteousness all the days of our life. Amen.

Wednesday Morning

Our voice shalt Thou hear betimes, O Lord; early in the morning will we direct our prayer unto Thee, and look up.

We bless Thee, O heavenly Father, that Thou hast kept us the night past, and still preservest our lives; we beseech Thee to receive us this day and forever under Thy gracious care. Rule and govern us by Thy Spirit; chase away all darkness and unbelief from our minds; deliver us from evil affections and carnal desires, and fill our hearts with a lively sense of the things of

447

heaven, and a true understanding and knowledge of Thy blessed Word.

And, as we pray that we may be thus enlightened, so we beseech Thee to give us grace to live agreeably to what we know. Suffer us not to be of the number of those who profess to know God with their mouths, and deny Him by their deeds. Let us not be like that son who said to his father that he would labor in the field, yet went not at all to the work. Rather do Thou make our hearts like that good and fruitful land, which yieldeth in its season a rich and abundant increase.

Grant, O Lord, that we may be justified and saved by a right and perfect faith in Thy blessed Son; and may so walk in the light of Thy truth, to the praise of Thy name, and the benefit of all around us, that they, seeing our good works, may glorify Thee, O God, through Jesus Christ our Savior and Redeemer. Amen.

Wednesday Evening

Let our prayer, O Lord, be set forth in Thy sight as incense, and let the lifting up of our hands be as an evening sacrifice.

Holy, holy, holy, Lord God, we, miserable sinners, must acknowledge that we have offended Thee this day, in thought, word, and deed: Lord, for Thy mercies' sake, forgive us, cleanse us from our wickedness, and strengthen our weakness, that we may overcome all the temptations which daily surround us, and continue constant in our obedience. Accept of our humblest praise and thanksgiving, O Lord, for all the goodness Thou hast this day shewed us; for all the helps of grace Thou hast vouchsafed us; for whatever we have done this day, which is in any measure acceptable to Thee; for whatever progress we have made in sanctification; for Thy preservation of us from all the miseries and dangers to which we are every moment exposed.

O heavenly Father, to Thy almighty protection we recommend ourselves, and all our relations, and all that belong to this place. O Thou that never slumberest or sleepest, watch over us and preserve us from sin and danger.

Lord, let it be Thy good pleasure to refresh us this night with such seasonable rest, that we may rise in the morning more fit for Thy service. O pardon our failings, and hear our prayers, for the sake of Thy Son Jesus Christ our Lord. Amen.

Thursday Morning

Almighty God, whose eyes are over the righteous, and whose ears are open to their prayers, satisfy us with Thy mercy, that we may rejoice and be glad; and never let us,

by evil-doing, cause Thee to turn away Thy face from our prayers.

We humbly beseech Thee to give us that love and charity which cometh out of a pure heart, a good conscience, and faith unfeigned. Pour into our hearts this spirit of Christian love, that we may love Thee, Lord our God, with all our heart, and mind, and soul, and strength; doing always that which is pleasing in Thy sight. Make us to love our neighbors as ourselves: to be all of one mind; having compassion one of another; sincere in brotherly love. Keep our tongue from evil, and our lips that they speak no guile. Teach us to seek peace with all mankind. We pray Thee also for the spirit of contentment in our several callings, that we may live quietly and thankfully in the same.

Gracious Lord, so order our lives in all things according to Thy holy will, that we may be always ready for the hour of death, and for the day of judgment. Grant this, we beseech Thee, O merciful God, for Jesus Christ's sake. Amen.

Thursday Evening

O God, be merciful, and bless us, and shew us the light of Thy countenance, and be gracious unto us; for the sake of Jesus Christ. Behold, we turn unto Thee, for Thou art the Lord our God. Shame hath covered our face, for we have sinned against the God of our fathers: we have not obeyed the voice of the Lord. We confess that our nature is corrupt, our desires are crooked and perverse. O Lord; the flesh lusteth against the spirit; the devil seeketh whom he may devour; the world persuadeth to vanities, and we forget our God. Acknowledging our own helplessness, we heartily pray Thee to take us under Thy protection, and endue us with strength from above; create in us clean hearts, and deliver us from all ungodly thoughts. Breathe into our souls, by Thy Spirit, holy and heavenly desires, that out of the good treasure within we may bring forth good things, to the praise and glory of Thy name.

The shadows of evening are coming around us, and that night is also pressing on in which no man can work. Prepare us against the hour of which no man knoweth, that we may be ready, like servants waiting for their Lord, who go out and meet him with joy. Blessed are those servants! O God, let their blessedness be ours, and hear us while we ask it for the sake of Jesus Christ our Lord and Savior. Amen.

Friday Morning

O Lord, be gracious unto us, for we wait upon Thee; be Thou our strength in the morning, and our salvation through the troubles and dangers of this day.

Merciful Father, we thank Thee for the blessings Thou hast bestowed upon us all the days of our life. That we have churches to go to, that we have pastors to teach us, and schools where our children may learn Thy Word; that we know Thy holy will; that the words of saving truth have come to us and ours; these are Thy mercies, O God, for which we bless and praise Thy name. Grant that we may never pervert to evil purposes Thy good and gracious gifts; nor be of the number of those who abuse the blessings which we enjoy.

Good and evil, life and death, poverty and riches, are of Thee, O Lord!—Thou liftest up and puttest down; Thou dost correct and chasten, and try the children of men, as seemeth right in Thy sight. Create in us obedient, faithful, and contented spirits. Give us hearts to love and obey them that are over us in the Lord; bless our Government and all who bear rule in the land: and finally grant that we, Thy servants, living here in quietness and lowliness of mind, may, at the last day, through Thy grace, be raised up to everlasting glory. We ask these blessings in the name, and for the sake of our Lord Jesus Christ. Amen.

Friday Evening

O Lord God of heaven, we, Thy creatures, whom Thou hast redeemed, offer up our evening sacrifices of prayer and praise, beseeching Thee to remember Thy promises of mercy, and to pardon our transgression, and to save us from the power of sin for the time to come. Incline our hearts to fear Thy name, remembering that, whether we sleep or wake, whether we live or die, we are always Thine. Thou art about our path, and about our bed, and knowest all our ways. We pray Thee, therefore, to take charge of us. Give us grace that we may cast away the works of darkness, and put upon us the whole armor of light, that through Thy Spirit assisting us, we may walk as children of light. By Thy great mercy defend us from all perils and dangers of this night. Grant, O Lord, that we may continually increase more and more in godly knowledge, and that we may always be found to walk and live after Thy will and pleasure, through Jesus Christ our Lord.

We commend to Thy favor and protection our friends, and all who have ever done us good. We implore the same mercies, together with Thy pardon, on those who wish, or intend to do us evil. We entreat Thee on behalf of the poor and afflicted in every place, deliver them, O God, in Thy good time, and bring them and us to that blessed place of rest, where sorrow and tears shall be done away, through Jesus Christ our Lord. Amen.

Saturday Morning

O come, let us worship and fall down, and kneel before the Lord, who hath turned the darkness into light, and renewed the face of the earth. Let us draw nigh unto Him with faith, with pure hearts and holy hands, in the Name of Jesus Christ.

Morning and evening praise Thee, O God! Great and wonderful are Thy doings; the earth is full of Thy mercies; and all things work together for good to them that keep Thy commandments, and abide in Thy fear.

Grant, Lord, that we may covet earnestly those things that please Thee; that we may know them truly, and fulfill them perfectly, to the praise of Thy holy Name. Remove from us vanity and lies; feed us with food convenient for us, make us thankful for the blessings we enjoy: and teach us, in whatever state we are, therewith to be content.

In Thee, O Lord, do we place our trust; let us never be put to confusion; deliver us in Thy righteousness, and incline Thine ear and hear us. Preserve us and all who belong to us, in our going out and coming in, from this time forth forevermore, and finally receive us to Thy mercies in heaven; for the sake of Him who loved us, and gave Himself for us, Jesus Christ our Lord. Amen.

Saturday Evening

Let us lift up our hands this night unto God in heaven, let us offer Him our evening sacrifice of praise, through our only mediator Jesus Christ.

O God, the Father of mercies, the God of all consolation and love, how many are the blessings we have received from Thee during the past week, notwithstanding all our sins. How great things hast Thou done for our bodies and our souls. What shall we render unto Thee for all we have received? Accept, O Lord, our confessions, our prayers, and praise: and sanctify us in heart and soul, that we may evermore give Thee that service which is meet for the holy and righteous God of heaven and earth.

Tomorrow is Thy day of sacred rest. Make us to remember Thee on our beds, to think of Thee in the night season, and to be ready to draw nigh unto Thee on the morrow in Thy holy house. Six days of labor have again passed away, and our lives, like the week, are hastening to their close. Our years decline apace, and we know not which of this family the righteous Lord may first take away. Again, therefore, we commend ourselves to Thy keeping; humbly beseeching Thee to continue Thy lovingkindness towards us, and to give us grace to walk worthy of our calling as Christians; that when we die we may enter into Thy presence with the spirits of just men made perfect, through the merits and mediation of our Lord Jesus Christ. Amen.

Prayers at Table

Come, Lord Jesus, be Thou a Guest
Bless Thou, and all our gifts are blest.

———

We thank Thee, Lord, for this our food,
For life and health, and every good:
May manna to our souls be given,
The Bread of Life, sent down from heaven.

Before Church Time

O my God, I humbly beseech Thee, prepare my soul to worship Thee this day with godly fear. Purify my heart from all vain or sinful thoughts; fix my affections on things above; and O Lord, give me grace to receive Thy Word which I shall hear this day into an honest and good heart, and to bring forth the fruit thereof with patience.

Hear me, O God, for the sake of Jesus, my Savior. Amen.

For a True Confession

Hear the voice of my humble petition, O Lord, when I cry unto Thee, and when I lift up my hands towards Thy mercy seat.

Behold, Lord, I search mine own heart; but alas it is deceitful and desperately wicked: how can I know it? Thou, therefore, that searchest the deep places of my being, discover to me all the evils and deceits of my own heart that I may confess them, obtain mercy and forsake them.

Lord hear me, Lord help me for the merits of Jesus my Savior. Amen.

Before Communion

O Holy Spirit, be Thou near me as I approach this seat of mercy, the Altar of the Sacrament.

I tremble as the priest approaching the temple veil, yet I come for Thou in the Word hast said "Come!" Just as I am I come.

My soul has heard the pardoning word and I believe the forgiveness of my sins. Tell me again of mercy for sinners and make assurance still more sure in this sacred pledge, the Body once broken and the Blood once shed upon the Cross.

Let me arise from the Altar cleansed and strengthened and ready for the pilgrimage in love and helpfulness toward all that are on the way with me.

Let Christ who gives Himself to me make His abode in my heart through undying faith. Amen.

After Communion

My soul is quiet before Thee, O God. Thanks be to Thee for all Thy mercies. Thanks for this unspeakable gift. Keep me

from sin, lead me in the way that is right, make me strong, let Christ live and rule in me! Amen.

In Time of Illness

Whom have I in heaven but Thee? And there is none upon earth that I desire beside Thee. My flesh and my heart faileth: but God is the strength of my heart and my portion forever.

Blessed is he whose transgression is forgiven, whose sin is covered. Blessed is the man unto whom the Lord imputeth not iniquity. Speak so to me O God! If there be a veil of guilt over my soul, a shadow of deceit between Thee and me, tear it away! Let Thy truth shine through!

Help me to number my days and know my frailty; to look back across the dark places of life and acknowledge my sin.

Walk before me through the inner rooms of my being. Search me, and know my heart: try me, and know my thoughts: and see if there be any wicked way in me, and lead me in the way everlasting. Amen.

I believe that Jesus is my Lord, who has redeemed me, a lost and condemned creature, purchased and won me from all sins, from death, and from the power of the devil, not with gold or silver, but with His holy, precious blood, and with His innocent sufferings and death; in order that I might be His own, live under Him in His kingdom, and serve Him in everlasting righteousness, innocence, and blessedness, even as He is risen from the dead, lives and reigns to all eternity. Amen.

Who shall separate us from the love of Christ? Shall tribulation or distress or peril? Nay in all these things we are more than conquerors, through Him that loved us. For I am persuaded that neither death, nor life, nor angels, nor principalities, nor powers, nor things present nor things to come, nor height, nor depth, nor any other creature, shall be able to separate us from the love of God, which is in Christ Jesus our Lord. (Rom. 8.)

Abide with me! Fast falls the eventide;
The darkness deepens; Lord, with me abide!
When other helpers fail, and comforts flee,
Help of the helpless, O abide with me!

Hold Thou Thy cross before my closing eyes,
Shine through the gloom and point me to the skies,
Heaven's morning breaks, and earth's vain shadows flee;
In life, in death, O Lord, abide with me!

Into Thy hands I commend my spirit; for Thou hast redeemed me, O Lord, Thou God of truth. Amen.

INDEX OF AUTHORS, TRANSLATORS,
AND SOURCES OF HYMNS

Index of Authors, Translators, and Sources of Hymns

Index of Composers and
Sources of Tunes

456

Index of Tunes with Meters

460

461

462

463

Index of First Lines of Hymns

464

466